575

RICK URBAN

The Anatomic and Mechanical

Fundamentals of Human Motion

Katharine F. Wells, Ph.D.

Associate Professor, Department of
Physical Education, Wellesley College

Kinesiology

THIRD EDITION

W. B. Saunders Company

Philadelphia and London

Preface to the Third Edition

During the five years since the second edition of this book was published there has been a notable increase in electromyographic investigations. These have been responsible for significant contributions to our knowledge of muscular action. Electromyography is a technique which permits investigation of several muscle groups at a time and which can be applied to movement patterns or sequences such as a tennis serve, a golf drive, a gymnastic exercise, a dance technique, walking, running, and the like. It gives precise information about the timing and intensity of the muscular contraction and provides objective records for future use and comparison. It is proving to be an immensely valuable tool for kinesiologic research.

In preparation for this third edition the author searched the literature of recent years for reports of electromyographic studies. Some of these have been summarized in the supplementary sections, and all have served as a basis for verifying and correcting muscular actions as stated throughout the text.

Two major changes which were made in the second edition have been retained. These are the rearrangement of content and the new nomenclature for muscular attachments. In the present edition, however, as a convenience to those who prefer using the standard terminology, the initials O and I are inserted parenthetically to indicate origins and insertions. The movements of the thumb at the carpometacarpal joint have been re-defined so as to agree with the definitions used by the majority of physical and occupational therapists. This change seemed expedient in view of the fact that the therapists, probably more than any other readers of this book, are the ones most concerned with the movements of the thumb and fingers.

v

The chapter on applications of kinesiology to physical therapy and occupational therapy has been expanded in the hope of increasing its usefulness to students who are preparing to enter these professions.

The author would like to express her appreciation to Mr. William A. Osburn for his drawings which help to give this new edition a new look, and also to the many persons whose thoughtful questions and suggestions served as guides in the revision of the book.

Wellesley, Massachusetts   KATHARINE F. WELLS

Preface to the First Edition

THIS BOOK is intended as a kinesiology text both for the teacher and for the student. The book is divided into four parts. The first part deals with the basic mechanics of human motion, the second with the action of the joints and muscles, the third with major types of motor skills, and the fourth with the applications of kinesiology to physical education activities, to the techniques of physical and occupational therapy, and to daily life skills. For those who like to teach the anatomic aspects of movements before the mechanical, Parts I and II can easily be used in the reverse order. Also, the topics in the anatomic section itself can be taken up in any order the instructor desires. Some may prefer to start with the upper extremity, some with the lower. The arrangement of this text need not deter the instructor from following the order of his preference.

It is believed that there is enough material in this book to use it as a text for a full year's course, yet, at the same time, by judicious selection of the subject matter, by omission of the supplementary material and by the substitution of classroom demonstrations for some of the laboratory exercises, the book should serve equally well as a text for a one semester course in kinesiology. It is left to the discretion of the instructor to select the material that meets his particular needs.

In its original form this textbook was an unpublished handbook-laboratory manual. It was used by the author in her kinesiology classes for three years before it was expanded to its present form. The original manual did not serve as an independent textbook. It was intended to be used as a companion book to a kinesiology or anatomy text. Since this limited its usefulness, however, it was decided to expand it to what is intended as a complete and independent textbook. For those who like to use a single textbook for a course it should suffice. To help the student (and the instructor) in his collateral reading, each chapter in this text contains a comprehensive bibliography. In many cases there is also a list of readings which are particularly recommended. These bibliographies and reading lists provide a rich source of information for the inquiring student.

In regard to the value of laboratory exercises and projects as a means of learning, James B. Stroud, in his book "Psychology in Education," points out that, "Effectiveness of instruction is not determined so much by what the teacher does, as by what he leads the pupil to do——." Again, "perhaps one of the most successful procedures for infusing learning with significance has been the constructive activities.——The activity is thus a means of making learning meaningful and of giving it a purpose." In accord with this point of view numerous laboratory exercises are suggested. In conformity to the same principle, only a few complete analyses of skills are presented, for it is the writer's contention that the student will gain far more from making one complete analysis himself than from reading a dozen or more ready-made analyses.

As a further means of enriching the kinesiology course a number of the chapters include supplementary material in the form of brief descriptions of research projects in the field of anatomy and kinesiology. A few of these were carried out by the author, but the majority were conducted by other investigators and reported in the professional journals. The purpose of including this material is to broaden the instructor's background and to provide supplementary reading assignments for advanced students.

It has been the intention of the author to write simply and to use non-technical terminology whenever this conveyed the meaning as clearly and specifically as technical terms. The latter have been used, however, whenever they served to avoid ambiguity. For instance, terms like "proximal" (meaning nearest to the body) and "distal" (meaning farthest from the body) have been used in preference to the terms "upper" and "lower," which might easily be misinterpreted. While it is desirable for the kinesiology student to enlarge his scientific vocabulary, a text which confronts him with a staggering list of new and strange words defeats its purpose. Textbooks should stimulate the curiosity of their readers, not frighten them with a forbidding vocabulary. For the same reason, the use of mathematical formulae has been studiously avoided. True, these might clarify certain explanations for the mathematically trained reader, but they tend to confuse and discourage the uninitiated.

The author acknowledges her indebtedness to many individuals without whose help it is doubtful if this book could have been written. She wishes to express her grateful appreciation particularly to Professor C. H. McCloy of the State University of Iowa for his continued guidance, encouragement and criticism, also for his generous permission to use material from his course in The Mechanical Analysis of Motor Skills; to Marjorie D. Sanger and Evelyn K. Dillon for their critical reading of the manuscript and for their constant help and encouragement throughout its preparation; to Constance K. Greene, Ada R. Hall and Mary E. Nesbitt for their helpful advice concerning the sections on neuromuscular action and physical therapy; and finally to the students in her kinesiology classes of the last three years who served patiently as "guinea pigs" and who made many constructive suggestions concerning the laboratory exercises.

For the illustrations, which add immeasurably to the usefulness of the text, grateful acknowledgment is made to Miss Mildred Codding, who made the anatomic drawings, to Mrs. George Homans, who printed the labels for these, to Mrs. Margareta F. Lyons, who made most of the non-anatomic sketches, to Dale Ballantyne, whose illustrations for the author's doctoral dissertation served as the basis for several of the sketches in this book, and to Miss Irene MacLaurin, who took a number of photographs specifically for this text. Many of the anatomic sketches are adapted from illustrations in standard texts by Braus, Bresnahan and Tuttle, Brubaker, Gray, Molliere, Ranson, Sobotta and Spalteholtz.

The author is under obligation to a number of individuals for the use of photographs and to several publishers for permission to reproduce copyrighted materials. To all writers and teachers from whom the author, either wittingly or unwittingly, has derived ideas which have provided the necessary background for the writing of this book she humbly acknowledges her indebtedness.

KATHARINE F. WELLS

Contents

II · The Mechanics of Human Motion

III · Underlying Principles of Basic Motor Skills

IV · Applications of Kinesiology

Introduction to the Study of Kinesiology

K INESIOLOGY, as it is known in physical education, orthopedics and physical medicine, is the science of human motion. In the early days of physical education, when few activities were taught besides gymnastics and the dance, the content of a course in kinesiology was confined chiefly to functional anatomy. Gradually, as sports assumed a more important place in the physical education curriculum, the concept of kinesiology was broadened to include the study of mechanical principles which applied to sport techniques. The principles were applied not only to the movements of the body itself, but also to the movements of the implements, balls, and other equipment used in connection with the sport. In like manner, the development of the kinesiology course in schools of physical therapy and occupational therapy has kept pace with the development of their expanded curricula. Having started as "muscle reeducation," it has come to include the application of mechanical principles to postural adjustments, to the gait, to the use of tools and household implements, and to the modifications of vocational and homemaking activities necessitated by limitations in neuromuscular capacity and skeletal structure.

The unique contribution of kinesiology is that it selects from sciences such as anatomy, physiology and physics those principles which are pertinent to human motion and systematizes their application. The body, being a living machine, is subject to the laws both of living matter and of mechanics. Hence the analysis of human motion is based on anatomic, physiologic and mechanical

1

principles. The studying of any science is like the opening of a door to a new world. This is no less true of kinesiology than of chemistry, physics or botany. The same perfection, the same orderliness, the same attention to detail that are manifested by these other sciences are likewise manifested by kinesiology. The mechanisms which are involved in activities such as walking, throwing a baseball or lifting a trunk are no less awe-inspiring than are the mechanisms involved in metabolism or photosynthesis. Nothing is haphazard; nothing is left to chance. Every structure which participates in the movement of the body does so in obedience to physical and physiologic principles. The student of kinesiology, like the student of anatomy and physiology, can only stand in reverent wonder at the intricate mechanism of the body, and in the words of the psalmist exclaim to his creator, "I will praise thee, for I am fearfully and wonderfully made."

But kinesiology is not studied merely for the purpose of inciting our interest in a fascinating and mysterious subject. It has a useful purpose. We study kinesiology in order to learn how to analyze the movements of the human body and to discover their underlying principles. The study of kinesiology is an essential part of the educational experience of students of physical education and physical medicine. For the physical educator it has a dual purpose: on the one hand, the purpose of perfecting performance in motor skills, and on the other, the purpose of perfecting the performer. Kinesiology helps to prepare the physical educator to teach effective performance in both fundamental and specialized motor skills. Furthermore, it enables him to evaluate exercises and activities from the point of view of their effect on the human structure. As Dr. William Skarstrom used to say to his kinesiology students, the human machine has this advantage over the manufactured machine: Whereas the latter wears out with use, the former improves with use (up to a certain point, of course), *provided it is used in accordance with the principles of efficient human motion.* The function of kinesiology, therefore, is to contribute not only to successful participation in various physical activities, but also to the improvement of the human structure through the intelligent selection of activities and the efficient use of the body.

For the physical therapist and the occupational therapist the purpose of studying kinesiology (whether called by that name or by some other) is not unlike that for the physical education teacher. The difference is in the emphasis, rather than in the purpose. The therapist is primarily concerned with the effect that exercises and other techniques of physical medicine have upon the body. He—or she—is concerned particularly with the restoration of impaired function and with methods of compensating for lost function. As with the physical educator, effective performance is likewise a goal for the therapist. But to the therapist "effective performance" refers not so much to *skillful* performance in athletic activities, as to *adequate* performance in the activities associated with daily living. Whereas the educator applies his knowledge of kinesiology chiefly to the movements of the normal body, the therapist, on the other hand, is concerned with the movements of a body which has suffered an impairment in function.

The educator and the therapist have at least one purpose in common in studying kinesiology. Both are concerned with posture and body mechanics, hence both are interested in discovering the anatomic and mechanical bases for training in this area. Both apply their knowledge of kinesiology to analyzing the postural needs of others, to the intelligent selection of posture exercises based on individual need, and to the mechanically efficient methods of using the body in daily life skills.

The most satisfactory way of studying kinesiology is by supplementing book study with laboratory experimentation. It is a truism that we learn best by doing. When time must be conserved, demonstration may be substituted for some of the experimental work, but it should never replace it entirely.

The use of motion picture films is another good device for supplementing book study. It is particularly helpful if a hand projector can be used, or a projector which can be stopped at will, thus making it possible to analyze positions and body relationships.

Whatever method of teaching or of study is employed it is well for the student to keep in mind the aims of a kinesiology course and the applications which he intends to make of what he learns. He must remember that the analysis of motion is not an end in itself, but rather a means to the learning of new movement patterns and the improvement of old ones. This is as true for the physical therapist teaching "polio" victims and paraplegics to walk again as it is for the physical educator teaching a sport technique. Finally, he must remember that the skill itself is of less importance than the one who practices it. Kinesiology serves only half its purpose when it provides the background for learning or teaching motor skills. It must also serve to lay the foundation for perfecting, repairing, and keeping in good condition that incomparable mechanism—the human body.

Demonstrations and Laboratory Exercises

Purpose. To familiarize the student with the method of observing and palpating muscles.

1. Have the subject bend his arm at the elbow while you resist the action by holding his wrist. With your other hand, feel the subject's forearm flexors (bi-

ceps and brachialis). While his arm is bent, release and reapply the resistance several times so that he will alternately relax and contract his muscles.

2. Have the subject bend his head to the right and turn his chin to the left, while you resist both motions with your hands. Observe the long muscle going from behind the ear diagonally downward and forward to the sternum. This is the sternocleidomastoid muscle. It bends the head to the same side and rotates it to the opposite side.

3. Have the subject raise his arm sideward against resistance. Observe and feel the bulky muscle (the deltoid) on the upper part of the arm, just below the shoulder.

4. Have the subject lower his arm sideward against resistance. Observe and feel the tendons forming the anterior and posterior borders of the axilla. The former is part of the pectoralis major, and the latter of the latissimus dorsi.

5. Have the subject rise on his toes. Observe and feel the muscle in the calf of the leg. This is the gastrocnemius.

I · Anatomic Fundamentals of Human Motion

1 · Fundamental Concepts

IF THE STUDY of kinesiology is to be meaningful to the student, it is advisable for him to grasp certain concepts at the outset of his study, for without an understanding of these concepts he is likely to get lost in ambiguities. If we are to understand one another, we must talk the same language, use the same vocabulary. We must agree on basic definitions and points of reference.

The concepts which are considered essential to the study of kinesiology, as outlined in this text, are the starting positions of the body, the center of gravity, the line of gravity, the orientation planes in which movements of the body occur, and the axes of motion about which they occur. Agreement on these basic points of reference makes it possible to define positions and movements of the body precisely, without the necessity of resorting to gestures and diagrams.

Starting Position. There are two standing positions which are commonly used as starting positions for fundamental movements of the body. These are the fundamental standing position and the anatomic position. It is important to state which of these is intended whenever suggesting a movement for analysis, particularly a movement of the upper extremity.

In the fundamental standing position the individual stands erect, either with the feet slightly separated and parallel or with the heels touching and the toes pointing slightly outward, the arms hanging easily at the sides, palms facing the body (Fig. 1, *A*). This is the position usually assumed for gymnastic exercises. The military and the old-fashioned formal gymnastic positions are more vigorous and tense variations of this.

The anatomic position is the one usually depicted in anatomy

7

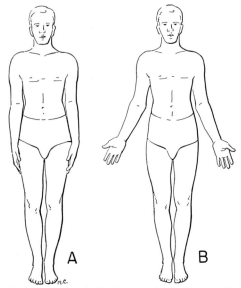

Figure 1. Standing positions. *A,* Fundamental standing position; *B,* anatomic standing position.

textbooks. The individual is erect with the elbows fully extended and the palms facing forward. The legs and feet are the same as in the fundamental standing position (Fig. 1, *B*). When making a kinesiologic analysis of the fundamental movements occurring at the elbow, wrist and finger joints, the anatomic position is the one accepted as the point of reference.

The Center of Gravity. The center of gravity is defined as "an imaginary point representing the weight center of an object"; also as "that point in a body about which all the parts exactly balance each other"; and as "the point at which the entire weight of the body may be considered as concentrated." In a perfect sphere or cube the center of gravity is located at the exact center. Its precise location in the human body depends upon the individual's anatomic structure, posture, position, and the presence of external weights which he is supporting. In a person of average build, standing erect with the arms hanging at the sides, the center of gravity is located in the pelvis in front of the upper part of the sacrum. It is usually lower in women than in men because of their heavier pelves and thighs and shorter legs.

The Line of Gravity. The line of gravity is an imaginary vertical line which passes through the center of gravity. Hence its location is dependent upon the position of the center of gravity. It is a fairly simple matter to determine experimentally the location of an individual's line of gravity with reference to his base of support. Directions for a common method of doing this are given in Chapter 17.

Orientation Planes of the Body and Axes of Motion.   There are three planes, corresponding to the three dimensions of space. Each plane is perpendicular to each of the other two. There are likewise three axes of motion, each perpendicular to the plane in which the motion occurs. The planes and axes of the body are defined as follows:

Planes (Fig. 2, *A, B, C*)

1. The sagittal or anteroposterior plane is a vertical plane passing through the body from front to back, dividing it in half.

2. The frontal or lateral plane is a vertical plane passing through the body from side to side, dividing it in half.

3. The horizontal or transverse plane is a horizontal plane which passes through the body, dividing it into upper and lower halves.

Since each plane bisects the body, it follows that each plane must pass through the center of gravity. Hence the center of gravity may be defined as the point at which the three planes of the body intersect one another. When describing a movement in terms of a plane,

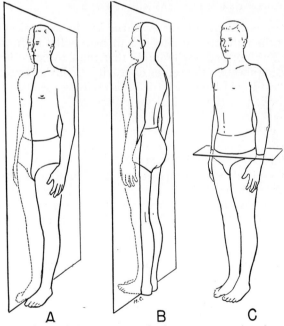

Figure 2.   The planes of the body. *A,* Sagittal or anteroposterior plane; *B,* frontal or lateral plane; *C,* horizontal or transverse plane.

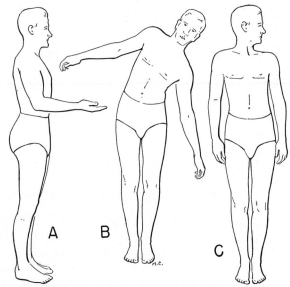

Figure 3. Movements of the body in the three planes. *A,* Movement of the forearm in the sagittal plane around a frontal-horizontal axis. *B,* Movement of the trunk in the frontal plane around a sagittal-horizontal axis. *C,* Movement of the head in the horizontal plane around a vertical axis.

such as "a movement of the forearm in the sagittal plane," we mean that the movement occurs in a plane parallel with the sagittal plane. It does not necessarily imply that the movement occurs in a plane passing through the center of gravity. If the latter is intended, the term "cardinal plane" is used. Thus nodding the head is a movement occurring in the cardinal sagittal plane.

Axes

1. The vertical axis is perpendicular to the ground.

2. The frontal or lateral horizontal axis passes horizontally from side to side.

3. The sagittal or anteroposterior horizontal axis passes horizontally from front to back.

A rotatory (axial, angular) movement of a segment of the body occurs *in* a plane, and *around* an axis. The axis around which the movement takes place is always at right angles to the plane in which it occurs.

Fundamental Movements of the Major Body Segments.   *Note:* The anatomic position is the basic point of reference for these movements.

Movements in the Sagittal Plane about a Frontal-Horizontal Axis (Fig. 3, *A*)

FLEXION.   The angle at the joint diminishes. (The shoulder is an exception.)

EXTENSION.   The return from flexion.

HYPEREXTENSION.   The continuation of extension beyond the starting position.

Movements in the Frontal Plane about a Sagittal-Horizontal Axis (Fig. 3, *B*)

ABDUCTION.   Movement away from the midline of the body.

ADDUCTION.   Movement toward the midline of the body.

LATERAL FLEXION.   Refers to lateral bending of the head or trunk.

Movement in the Horizontal Plane about a Vertical Axis (Fig. 3, *C*)

ROTATION.   Rotatory movement of a segment about its own longitudinal axis. In outward rotation the anterior aspect turns laterally; in inward rotation it turns medially. Outward and inward rotation of the forearm are called supination and pronation respectively.

Circumduction.   An orderly sequence of the movements which occur in the sagittal and frontal planes, so that the segment as a whole describes a cone.

Demonstrations and Laboratory Exercises

1. Construct a simple device to illustrate the planes and axes.

2. Working with a partner, take turns performing simple movements of the head, trunk, upper extremity and lower extremity, and identifying the planes and axes concerned.

Bibliography

1. Cates, H. A.: Primary Anatomy. 3rd ed. Baltimore, Williams & Wilkins Company, 1955, pp. 19, 73–75.

2. Steindler, A.: Kinesiology of the Human Body. Springfield, Ill., Charles C Thomas, 1955. Lecture 7.

2 · The Joints: Their Structure and Function

The STUDENT of kinesiology will have a clearer understanding of human motion if he has acquired the ability of visualizing the action of the joints in each movement he observes. This ability will stand him in good stead not only in the analysis of specific movement skills, but also in the understanding of joint injuries and of abnormalities in joint motion. Such an understanding can be based only on a sound foundation in the structure and function of each joint in the body. Fortunately this is not such a staggering task as it sounds. Although there are many joints in the skeletal framework, there are relatively few *types* of joints. By first studying the classification of joints one finds the study of individual joints greatly simplified.

Nature has shown an amazing versatility in designing joints to meet a variety of purposes. There are hinge joints, pivot joints and ball-and-socket joints, to name a few. Within these categories there are modifications in the shapes of the articulating bony surfaces, the thickness of cartilaginous plates and disks, and the arrangement of ligaments.

Too often the student thinks of kinesiology as being primarily a study of muscular action and he tends to overlook, or at least to underrate, the importance of studying the joints. As a result, he has such a hazy conception of the mechanics of joint function that he is seriously handicapped later in his profession. He will not understand the exact nature of the strain likely to be put upon some joints by certain activities, nor the nature of injuries after they have occurred. It is for this reason that the structure and function of the joints are treated in considerable detail in this text. If the student will approach the study of this section in the spirit of the youngster who takes the mechanical toy apart to see how it works, or in the spirit of the youth who, for the same reason, tinkers with the engine of his jalopy, his investigation will be equally rewarding.

Definitions. A skeletal joint is the union between two or more bones; between bone and cartilage; or between two or more cartilages. The word "articulation" (of Latin derivation) is a synonym for joint and may be used interchangeably with it.

"Arthrology" comes from the Greek word for joint and refers to the branch of anatomy which deals with the study of joints. The term "syndesmology," used in some anatomy textbooks, more accurately applies to the study of ligaments.

Classification. Joints may be classified according to their structure, more specifically according to the way in which the bones (or cartilages) are united. The classifications in two well-known anatomy texts[1, 2] are based on the presence or absence of a joint cavity, i.e., a space between the articulating surfaces of the bones. Each type of joint is further subdivided either according to shape or according to the nature of the tissues which connect the bones. These classifications, with their subdivisions, may be grasped more readily if presented in outline form.

    I. Diarthrosis (from the Greek, meaning a joint in which there is a separation, or articular cavity) (Fig. 4)
      A. Characteristics
        1. An articular cavity is present.
        2. The joint is encased within a sleevelike ligamentous capsule.
        3. The capsule is lined with synovial membrane which secretes synovial fluid for lubricating the joint.
        4. The articular surfaces are smooth.
        5. The articular surfaces are covered with cartilage, usually hyaline, but occasionally fibrocartilage.

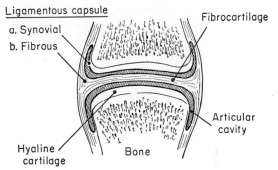

Figure 4. Frontal section of a diarthrodial joint having fibrocartilage.

B. Classification*

1. Irregular (arthrodial; plane). The joint surfaces are irregularly shaped, usually flat or slightly curved. The only movement permitted is of a gliding nature, hence it is nonaxial. Example: the carpal joints (Fig. 88).

2. Hinge (ginglymus). One surface is spool-like; the other is concave. The concave surface fits over the spool-like process and glides partially around it in a hinge type of movement. This constitutes movement in one plane about a single axis of motion, hence it is uniaxial. The movements that occur are flexion and extension. Example: elbow joint (Fig. 78).

3. Pivot (trochoid; screw). This kind of joint may be characterized by a peglike pivot, as in the joint between atlas and axis, or by two long bones fitting against each other near each end in such a way that one bone can roll around the other one, as do the radius and ulna of the forearm. In the latter type a small concave notch on one bone fits against the rounded surface of the other. The rounded surface may either be the edge of a disk (like the head of the radius), or it may be a rounded knob (like the head of the ulna). The only movement permitted in either kind of pivot joint is rotation. It is a movement in one plane about a single axis, hence the joint is uniaxial. Examples: atlantoaxial and radioulnar joints (Figs. 23 and 78).

4. Ovoid (condyloid; ellipsoidal). An oval or egg-shaped convex surface fits into a reciprocally shaped concave surface. Movement can occur in two planes, forward and backward, and from side to side. The former movement is flexion and extension, and the latter abduction and adduction, or lateral flexion. The joint is biaxial. When these movements are performed in succession, they constitute circumduction. Example: wrist joint (Fig. 88).

5. Saddle (reciprocal reception). This may be thought of as a modification of an ovoid joint. The two ends of the convex surface are tipped up, making the surface concave in the other direction, like a western saddle. Fitting over this is a reciprocally concave-convex surface. Like the ovoid joint, this is a biaxial joint, and it permits flexion and extension, abduction and adduction, and circumduction. The difference between the two is that the saddle joint has greater freedom of motion. Example: carpometacarpal joint of thumb (Fig. 91).

6. Ball-and-socket (spheroidal; enarthrodial). In this type of joint the spherical head of one bone fits into the cup or saucerlike cavity of the other bone (Figs. 56 and 104). It is very like the swivel joint on the top of a camera tripod. It permits flexion and extension, abduction and adduction, circumduction (the sequential combination of the preceding), and rotation. It is a triaxial joint, since it permits movement about three axes.

C. Summary classification of diarthrodial joints

Number of Axes	0 Non-axial	1 Uniaxial	2 Biaxial	3 Triaxial
Classification.........	Irregular	Hinge Pivot	Ovoid Saddle	Ball and socket

* This classification is based on the one in Morris' Human Anatomy.

II. Synarthrosis (from the Greek, meaning literally "with joint," or according to our usage, a joint in which there is no separation or articular cavity)

  A. Characteristics

    1. In two of the types (cartilaginous and fibrous) the two bones are united by means of an intervening substance, such as cartilage or fibrous tissue, which is continuous with the joint surfaces.

    2. The third type (ligamentous) is not a true joint, but is a ligamentous connection between two bones which may or may not be contiguous.

    3. There is no articular cavity, hence no capsule, synovial membrane or synovial fluid.

  B. Classification

    1. Cartilaginous (synchondrosis; from the Greek, meaning "with cartilage")

    Only the joints which are united by fibrocartilage permit motion of a bending and twisting nature. Those united by hyaline cartilage permit only a slight compression. Example of hyaline type: epiphysial unions. Example of fibrocartilaginous type: articulations between the bodies of the vertebrae (Fig. 15).*

    2. Fibrous (suture; from the Latin word for "seam"). The edges of bone are united by means of a thin layer of fibrous tissue which is continuous with the periosteum. No movements are permitted. Only example: the sutures of the skull.

    3. Ligamentous (syndesmosis; from the Greek, meaning "with ligament"). Two bones, which may be adjacent or which may be quite widely separated, are tied together by one or more ligaments. These ligaments may be in the form of cords, bands or flat sheets. The movement that occurs is usually limited and of no specific type. Examples: coracoacromial union (Fig. 58); midunion of radius and ulna (Figs. 79 and 80).

  C. Summary

    The synarthrodial joints of greatest concern to the kinesiologist are those of the vertebral bodies. Owing to the thickness of the intervertebral disks, these permit a moderate amount of motion simulating that of ball-and-socket joints. The movements are flexion and extension, lateral flexion, circumduction and rotation.

* In some anatomy texts these are classified separately as amphiarthrodial joints.

Suggestions for Studying the Structure and Function of the Joints.

In order to understand thoroughly the structure of a joint, the student should supplement his book study with first-hand study of a skeleton or of the disarticulated bones which enter into the formation of each joint. Following this preliminary study, the student will find it extremely helpful to "construct" a joint by taking the disarticulated bones and fastening them together with pieces of adhesive tape, carefully placed to represent the specific ligaments of the joint. Pieces of felt, cut in the proper shape, may be used to represent the fibrocartilage. This method of studying a joint is particularly helpful in regard to the knee, hip and shoulder joints.

The movements of each joint should be studied both on the skeleton and on the living subject. When using the latter method, the student should take into consideration all the joints involved in the movement being studied. For instance, in studying the movements of the elbow, the articulation between the humerus and the radius must not be overlooked. The close relationship that exists between certain joints should be noted, as for instance the relationship between the elbow joint and the proximal radioulnar articulation. The tilting of the pelvis which accompanies many movements of the lower extremity should be recognized; likewise the movements of the shoulder girdle which accompany those of the shoulder joint. There is a particular pitfall awaiting those who study the movements of the shoulder joint only by observing the living subject. If not forewarned, they are very likely to overlook the part played by the shoulder girdle in movements of the arm on the body. The action of the shoulder girdle may easily be detected if the student will palpate the scapula and the clavicle in all movements of the upper arm. He can follow the movements of the scapula by placing his thumb at the inferior angle, one finger on the root of the scapular spine, and another on the acromion process, and by keeping them firmly in contact with these points as the scapula moves.

The x-ray also affords a valuable method of studying the structure and function of the joints. Of even greater value will be the x-ray motion picture when it is made available for such purposes.

Supplementary Material

Method of Measuring Joint Motion.   The literature on the measurement of joint motion reveals a notable lack of uniformity in technique and a corresponding disagreement regarding the normal range of motion. In many instances the norms quoted appear to be set up arbitrarily, rather than as the result of experimentation. While much has been achieved in the past decade in standardizing the techniques of measurement, there is still a need for tables of norms for both sexes and for a complete age range, based on actual measurement. The student who is interested in investigating this field will find a wealth of material in the literature listed in the bibliography. One of the most complete and scientific investigations to date is that of Moore at the Division of Clinical Research, Baruch Center of Physical Medicine, Medical College of Virginia.

Range of Motion.   1. *The Range of Motion in Selected Joint Movements.* An investigation was conducted by the author to note the range of motion in certain selected joint movements and to observe the extent of individual differences. The movements measured were: flexion, outward and inward rotation, and horizontal extension-abduction of the arm at the shoulder joint; flexion and abduction of the thighs; dorsal and plantar flexion of the foot. In each of the arm measurements the subject was required to perform the movement with both arms, although the measurement was taken on only the left. The purpose of this was to prevent the tendency to rotate the body toward the side being measured in an attempt to get an apparent increase of motion. Twenty-four young women were used as subjects. All measurements were made with a protractor.

a. FLEXION AT THE SHOULDER JOINT.   The subject sat on a bench with the head and back braced against the edge of an open door and raised both arms forward-upward as far as possible, keeping them shoulder distance apart, with the palms facing each other and the elbows fully extended. The angle between the upper arm and the vertical was measured with a plumb line protractor.

Range = 161° to 186°
Median = 172.5°

b. OUTWARD ROTATION AT THE SHOULDER JOINT. The subject assumed the same position as described above, except that the upper arms were raised sideward to shoulder level, with elbows bent at right angles and the forearms pointing forward with palms down. The upper arms were then rotated outward so that the forearms moved in an arc, upward and backward as far as possible, with the upper arms remaining at the horizontal. The angle between the forearm in its final position and the horizontal was measured with a plumb line protractor.

Range = 90° to 138°
Median = 99°

c. INWARD ROTATION AT THE SHOULDER JOINT. The starting position for this measurement was the same as that for outward rotation. The upper arms were rotated inward so that the forearms moved forward-downward as far as possible, with the upper arms remaining at the horizontal. The angle between the final position of the forearm and the horizontal was measured with a plumb line protractor.

Range = 75° to 148°
Median = 108°

d. HORIZONTAL EXTENSION-ABDUCTION AT THE SHOULDER JOINT. The subject lay on her back on a narrow bench with her knees drawn up and feet resting on the bench. The arms were extended sideward at shoulder level, then lowered toward the floor as far as possible. Care was taken to see that the bench was narrow enough so as not to interfere with free movement of the shoulder joints. The angle between the upper arm and the horizontal was measured with a plumb line protractor.

Range = 20° to 57°
Median = 44°

e. HIP FLEXION WITH STRAIGHT KNEE. As a measure of hip and hamstring flexibility hip flexion was measured with the knee kept in complete extension. The subject lay on a narrow bench and raised the right leg from the hip as far as possible, keeping the knee and the ankle fully extended. The angle between the midline of the lateral aspect of the thigh and the horizontal was measured with a plumb line protractor.

Range = 53° to 114°
Median = 92°

f. HIP ABDUCTION. The subject lay on her back on the floor and abducted both legs at the hip joints as far as possible, keeping the feet pointing upward, thus eliminating rotation at the hips. The angle between the two abducted thighs was measured with a Lufkin rule protractor, each arm of which had been extended by the attachment of a straight, narrow stick, long enough to reach past the patella.

$$\text{Range} = 59° \text{ to } 95°$$
$$\text{Median} = 78.5°$$

g. DORSAL FLEXION OF THE FOOT.   The subject sat on a long bench with the legs extended and the feet projecting beyond the edge of the bench. Keeping the right leg extended, the subject dorsiflexed her right foot. One arm of the protractor was held along the lateral surface of the foot in line with its long axis, and the measurement was taken between this and the vertical. If the foot reached or passed the vertical, the measurement was positive. If it failed to reach the vertical, it was negative.

$$\text{Range} = -4° \text{ to } 15°$$
$$\text{Median} = 5°$$

h. PLANTAR FLEXION OF THE FOOT.   The subject sat on a long bench with the legs extended and the feet projecting beyond the edge of the bench. Keeping the right leg extended, the subject plantar-flexed her right foot. One arm of the protractor was held along the lateral surface of the foot in line with its long axis, and the measurement was taken between this and the vertical.

$$\text{Range} = 47° \text{ to } 80°$$
$$\text{Median} = 61°$$

2. *Comparison of Shoulder Flexibility before and after Corrective Exercises.* In a class in corrective physical education the author made several pertinent measurements at the beginning and end of the season of instruction. Among these was the measurement of forward elevation of the arm on the body. This involves, chiefly, flexion at the shoulder joint, but also includes some movement of the scapula, especially upward rotation. Individuals with resistant forward shoulders have limited motion in the shoulder joint. It is particularly difficult for them to get their arms to an upward vertical position, or beyond, when the arms are kept only shoulder distance apart. The measurements were made on thirty girls, aged 16 to 18, in the following manner. The subject presented her left side to the examiner and raised both arms forward, upward and backward as far as possible without bending the elbows. Using a large semicircular protractor with a movable arm, the examiner held the protractor with its center opposite the center of motion at the shoulder joint and with the base line parallel with the axis of the subject's upper trunk. She then moved the arm of the protractor until it was in line with the subject's arm and read the anterior angle between the subject's arm and trunk. The results of the two sets of measurements were as follows:

	RANGE	MEDIAN
Measurements made in November 1948	129° –170°	142.5°
Measurements made in March 1949	141.5°–175°	162.5°

3. *Comparison of Measurements of Forward Elevation of the Arm Made by Different Investigators.*   A comparison of measurements of a selected joint movement may be of interest to the reader. It should be noted, however, that the techniques used were not standardized and that the measurements were based on relatively small samples, not selected at random. Forward elevation of the arm is

the movement selected. The techniques of the three investigators were different, but had this in common: they used either the vertical or the horizontal as a point of reference rather than the long axis of the trunk.

a. Experimenter: Van Horn

Number, age and sex of subjects: 165 women, aged 16 to 18 inclusive.

Technique: The subject lay on a narrow board with the knees drawn up and the back kept in contact with the board. The angle between the horizontal surface of the board and the subject's arm was measured with a protractor.

Measurements:

	Range	*Median*
R:	159°–196°	178°
L:	155°–198°	177°

b. Experimenters: Glanville and Kreezer

Number, age and sex of subjects: ten men, aged 20 to 40 inclusive.

Technique: The subject lay on his back on a table with the shoulder over the edge of the table. The measurement was made with an arthrometer having a circular scale and a weighted metal pendulum type of indicator. This instrument was strapped to the lateral surface of the subject's arm, just proximal to the elbow.

Measurements:

	Range	*Mean*
R:	164°–191°	179°
L:	165°–187°	180°

c. Experimenter: Wells

Number, age and sex of subjects: 24 young women, aged 17 to 20.

Technique: The subject sat on a gymnasium bench with the head and back braced against the edge of an open door and raised both arms forward-upward as far as possible, keeping them shoulder distance apart with the palms facing and the elbows fully extended. The anterior angle between the upper arm and the plumb line was measured with a plumb line protractor.

Measurements:

	Range	*Median*
L:	161°–180°	172.5°

It is interesting to see that, in spite of the small groups of subjects and in spite of the differences in techniques, the results are fairly consistent. It is also interesting to note the contrast between the results of these three investigations and the one made by the author on the students in the corrective class. There are doubtless two factors that account for the appreciably lower scores made by the latter group. The first is the fact that the group was selected on the basis of poor posture. The second is the fact that the subject's own trunk was taken as the point of reference. This ruled out the influence of hyperextension of the spine on the position of the arm. Although the latter technique requires the use of subjective judgment in aligning the protractor with the subject's trunk, it is probably a more valid measure of the range of joint motion. This is the technique used by Kraus and Weber at the Vanderbilt Posture and Corrective Exercise Clinic.

Demonstrations and Laboratory Exercises

1. Dissect a joint obtained from the butcher and identify the following types of tissue: tendon, ligament, fibrocartilage, hyaline cartilage and synovial membrane. Identify the type of joint and name its movements.

2. By studying a skeleton and observing a living subject, classify the following joints without referring to a textbook: hip, elbow, knee, ankle, wrist, radioulnar, metacarpophalangeal joint of finger, shoulder joint. (Do not confuse the motion at the elbow or wrist joints with that at the radioulnar joints.)

3. From a disarticulated skeleton select the necessary bones to illustrate each type of joint.

4. Using a movable arm type of protractor, measure the range of motion in the same joint movements that were described in the supplementary section of this chapter.

Bibliography

Joint Structure and Function

1. Gray, H.: Anatomy of the Human Body. 26th ed. Philadelphia, Lea & Febiger, 1954.
2. Morris' Human Anatomy. 11th ed. New York, McGraw-Hill Book Company, Inc., 1953.
3. Sibley, K.: Elementary Human Anatomy. New York, A. S. Barnes & Co., 1935.
4. Sobotta, J.: Atlas of Human Anatomy. Translated from latest German edition by E. Uhlenhuth. New York, Hafner Publishing Co., 1957.
5. Steindler, A.: Kinesiology of the Human Body. Springfield, Ill., Charles C Thomas, 1955, pp. 58–63.
6. Walmsley, T.: Mechanism of Diarthrosis. J. Bone & Joint Surg., *10:* 40–45, 1928.

Range of Joint Motion and Its Measurement

7. Dorinson, S. M., and Wagner, M. L.: An Exact Technic for Clinically Measuring and Recording Joint Motion. Arch. Phys. Med. *29:* 468, 1948.
8. Glanville, A. D., and Kreezer, G.: Maximum Amplitude and Velocity of Joint Movements in Normal Male Human Adults. Human Biology, *9:* 197–211, 1937.
9. Hand, J. C.: A Compact Pendulum Arthrometer. J. Bone & Joint Surg., *20:* 494–495, 1938.
10. Hurt, S. P.: Joint Measurement. Am. J. Occupational Therapy, *1:* 209–214, 1947.
11. Kraus, H., and Eisenmenger-Weber, S.: Evaluation of Posture Based on Structural and Functional Measurements. Physiotherapy Rev., *25:* 267–271, 1945.
12. Leighton, J. R.: A Simple Objective and Reliable Measure of Flexibility. Research Quarterly, Am. Assn. for Health, Phys. Ed. and Rec., *13:* 205–216, 1942.
13. Molander, C. O., and Weinmann, B.: A New Chart System of Recording Joint Measurements. Physiotherapy Rev., *21:* 88–90, 1941.
14. Moore, M. L.: The Measurement of Joint Motion. Part I: Introductory Review of the Literature. Phys. Therapy Rev., *29:* 195–205, 1949.
15. ———: The Measurement of Joint Motion. Part II: The Technic of Goniometry. Phys. Therapy Rev., *29:* 256–264, 1949.
16. Van Horn, E. C.: Preliminary Work toward the Development of a Table of Norms of the Range of Motion in the Shoulder Joint. Unpublished Seminar Study, Wellesley College, 1947.
17. West, C. C.: Measurement of Joint Motion. Arch. Phys. Med., *26:* 414–425 (July) 1945.

3 · The Muscular System

Definition.   A muscle may be described as a bundle of red contractile fibers held together by a sheath of connective tissue. It is attached to bone by means of tendons or aponeuroses (fibrous sheets) which stem from the connective tissue sheath.

The Properties of Muscular Tissue.   Like an elastic band, muscular tissue can be stretched, and will return again to its normal resting length when the stretching force is removed. This characteristic of muscular tissue involves two properties, *extensibility* and *elasticity*. Unlike the elastic band, it can shorten beyond its normal resting length by pulling from both ends in toward the center. This is a chemical process, and it results (unless prevented) in the total muscle becoming shorter and, at the same time, greater in circumference. This property is known as *contractility*. Experimenters have found that the average muscle fiber can shorten to approximately one-half its resting length and can be stretched until it is half again as long as its resting length.[1, 12] The range between the minimal and maximal lengths of a muscle fiber is known as its amplitude.[11]

Physiologic Principles of Muscular Contraction.   Whenever a muscle fiber contracts, it contracts maximally. This is known as the *all-or-none* principle of muscular contraction. Gradations in muscular contraction are related to the number of fibers in the muscle which contract, not to variations in intensity.

When a muscle contracts repeatedly, the first few contractions are each progressively greater than the preceding, until the maximal response is reached. The inability of the muscle to attain its maximum response immediately is thought to be due to the viscosity of the muscle. This phenomenon, known as the *treppe* or staircase phenomenon, is one reason for recommending a warm-up as preparation for strenuous activity.

Of significance to the physical educator and the physical therapist is the fact that a muscle can exert greater force when it is on a stretch than when it is shortened. It exerts its maximum force when the resistance to its action is so great that no shortening can take place. As the muscle shortens, its force diminishes progressively. This characteristic of muscular action to exert greater force when it is on a stretch, or when it encounters an appreciable resistance, gives the clue to the condition under which muscles are strengthened. It also forms the basis for the DeLorme heavy resistance exercises. The increase in strength can be surprisingly rapid if the loads are increased in exactly the right relation to the capacity of the muscles.[10]

Structural Classification of Muscles.　　The arrangement of the fibers and the method of attachment vary considerably among the different muscles. These structural variations form the basis for a classification of the skeletal muscles.

Longitudinal.　　This is a long straplike muscle whose fibers lie parallel to one another. Two examples are the rectus abdominis on the front of the abdomen, and the sartorius, which slants across the front of the thigh.

Quadrate or Quadrilateral (Fig. 5, *E* and *F*).　　Muscles of this type are four-sided and are usually flat. They consist of parallel fibers. Examples include the pronator quadratus on the front of the wrist, and the rhomboid muscle between the spine and the scapula.

Triangular or Fan-Shaped (Fig. 5, *D*).　　This is a relatively flat type of muscle whose fibers radiate from a narrow attachment at one end to a broad attachment at the other. The pectoralis major on the front of the chest is an excellent example.

Fusiform or Spindle-Shaped (Fig. 5, *A*).　　This is usually a rounded muscle which tapers at either end. It may be long or short, large or small. Good examples are the brachialis and the brachioradialis muscles of the arm.

Penniform or Feather-like (Fig. 5, *B*).　　In this type of muscle a series of short parallel fibers extends diagonally from the side of a long tendon, giving the muscle as a whole the appearance of a wing feather. Examples: extensor digitorum longus and tibialis posterior muscles of the leg.

Bipenniform (Fig. 5, *C*).　　This is a double penniform muscle. It is characterized by a long central tendon with the fibers extending diagonally in pairs from either side of the tendon. It is like a symmetrical tail feather. Examples: flexor hallucis longus and rectus femoris.

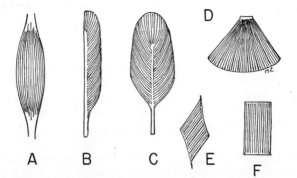

Figure 5. Examples of muscles of different shapes and internal structure. *A,* Fusiform or spindle; *B,* penniform; *C,* bipenniform; *D,* triangular or fan-shaped; *E,* rhomboidal; *F,* rectangular.

Multipenniform.   In this type of muscle there are several tendons present, with the muscle fibers running diagonally between them. The middle portion of the deltoid muscle is an example of a multipenniform muscle.

Fascia.   Closely associated with the musculature is the deep fascia, a type of fibrous connective tissue which forms both the enveloping sheaths for the muscles, nerves and blood vessels, and the partitions which separate muscles and muscle groups from each other. The term "fascia" comes from the Latin word for band, meaning something which binds together like a bandage. This gives a good picture of the function of fascia in the body.

Although fascia does not have the ability to contract, it does sometimes serve as an extension of a muscle. The fascia on the side of the thigh, for instance, is tightened by the contraction of the tensor fasciae latae and the gluteus maximus muscles (Figs. 111, 112, 113), and the influence of these muscles is thus extended to the side of the leg just below the knee, where the strip of fascia, known as the iliotibial band, is attached. The effect of this tightening of the fascia is to stabilize the knee joint. It is an example of the part played by fascia in increasing postural stability. The fasciae of greatest interest to the student of kinesiology are probably the plantar fascia on the sole of the foot, the lumbodorsal fascia in the back, the fascia lata and the iliotibial band, on the lateral side of the thigh. More will be said about these fasciae in connection with the muscles with which they are associated.

The Action of the Muscles in Moving Bones.   In the simplest arrangement, a muscle spans a joint and attaches to the two contiguous bones. When the muscle is stimulated by the motor nerves, which innervate its fibers, it contracts and thus pulls on the two bones to which it is attached. If no opposing or stabilizing force were present, the two bones would both move. For instance, a muscle which spanned the inner aspect of a hinge joint would cause the two bones to fold together, both of them participating in the movement. Likewise, a muscle which spanned the outer aspect of a hinge joint would pull these bones back to their original position. If one thinks in terms of using the hand for a particular task, it would immediately be apparent that it would be most inconvenient if, every time the forearm moved, the upper arm were to move too. If such were the case it would be difficult to perform movements of precision or power. A more effective movement results when a muscle moves only one of the bones to which it is attached. This it does when the other bone is stabilized, that is, held motionless either by the action of other muscles or by the greater weight or more limited mobility of the second bone. This is essentially the manner in which all movements of the body segments take place.

Direction of Pull.   Which bone is to remain stationary and which one is to move, or in other words, which muscle attachment is to be stabilized and which is to move, depends upon the requirements of the total movement. In most of the movements of the arms and legs the more distal bones are the ones that move. But this is not always the case. There are a number of familiar movements which require that the more distal bone be stationary in order that the more proximal one may move effectively. In chinning one's self, for instance, the forearm is stationary while the upper arm moves toward it.

Muscular Attachments.   It has been customary to name the attachments of the muscles "the origin" and "the insertion," the origin being the attachment which is usually stabilized, and the insertion being the attachment which usually moves. This terminology has had the unfortunate result of giving students the erroneous idea that the muscle can pull in only one direction. They have had difficulty in grasping the true concept of muscular contraction, namely, that the muscle tends to pull equally from its attachments toward the center, and would do so if the bones to which it was attached were equally free to move.

In an attempt to prevent a misconception of muscular contraction, a departure from the usual system for naming the attachments of the muscles is suggested here. It is hoped that students who have previously learned the terms "origin" and "insertion" will attempt to substitute the terminology suggested below.*

* As a concession to those who find the new terms more confusing than helpful, also as an aid to students who wish to relate the new terms to the old, the letters "O" and "I" are inserted parenthetically, following the new terms.

Attachments of Muscles of the Head, Neck and Trunk:
Upper attachment
Lower attachment   } for muscles which run more or less vertically

Medial attachment }
Lateral attachment } for muscles which run more or less horizontally

Attachments of Muscles of the Extremities:
Proximal attachment
Distal attachment

Attachments of the Diaphragm:
Peripheral attachment
Central attachment

Bones as Levers.   From the mechanical point of view, the bones serve as levers, a lever being any rigid bar which turns about a fixed point (i.e., a fulcrum) when force is applied to it. In the bony lever the fixed point is the joint at which the movement is taking place, and the force applied to the lever is the pull exerted by the contracting muscle. The mechanical laws which govern the action of levers are discussed in Chapter 13.

Angle of Pull (Fig. 6).   The angle formed between the muscle's line of pull and the mechanical axis of the bony lever is known as the muscle's angle of pull. It represents the direction of the application of force. As the bone moves, the angle of pull keeps changing. This is inevitable when the muscle's other point of attachment is kept stationary. The size of the angle has a direct bearing on the effectiveness of the muscle's pull in moving the bony lever. Except when the pull is at right angles to the mechanical axis of the lever, some part of the force exerted by the muscle is wasted, so far as motion is concerned. More often than not, the angle of pull is less than a right angle. This means that the portion of force which is not contributing to the movement of the bone is tending to pull lengthwise through the bone in the direction of the joint. This has a stabilizing effect, as it counteracts any tendency toward dislocation. The components of muscular force and their relation to the angle of pull are discussed in Chapter 15.

Muscle Tension.   When a muscle contracts, it is said to exert tension. As the muscle shortens, there is a proportional decrease in its tension. Hence a muscle exerts maximum tension when it is on the greatest stretch, that is, within normal physiologic limits. The effectiveness of a muscle in moving a bodily segment depends not alone upon the tension it is able to exert, but also upon the leverage and the angle of pull as well. This is discussed further in Part II.

Types of Muscular Contraction.   Although the word "contraction" literally means shortening, there are three types of so-called

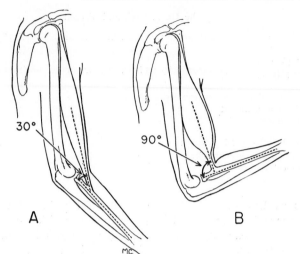

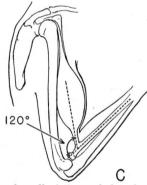

Figure 6. Angles of muscle pull. *A,* An angle less than 45 degrees; *B,* an angle of 90 degrees; *C,* an angle greater than 90 degrees.

muscular contraction, only one of which involves a shortening of the fibers.

1. *Shortening or Concentric Contraction* (also called phasic or isotonic contraction). The muscle actually shortens, and when one end is held still, the other pulls the bone and turns it about the joint. The bone thus serves as a lever and the joint as its fulcrum. This is the usual type of contraction seen in physical activities.

2. *Lengthening or Eccentric Contraction.* This is a gradual releasing of the contraction, as when one lowers a weight slowly or gives in to an external force which is stronger than that of the contracted muscle. The term "lengthening" is misleading, since the muscle does not actually lengthen. It merely returns to its resting length.

3. *Static Contraction* (also called tonic or isometric contraction).   The muscle remains in partial or complete contraction without changing its length. There are two different conditions under which this type of contraction is likely to take place.

a. Muscles which are antagonistic to each other contract with equal strength, thus balancing each other. The part affected is held tensely in place without moving. Tensing the biceps is an example of this.

b. A muscle is held in partial or complete contraction against another force, such as the pull of gravity or an external force. Examples of this are holding a book with outstretched arm; a tug of war between two equally matched opponents; and attempting to move an object which is too heavy to move.

A Functional Classification of Muscles.

Whether a muscle will cause flexion, extension, abduction or any other movement when it contracts, is determined not by anything inherent in its structure, but by the relation of the muscle's line of pull to the joint's axis of motion, and to the movements permitted by the structure of the joint. Thus a muscle on the front of the knee joint can only extend, whereas one on the front of the elbow joint flexes. A muscle on the lateral side of the hip joint abducts; one on the medial side, adducts; and so forth. A muscle on the lateral side of the knee joint, however, could not abduct because the structure of the knee is such that abduction is impossible. Because of the interrelationship between muscle function and joint structure, a functional classification of the muscles corresponds closely to the structural classification of the diarthrodial axial joints.

Joints	*Muscles*
Uniaxial	
Hinge...............	Flexors and extensors
Pivot..................	Rotators
Biaxial	
Ovoid..................	Flexors; extensors; abductors; adductors
Saddle................	Same as for ovoid joints
Triaxial*	
Ball-and-socket.........	Flexors; extensors; abductors; adductors; rotators

Reversal of a Muscle's Customary Function.

Occasionally it happens that the relation of a muscle's line of pull to the joint's axis of motion becomes reversed as the joint assumes certain positions. For instance, the clavicular portion of the pectoralis major is ordinarily a flexor, adductor, and horizontal flexor-adductor of the arm at the shoulder joint. When the arm is elevated sideward to

* Although the joints of the spinal column consist of cartilaginous and nonaxial diarthrodial joints, the movements of the spine are similar to those of a triaxial joint. This is because of the ball-and-socket nature of the nucleus pulposus in the intervertebral disks.

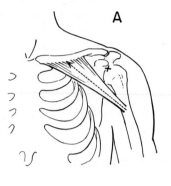

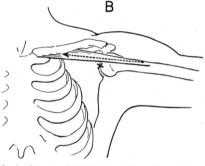

Figure 7. The clavicular portion of the pectoralis major muscle reversing its customary function. *A,* The line of pull is below the center of the shoulder joint. *B,* The line of pull is above the center of the shoulder joint.

a position slightly above shoulder level, however, the line of pull of the clavicular portion of the pectoralis major shifts from below to above the axis of the shoulder joint (Fig. 7). Contraction of the muscle in this position contributes to *abduction* of the humerus, instead of to adduction. Thus the student will see that he cannot take the muscular actions for granted, but must always consider the relation of the muscle's line of pull to the joint's axis of motion at each stage of a movement.

The Coordination of the Muscular System. Not all muscular action is for the purpose of causing motion. In nearly every movement of the body there are some muscles which have other functions, such as steadying and supporting a part, stabilizing a bone to which another muscle is attached, or neutralizing the unwanted action of a muscle which normally causes several movements. Accordingly, the muscles which make their various contributions to a movement may be classified respectively as movers, stabilizers and neutralizers.

Movers. A mover is a muscle which is directly responsible for effecting a movement. In the majority of movements there are several movers, some of them of greater importance than others. These are the principal movers. The muscles which help to perform the movement, but which seem to be of less importance, or which contract only under certain circumstances, are the assistant movers. Muscles which help only when an extra amount of force is needed, as when a movement is performed against resistance, are sometimes called emergency muscles. This distinction between the various muscles which contribute to a movement is entirely arbitrary. There may well be some difference of opinion as to whether a muscle is a principal or an assistant mover in a given movement.

Fixator, Stabilizing and Supporting Muscles. This group includes the muscles which contract statically to steady or support some part of the body against the pull of the contracting muscles, against the pull of gravity, or against the effect of momentum and

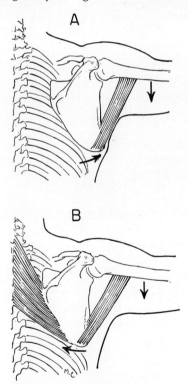

Figure 8. If the scapula were not stabilized, the teres major would increase the upward rotation of the scapula as it adducted the humerus. This dual action on the humerus and scapula is shown in *A*. In *B*, the scapula is stabilized by the scapular adductors and downward rotators. This permits the teres major to concentrate its force on the adduction of the humerus.

recoil in certain vigorous movements. One of the most common functions of these muscles is the steadying or fixating of the bone to which a contracting muscle is attached. It is only by the stabilizing of one of its attachments that the muscle is able to cause an effective movement of the bone at which it has its other attachment (Fig. 8).

Neutralizers. A neutralizer is a muscle which acts to prevent

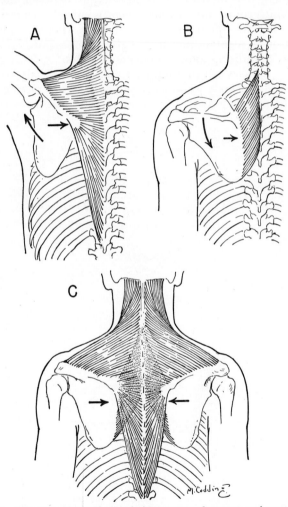

Figure 9. The trapezius and rhomboids as mutual movers and neutralizers. *A*. The trapezius alone adducts the scapula and rotates it upward. *B*, The rhomboids alone adduct the scapula and rotate it downward. *C*, Together the trapezius and rhomboids adduct the scapula without rotating it either upward or downward.

an undesired action of one of the movers. Thus if a muscle both flexes and abducts, but only flexion is desired in the movement, an adductor contracts to neutralize the abductory action of the mover.

Occasionally two of the movers have one action in common, but second actions which are antagonistic to each other. For instance, one muscle may upward rotate and adduct, the other may downward rotate and adduct. When they contract together to cause adduction, their rotatory functions counteract each other (Fig. 9). Muscles which behave this way in a movement are mutual neutralizers as well as movers. Some writers call muscles which have this neutralizing function, synergists.[13] The term "synergist" is also used by some for muscles that stabilize bones; and by others for any muscles that work together to contribute to a movement, regardless of the specific function of each.[11, 12] Because of this confusion, the use of the term has purposely been avoided in this text.

Antagonists. An antagonist is a muscle which causes the opposite movement from that of the muscle acting as a mover. Thus in a movement of flexion, the flexors are the movers and the extensors are the antagonists. In accordance with the physiologic principle known as reciprocal innervation, when a muscle contracts, its antagonist automatically relaxes (see p. 44).

Having stated the general rule, it is now necessary to describe what may at first appear like a contradiction. If a movement performed with great force and rapidity is not checked, it will subject the ligamentous reinforcements of the joint to sudden strain. The tissues would probably be severely damaged. This is particularly true of quick movements of the arm or leg because of the tremendous momentum that can be developed in a long lever. To prevent such injury the muscles which are antagonistic to the movers contract momentarily to check the movement. As they contract, the movers relax, if indeed they have not already relaxed, allowing momentum to complete the movement. The situation is a little like taking the foot off the accelerator in order to put it on the brake. At the moment when the movement is being checked, the so-called antagonistic muscles are not antagonistic at all, but are serving temporarily as movers in eccentric contraction. Thus, in a vigorous movement, the antagonistic muscles may be said to perform two functions. Their first function is to relax in order to permit the movement to be made without hindrance; their second function is to protect the joint by acting as a brake at the completion of the movement.

Relation of Gravitational Force to Muscular Action. Any movement which *could* be performed by the force of gravity, but which is controlled muscularly, is performed (i.e., controlled) by the muscles which are ordinarily antagonistic to the movement in

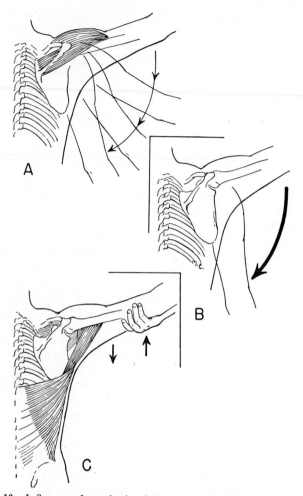

Figure 10. Influence of gravitational force on muscular action in sideward depression of the arm (adduction of the humerus). *A,* Eccentric contraction of the abductors in slow lowering of the arm. *B,* Absence of muscular action when the arm is dropped to the side. *C,* Concentric contraction of the adductors when the movement is performed against resistance.

question. For instance, a slow sideward lowering of the arm from an overhead position involves adduction at the shoulder joint (Fig. 10, *A*). Yet it is the abductors (deltoid and supraspinatus) which control the movement. They exert their control by means of eccentric or lengthening contraction (p. 26). If the arm were allowed to fall to the side, gravity alone would be responsible for the movement (Fig. 10, *B*). If it were brought down quickly and vigorously, or if it were lowered forcefully against an external resistance, the adductors would be the movers (Fig. 10, *C*). In analyzing movements, therefore, it is essential to note the part played by the force of gravity or by resistance. In all movements controlled against the pull of gravity the usual muscular action is reversed.

Pulley or Tendon Action of Two-Joint Muscles. Another type of coordination of the muscular system is seen in the so-called pulley or tendon action of the two-joint muscles, that is, the muscles that pass over and act upon two joints. Examples of these are the hamstrings (semitendinosus, semimembranosus, and biceps femoris), which flex the leg at the knee and extend the thigh at the hip; the rectus femoris, which flexes the thigh and extends the leg; the sartorius, which flexes both the thigh and the leg; the gastrocnemius, which helps to flex the leg in addition to its primary function of extending the foot; and the long flexors and extensors of the fingers. The latter are actually multi-joint muscles, since they cross the wrist and at least two of the joints of the fingers. A characteristic of all these muscles, whether they act on joints that flex in the same direction, as in the case of the wrist and fingers, or in the opposite direction, as in the case of the knee and hip, is that they are not long enough to permit complete movement in both joints at the same time. This results in the tension of one muscle being transmitted to the other, in much the same manner that a downward pull on a rope which passes through an overhead pulley is transmitted in the form of a pull in the reverse direction to the rope on the other side of the pulley. Thus if the hamstrings contract to help extend the hip, tension is transmitted to the rectus femoris, causing it to extend the knee. Or if the rectus femoris contracts to help flex the hip, tension is transmitted to the hamstrings, causing them to flex the knee. This explanation is, of course, an over-simplification of what actually happens in the movements of the body.

When one-joint muscles contract, their shortening is accompanied by a corresponding loss of tension. In quick movements of the limbs, one-joint muscles lose their tension rapidly. The advantage of two-joint muscles is that they can continue to exert tension without shortening. The two-joint muscles have two different patterns of action. These have been described by Fenn, Steindler and others as concurrent and countercurrent movements.

An example of concurrent movement is seen in simultaneous extension of the hip and knee; also in simultaneous flexion of these joints. As the muscles contract they act on each other in such a way that they do not lose length, and therefore retain their tension. It is as though the pull traveled up one muscle and down the other in a continuous circuit. In simultaneous extension of the hip and knee, for instance, the rectus femoris' loss of tension at the distal or knee end is balanced by a gain in tension at the proximal or hip end. Similarly, the hamstrings, which are losing tension at their proximal end, are gaining it at their distal end.

The countercurrent pattern presents a different picture. In this type of movement, while one of the two-joint muscles shortens rapidly at both joints, its antagonist lengthens correspondingly and thereby gains tension at both ends. An example of this is seen in the rapid loss of tension in the rectus femoris and corresponding gain of tension in the hamstrings, when the hip is flexed and the knee is extended simultaneously. A vigorous kick is a dramatic illustration of this kind of muscle action. The backward swing of the lower extremity preparatory to kicking is a less spectacular but equally valid example. The forward swing in walking is another. In both patterns of movement the one- and two-joint muscles appear to supplement each other, and thus, by their cooperative action, to produce smooth, coordinated, efficient movements.

The Study of Muscular Actions by Electromyography.   Muscular action has been studied by dissection, by experiments on the cadaver, by electrical stimulation of normal muscles, by deduction based on a knowledge of anatomy and mechanics, and by the observation and palpation of the muscles on living, moving subjects. In recent years a new method has been developed and is being used to an increasing extent. This is electromyography, the technique whereby the action potentials of contracting muscles are recorded. It reveals both the relative intensity and the duration of the contraction. Thus it is a precise, accurate tool for analyzing the activity of individual muscles in a given movement. It is also a useful means of studying abnormal movement patterns and of comparing them with the normal. Its limitations are the same as those of palpation in that it is limited to the study of superficial muscles. The problem of testing the deeper muscles may be solved in the future, however. Another limitation lies in the fact that, in any given study, it can be applied to only relatively small groups of subjects. Since individual variations in muscular activity have been noted, this is a definite drawback. The investigator must refrain from making generalizations on the basis of single studies. As in all research, the results of one study need to be substantiated by those of other similar studies before positive conclusions can be drawn. The student of kinesiology will find it well worth his time to keep abreast of the literature in which electromyographic studies are reported, and to compare the results of studies on the same muscle groups.

Supplementary Material

In an article on the mechanics of muscular contraction Fenn described a simple experiment that demonstrates the influence of muscle length on the force which the muscle can exert. The strength of the rectus femoris and of the biceps femoris was tested in two positions by means of the Martin breaking-point test. The rectus femoris is situated on the front of the thigh and attaches to the pelvis just above the hip joint, and, by means of the patellar ligament, exerts its pull on the front of the tibia just below the knee joint. Hence it is a flexor of the hip and an extensor of the knee. The biceps femoris is situated on the back of the thigh and attaches above the hip and below the knee. It therefore is an extensor of the hip and a flexor of the knee.

For the first test the subject lay on his back on a table with his knees at the edge and his legs hanging down. For the second test he sat on the end of the table with his trunk flexed well forward from the hips. Thus the rectus femoris was on a greater stretch in the first position, and the biceps femoris in the second. The results showed that the rectus femoris exerted greater force in the first position than in the second, but the biceps femoris exerted greater force in the second position. These experiments could easily be duplicated in the classroom.

Demonstrations and Laboratory Exercises

1. Referring to a cadaver, a muscle manikin, muscle charts, or samples of meat obtained from a butcher, identify the structural type of several muscles. Also identify some deep fascia.

2. Take two sticks which are joined at one end by a hinge. Attach a single piece of elastic or a long rubber band to the opposite ends of the two sticks.

a. Separate the ends of the sticks as far as the elastic will permit and then demonstrate the way the elastic will pull both sticks together.

b. Demonstrate the way the elastic will move only one of the sticks if the other one is stabilized.

c. Repeat both a and b, using the arm of the skeleton instead of the sticks.

3. Fasten or hold an elastic on a skeleton to represent the line of pull of the clavicular portion of the pectoralis major. Note its relation to the center of motion of the shoulder joint. Now raise the arm sideward above the shoulder level. Again note the relation of the elastic to the center of the joint.

4. Get a subject to hold a heavy dumbbell in his right hand and slowly raise his arm sideward-upward without bending at the elbow. Keep your fingers on the clavicular portion of the pectoralis major. Does it contract? If so, at what position of the arm does it begin?

5. Flex the fingers hard. Keep them flexed and flex the hand at the wrist as far as possible. What happens to the fingers? Explain.

6. Extend the fingers, then hyperextend the hand at the wrist as far as possible. What happens to the fingers? Explain.

7. Get a subject to lie on the left side with the hip and knee in a partly flexed position and the right leg fully extended. The right thigh should now be flexed passively by an operator. The subject should attempt to keep the knee straight, but not to the point of interfering with the hip flexion. What happens? Where does the subject feel discomfort? Explain.

8. With the subject in the same starting position as in 7, have him flex both his right thigh and leg completely. The right thigh should now be passively extended by an operator, the subject attempting to keep the leg flexed at the knee. As the thigh becomes fully extended, what happens to the knee? Where does the subject feel discomfort? Explain. (Caution: Do not use acrobats or acrobatic dancers as subject for 7 or 8, or the experiments may not work. Why?)

Note: Laboratory exercises on the action of muscles as movers, stabilizers and neutralizers are not included here because, in order to do them, it is necessary to know the individual muscles. They will be found in the laboratory sections of the chapters that follow.

Bibliography

1. Arkin, A. M.: Absolute Muscle Power; The Internal Kinesiology of Muscle. Arch. Surg., *42:* 395–410, 1941.
2. Bowen, W. P., and Stone, H. A.: Applied Anatomy and Kinesiology. 7th ed. Philadelphia, Lea & Febiger, 1953, Chap. 3.
3. Brunnstrom, S.: Some Observations of Muscle Function; With Special Reference to Pluriarticular Muscles. Physiotherapy Rev., *22:* 67, 1942.
4. DeLorme, T. L., and Watkins, A. L.: Progressive Resistance Exercise. New York, Appleton-Century-Crofts, Inc., 1951, Chaps. 2 and 3.
5. Elftman, H.: The Action of Muscles in the Body. Biological Symposia, ed. by W. O. Fenn. Vol. 3: Muscle. Lancaster, Pa., The Jaques Cattell Press, 1941, pp. 191–209.
6. Fenn, W. O.: The Mechanics of Muscular Contraction in Man. J. Appl. Physics, *9:* 165–177, 1938.
7. Lombard, W. P.: The Action of Two-Joint Muscles. Am. Phys. Ed. Rev., *8:* 141–145, 1903.
8. Markee, J. E., et. al.: Two-Joint Muscles of the Thigh. J. Bone & Joint Surg., *37A:* 125–142, 1955.
9. McCloy, C. H.: Some Notes on Differential Actions of Partite Muscles. Research Quarterly of Am. Assn. for Health, Phys. Ed. and Rec., *17:* 254–262, 1946.
10. Morehouse, L. E., and Cooper, J. M.: Kinesiology. St. Louis, C. V. Mosby Company, 1950, Chaps. 10, 11 and 12.
11. Scott, M. G.: Analysis of Human Motion. New York, F. S. Crofts & Co., 1945, p. 384.
12. Steindler, A.: Kinesiology of the Human Body. Springfield, Ill., Charles C Thomas, 1955.
13. Wright, W.: Muscle Function. New York, Paul B. Hoeber, Inc., 1928, pp. 6–7.

Recommended Readings

Bowen, W. P., and Stone, H. A.: Applied Anatomy and Kinesiology. (See 2 above.)
Steindler, A.: Kinesiology of the Human Body. (See 12 above.) Lectures 4B and 5B. (For advanced students.)
Wright, W.: Muscle Function. (See 13 above.)

4 · Neuromuscular Function

$\mathbf{T}$HE STUDY of neuromuscular function belongs properly to a course in physiology, but certain aspects of it relate so closely to kinesiology that some mention of these facts should be made in a kinesiology text. It is important to realize, however, that a single chapter on neuromuscular function cannot do justice to this subject. The chapter should be looked upon merely as an introduction to neuromuscular function for those who have not yet studied physiology of movement, or as a brief review for those who have studied it.

It is well for the student to be aware of the fact that sciences which relate to the human body are not in "airtight compartments." The various bodily functions are described as separate systems for reasons of convenience, not because they are inherently separate, independent systems. Thus biologic chemistry, physiology, neurology, biomechanics, and others, are not isolated or unrelated sciences. They are collections of scientific facts and principles, having to do with the human body, which have been systemized into so-called sciences for purposes of study, reference and application. It is inevitable that there should be some overlapping, since the different aspects of the body which are described in these sciences are closely interrelated and interdependent. The very fact that hard and fast boundaries cannot be drawn between them serves to point up the high degree of integration within the human organism.

Only those aspects and characteristics of neuromuscular function which seem to have particular significance in the study of kinesiology are mentioned in this chapter, and the discussion of each is brief. For more thorough considerations of these topics the reader is referred to the bibliography at the end of the chapter.

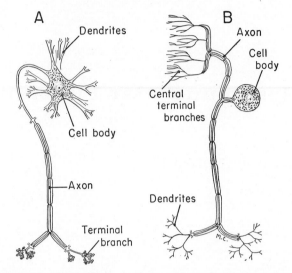

Figure 11. Nerve fibers. *A,* Motor neuron; *B,* sensory neuron.

The Motor Unit.   Since muscles provide the force for moving the anatomic levers, a brief review of the way in which they function has a logical place in a text on human motion. Skeletal muscles ordinarily contract only in response to nerve impulses coming from the central nervous system. The complex stimulus-response mechanism can best be understood in terms of the motor unit—that is, a single motor neuron (Fig. 11, *A*) and the muscle fibers which it supplies. The cell body of the neuron is located in the anterior horn of the spinal cord (or occasionally in the brain stem), and its other end terminates in a muscle. The terminal end branches within the muscle, and each branch terminates in a motor end-plate, which in turn makes direct contact with the sarcoplasm of a single muscle fiber. Because of the terminal branching of a neuron, each nerve fiber may innervate as many as a hundred or more muscle fibers. On the other hand, every muscle fiber is supplied by at least one nerve fiber (motor neuron). The number of muscle fibers innervated by a single nerve fiber is determined, not by the size of the muscle, but by the precision of its movements. Muscles which are called upon to perform movements requiring fine coordination have more nerve fibers per muscle fiber than do muscles which perform less skillful movements. In the small muscles of the hand, such as those used for threading a needle, there are fewer muscle fibers per nerve fiber than is the case in the rectus abdominis, for instance, or in the gluteus maximus.

Impulses travel along the motor neuron in one direction only, that is, from the spinal cord to the muscle fiber. When a stimulus reaches a muscle fiber, there is a brief latent period, followed by a period of contraction, which in turn is followed by a period of relaxation. Whenever a muscle fiber receives a stimulus, either it contracts completely or it does not contract at all. There is no such thing as partial contraction of a single muscle fiber. The tension in a fully contracted fiber is not always uniform, however, for it is influenced by such factors as fatigue and training. Nevertheless the fiber is always as completely contracted as it is able to be at that moment. Variations in the degree of contraction of a total muscle are achieved by means of the number of muscle fibers innervated and the frequency of nerve impulses to each fiber.

Innervation of Muscle. The motor neuron functions only in response to a stimulus. This stimulus may stem from volition (i.e., from the cerebrum), from the cerebellum and brain stem, or it may come as a simple reflex, initiated by pressure, pain, irritation, and so on. Volitional impulses originate in the central nervous system (brain and spinal cord). The reflexes from the brain stem and cerebellum smooth and coordinate movements. The stimuli for reflex movements come from the sensory nerves of the peripheral system. These sensory nerves conduct impulses of sensation from the surface of the body and from the sense organs (exteroceptive or cutaneous nerves), from the muscles and tendons, also from the mechanism for equilibrium located in the ear (proprioceptive nerves), and from the lining of the viscera (interoceptive nerves). Thus the exteroceptive nerves conduct sensations of touch, pain, temperature, taste, hearing and sight; and the proprioceptive nerves conduct sensations of deep pressure, changes in muscular tensions, and equilibrium. A sensory nerve, otherwise known as an afferent neuron (Fig. 11, *B*), is stimulated through its dendrites which are located in skin, muscles and sense organs. The impulses are then conducted along these dendrites to the cell body in a root ganglion,

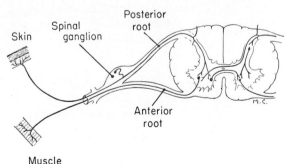

Muscle

Figure 12. Reflex arc mechanism.

and thence by axon to the dorsal (posterior) horn of the spinal cord, where the fiber ends in central terminal branches. These make synaptic connections either directly with the dendrites of a motor neuron, or indirectly by means of connector neurons. The motor neuron then carries the impulse to the muscle, which responds by contracting. This type of stimulus-response mechanism is known as a reflex arc (Fig. 12).

Nerve Trunks.   Motor neurons and sensory neurons serving the same region are united into nerve trunks. Each nerve trunk goes to the general region which it supplies and there separates into its various nerve fibers. At the distal extremity of the trunk the efferent or motor neurons emerge and pass to their respective muscles. By means of terminal branching, each neuron supplies several muscle fibers. The afferent or sensory neurons originating from the skin, muscles, tendons, and so forth, from this region converge to become part of this same nerve trunk. The nerve trunk, at its proximal or spinal end, enters the spinal column via the notch that lies beneath the pedicle, behind the body and in front of the inferior articular process of a vertebra. It then divides into two roots, the posterior root joining the posterior horn of the spinal cord, and the anterior root joining the anterior horn (Fig. 13). The posterior root is made up of sensory neurons, and the anterior root of motor neurons. Unlike the motor neuron, the cell body of the sensory neuron is not located within the spinal cord, but in the posterior root ganglion before it joins the cord. There are thirty-one pairs of spinal nerves in all—eight cervical, twelve thoracic, five lumbar, five sacral, and one coccygeal.

This is obviously an oversimplification of the nervous mechanism. For a thorough description, the reader should refer to a standard text on physiology, neurology, or physiology of exercise.

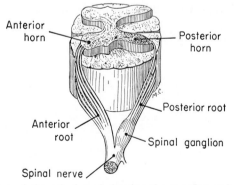

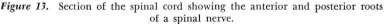

Figure 13. Section of the spinal cord showing the anterior and posterior roots of a spinal nerve.

Muscle Tonus (Tonic Contraction). The major functions of neuromuscular activity divide themselves into (1) tonic contractions, for the purpose of maintaining muscle tonus and controlling posture, and (2) phasic contractions, for effecting movements of the skeletal structure. All living muscles normally possess tonus, even when the individual is in a state of maximal voluntary relaxation. A complete absence of tonus is found only in pathologic conditions in which there is injury to some part of the motor unit. Flaccidity of the muscles results from conditions such as anterior poliomyelitis in which the motor cells in the anterior horn of the spinal cord are damaged. The degree of tonus in the normal muscle varies in relation to different factors, such as temperature and emotional states. It also varies from muscle to muscle at any given moment, the postural or antigravity muscles usually having greater tonus than the others.

Muscles depend for their tonus upon stimulation from the reflex arcs, and this tonus may be modified by impulses from the brain stem nuclei. The exact process is not completely understood, but it is believed that the muscle fibers contract in turn, a few at a time. Although each fiber that contracts undergoes maximum contraction, not enough fibers are active to produce any motion of the skeletal segment. The individual cannot control the degree of muscle tonus, for it is a reflex response, that is, a response to impulses from the reflex centers and peripheral nervous system rather than from the brain. The most important of these reflexes is known as a myotatic reflex. The stimuli responsible for muscle tonus come from changes in the tension of the muscle. These changes may be caused by stretching, in which case the response is called a stretch reflex.

Muscle tonus serves the purpose of maintaining the body postures and of preventing the full weight of body parts from falling on the ligaments. The antigravity muscles have more tonus than the other muscles, as the reader can ascertain for himself by comparing the firmness of the gastrocnemius, quadriceps femoris, abdominal muscles and sacrospinalis with that of the triceps, pectoralis major and sternocleidomastoid, for instance. The impulses responsible for the muscle tonus necessary for maintaining posture and preserving equilibrium are derived from the sensory receptors (proprioceptors) in muscles and tendons, from the mechanism for equilibrium located in the semicircular canals, and from visual stimulation.

Phasic Contraction. Phasic muscular contractions are the contractions that effect movements of the skeletal structure. They may be either reflex or volitional. Jerking the hand away after inadvertently touching a hot stove is an example of the former; tying one's shoelace an example of the latter. In the case of touching the hot stove the stimuli received by the receptors of the skin on the palm of the hand are conducted to the spinal cord transmitted within the cord to the motor neurons, and from the latter to the muscles responsible for removing the hand from the stove. It is interesting to note that it is not the muscles of the palm of the hand that are innervated in this case, but the muscles of the wrist, elbow and shoulder joints, and possibly even of the trunk and lower extremities. Thus, without the intervention of the brain, the nervous system "knows" which muscles to innervate in order to accomplish the purpose of removing one small part of the body from the offending environment. This type of reflex is known as a spinal reflex.

Volitional Movements.   Volitional movements, like the tying of one's shoelace, are initiated by impulses from the motor area of the cerebral cortex. These are transmitted down the spinal cord to the level where the motor cells controlling the proposed movement are located. The left side of the motor area controls movements of the right side of the body, and vice versa.

Reflexes.*   A reflex act is one which occurs without the aid of the volition. The mechanism for this is described in the section on innervation of muscle and is illustrated in Figure 12. The reflexes of particular interest to the kinesiologist are the flexor, extensor, stretch and postural reflexes.

Flexor Reflexes.   There are two manifestations of flexor reflexes in the movements of the body. One of these is the response to pain. It is due to the flexor reflex that we automatically withdraw a part of the body the instant it is hurt. If a pin pricks a finger or if we accidentally touch a hot stove, we do not have to think about removing our hand from the source of injury; we jerk it back almost before we know what has happened to it. In this sense the flexor reflex is a device for self-protection.

The other manifestation of flexor reflex action is in the flexion movements of the lower extremities in walking and running. For locomotor movements like these, the flexor and extensor reflexes alternate with each other to provide a smooth, coordinated movement pattern.

Stretch Reflex.   The stretch reflex is a proprioceptor reflex, depending upon stimulation from within the muscle itself for its innervation. When the tendon of a muscle is stretched as the result of the contraction of an antagonistic muscle, the pull of gravity, or some external force acting upon it, the impulses thus received are carried to the spinal cord, where they are transmitted to the motor neurons. These conduct motor impulses back down to the muscle,

* Most of the material in this section was obtained from Fulton's "Textbook of Physiology," Chapter 6.

and the muscle contracts. It is characteristic of the stretch reflex
that the response is limited to the muscle fibers which are stretched.
It is interesting to note that the stretch reflex is most fully developed
in the extensor muscles.

Extensor or Antigravity Reflex. As was stated above, the
stretch reflex is particularly well developed in the antigravity muscles. These include the extensor muscles of all the weight-bearing
joints, the supinators of the feet, the abdominal muscles and the
scapular adductors. In the upright position the pull of gravity
on the body tends to flex the joints of the spine, hips, knees and
ankles. This tendency serves as a stimulus to the antigravity muscles, which respond by an increase in tonus which enables them to
keep the weight-bearing joints in extension. Normally, the stretch
reflex also enables man to maintain good posture of the abdomen
and shoulders, but apparently it has been lost in many individuals
because of the long hours they have spent in sedentary occupations,
working with their arms in front of their bodies.

The extensor reflex is brought into action by other means than
the stretch reflex alone. Pressure against the sole of the foot elicits
the reflex contraction of the extensor muscles of the lower extremity.
Thus it cooperates with the stretch reflex in helping the body to
resist the force of gravity when it is in the upright, weight-bearing
position. This is of value in all forms of locomotion, as well as in
standing still.

Haynes has demonstrated that the voluntary contraction of certain of the muscles in the antigravity group has a tendency to cause
others to contract reflexly. Thus, if a person lying prone contracts
the extensors of the left lower extremity, the extensors of the right
one contract also. Or if he voluntarily contracts the gluteal muscles,
the other extensors contract reflexly.

Postural Reflexes. The postural reflexes represent the coordinated efforts of the body to resist the downward pull of gravity.
They include three categories of reactions. The first, known as local
static reactions, are controlled by the antigravity or extensor reflexes just described. Their effect is most noticeable in the stance.

The second group, known as segmental static reactions, has to do
with the effect of the movement of one extremity on the opposite
extremity. In four-footed animals it is responsible for the coordination of the limbs in locomotion, i.e., the tendency of the left foreleg
to extend as the right hind leg extends. In man it would seem to be
responsible for the swing of the arms in opposition to the movement of the legs.

The third group, coming under the heading of general static reactions, includes the tonic neck and labyrinthine reflexes. These
function in response to the position of the head in space, which, in

turn, influences the tonus of the neck muscles and the two mechanisms of the labyrinthine reflexes, namely, the semicircular canals and the otolithic chambers. The effect of stimulating these reflexes is to bring about a reaction of the limbs and trunk in response to the position of the head.

Spasticity of Muscles. Muscular spasticity is described by Magoun and Rhines as an exaggeration of spinal stretch reflexes. To understand this it is necessary to recognize the function of the two central mechanisms, the central inhibitory and the central facilitatory mechanisms. The former, located in the brain, serves to reduce spinal stretch reflexes. The latter appears to have several sources, some in the cord itself, some in the brain stem, some in the cerebellum, and some in the cerebral cortex. The impulses from any of these facilitatory mechanisms serve to augment stretch reflexes. When an interference, caused by disease or injury, cuts off the inhibitory influences, the normal stretch reflex augmented by impulses from any of the uninjured facilitatory mechanisms results in the exaggeration of stretch reflexes, known as spasticity. The fact that some facilitatory influences are derived from the spinal cord explains a phenomenon which surprises the partially informed layman, namely, spasticity of muscles resulting from an injury in which the spinal cord is severed.

Reciprocal Innervation and Inhibition. Were it not for the mechanism of reciprocal innervation and inhibition, the muscles contracting to move a segment of the body would have to work against the resistance of the normal muscle tonus of the antagonistic muscles. Thus, in flexion of the forearm at the elbow, the biceps and brachialis would have to overcome the resistance provided by the tonus of the triceps and anconeus. Nature is more efficient than this, however. By means of the phenomenon of reciprocal innervation and inhibition the muscles antagonistic to a movement are inhibited. The inhibition apparently comes about as the result of the function of the central inhibitory mechanism in the brain. This not only inhibits phasic contraction, but it inhibits tonic contraction also. Thus the muscle tonus of antagonistic muscles during movement is considerably less than their tonus in the normal resting state.

An application of this phenomenon is occasionally useful in stretching exercises such as "passive chest lifting" (p. 469). The stretching may stimulate a stretch reflex action causing increased tonus in the pectoral muscles. This can be avoided if the operator takes advantage of the mechanism for reciprocal innervation and inhibition. If he gets the subject to adduct the scapulae and if he synchronizes his pull on the elbows with the subject's contraction of the adductors, he will find that a greater range of motion is achieved than when the subject is merely passive. Another example of the inhibition of normal muscle tonus is seen in the comparison of active dorsiflexion of the foot with passive dorsiflexion, performed by an operator.

Functional Innervation of Muscles.   Beevor concluded from his experiments that muscles are innervated in their functional groups. According to this theory, if a movement such as forward elevation of the arm is desired, it is initiated by one center in the central nervous system, rather than by a center for each muscle involved in the movement. Wright pointed out, however, that such grouping is not fixed. As evidence of this she cited the possibility of reeducating a muscle which has been transplanted. The peroneus longus, for instance, normally a plantar flexor of the foot, can be taught to contract with the dorsiflexors when its tendon of insertion is transplanted in such a way that the line of pull of the muscle is shifted from behind, to in front of, the center of motion at the ankle joint.

Kinesthetic Sense.   In his chapter on Somatic Sensation, Ruch listed six senses in addition to the familiar five.* One of these is the "muscle, tendon and joint sense, or kinesthesia." This is also known as the "position sense," for it is the sense that gives us the awareness of the position of the parts of the body without the aid of vision or touch. Other terms commonly used are kinesthesis and proprioception. There are three types of receptors which record muscle sensations. One of these is located in the fleshy part of the muscle, another in the tendons close to the point of union with the muscle proper, and the third in the fasciae of the muscles. These receptors are responsible for making us aware of the state that a muscle is in, i.e., whether it is contracted or stretched, and the intensity of the contraction or stretch. They also make us aware of the stretch to which fascia is subjected. In addition to awareness of muscular and fascial sensations, the kinesthetic sense enables us to know, with a fair degree of accuracy, the position of any part of our body and the movement that a part of the body is undergoing, even when that part is moved by someone else and our own muscles are in a state of relaxation.

This awareness of position or movement and of intensity of muscular action is an important factor in the learning of new skills. In learning any given skill the memory of former sensations and the consciousness of present ones in the performance of this skill help us to judge the correctness of our movements. Glassow placed considerable emphasis on kinesthetic awareness, perception and memory in the learning of movement patterns.

Learning Motor Skills.   It is a matter of common observance that some movement skills require greater concentration than others,

* A Textbook of Physiology, edited by Fulton, Chapter 18.[2]

and that during the learning period all skills demand considerably more concentration than they do after they have been mastered. Even fairly complicated skills, like assembling a piece of machinery and knitting Argyle socks, can be so completely mastered that the performer can give his attention to a conversation or to planning a menu without making a mistake in his work.

The process of developing motor skills has been particularly well described by Morehouse and Miller. At first, when full attention must be given to the task, the movements are controlled by the motor area of the cerebral cortex. This phase usually requires that the sensations received from the vision be closely correlated with those received from the kinesthetic sense. The correct sequence of movements is gradually learned as the result of practice. As this step in the learning process takes place, the control of the movements shifts to the area anterior to the motor area. As perfection in the skill is attained, the individual relies almost entirely on the proprioceptive stimuli. The visual stimuli as such are discontinued, although, no doubt, the memory of previous visual stimuli still plays a part in the accuracy of the movements. Learning to type by the touch method is a familiar example of this learning process. Writing by longhand, eating, and dressing oneself are even more familiar illustrations.

Ballistic Movement. The concept of ballistic movement is one which has been described, not by physiologists, but by experimental psychologists.[2, 3, 8, 10, 12, 13, 14] They classify movements first into slow and rapid movements. The slow movements are said to be "moving fixations," because they involve the contraction of opposing muscle fibers. Rapid movements, they say, may be performed either ballistically or as moving fixations. Rapid movements are skillfully executed only when they are performed ballistically. By this they mean that the movement is initiated by muscular contraction, but that the muscles then relax and permit momentum to complete the movement. This type of movement is characteristic of throwing, striking and kicking. On a smaller scale it is represented by typewriting and piano playing. When these activities are performed nonballistically, that is, with a constant muscular contraction, they are uneconomical, hence not skillful. They are then tension movements. This characterizes the way in which beginners and young children frequently attempt new coordinations, especially when they are concentrating on accuracy of aim rather than on ease of motion. The psychologists recommend emphasizing form at the expense of accuracy in learning new skills. Otherwise, they say, bad habits of tensing the muscles are likely to be established.

Ballistic movements may be terminated by one of three methods: (1) by contracting antagonistic muscles, as in the forehand drive in tennis; (2) by allowing the moving part to reach the limit of motion, in which case it will be stopped by the passive resistance of ligaments or muscles, as in the case of a high kick; (3) or by the interference of an obstacle, as in the case of chopping a tree. In many movements found both in sports and in skilled labor, three types of muscular action cooperate to produce a single act. This kind of cooperation is seen especially in striking movements which require the use of an implement, such as a tennis racket, golf club or ax. Movements such as these involve (1) fixation to support the moving part and to maintain the necessary position; (2) ballistic movement of the active limb; and (3) fixation in the fingers as they grasp the implement. Hartson suggested that the purpose of the "follow through" in throwing and striking movements in sports is to assure a ballistic type of movement.

The investigations of these psychologists, based on action current analysis, raise many questions of interest to the kinesiologist and demonstrate a tool of research which is unfamiliar to the majority of physical educators, but which opens up an exciting new field of experimentation. The experiments from which the psychologists draw their conclusions were based for the most part on artificial movements of the hand or arm. Their findings have many implications for the physical educator, yet the latter should not accept them without further evidence—evidence based on actual sport movements. It would seem, for instance, that there may be some sport movements which cannot be categorized as either tension or ballistic movements. Where maximum speed or force is desired, it would seem necessary to exert muscular effort throughout the movement, yet undesirable to contract the antagonistic muscles. It would also seem that there are more factors in the "follow through" than are suggested by Hartson's hypothesis. Questions such as these await further research by investigators in the field of physical education.

Since demonstrations and laboratory exercises pertaining to neuromuscular function belong properly in a physiology laboratory, they are omitted here.

Bibliography

1. Beevor, C.: The Croonian Lectures on Muscular Movements. (Reprint.) New York, Macmillan Company, 1951.
2. Fulton, J. F. (Editor): A Textbook of Physiology. 17th ed. Philadelphia, W. B. Saunders Company, 1955.
3. Glassow, R. B.: A Laboratory Manual for a Course in Functional Kinesiology. Mimeographed by Kramer Business Service, Madison, Wisconsin, 1950.
4. Hartson, L. D.: Analysis of Skilled Movements. Personnel J., *11:* 28–43, 1932.
5. Hartson, L. D.: Contrasting Approaches to the Analysis of Skilled Movements. J. Gen. Psychol., *20:* 263–293, 1939.

6. Haynes, R. S.: Postural Reflexes in Relation to the Correction of Improper Body Position. Am. J. Dis. Child., *36:* 1095–1107, 1928.
7. Karpovich, P. V.: Physiology of Muscular Activity. 5th ed. Philadelphia, W. B. Saunders Company, 1959.
8. Magoun, H. W., and Rhines, R.: Spasticity; The Stretch-Reflex and Extrapyramidal Systems. Springfield, Ill., Charles C Thomas, 1948.
9. Morehouse, L. E., and Cooper, J. M.: Kinesiology. St. Louis, C. V. Mosby Company, 1950, Chap. 11.
10. Morehouse, L. E., and Miller, A. T.: Physiology of Exercise. 2nd ed. St. Louis, C. V. Mosby Company, 1953, Chaps. 1, 2 and 18.
11. Ralston, H. J.: Recent Advances in Neuromuscular Physiology. Am. J. Phys. Med., *36:* 94–120, 1957.
12. Sherrington, C. S.: Integrative Action of the Nervous System. New Haven, Yale University Press, 1948.
13. Sperry, R. W.: Action Current Study in Movement Coordination. J. Gen. Psychol., *20:* 295–313, 1939.
14. Stetson, R. H., and Bouman, H. D.: The Action Current as a Measure of Muscle Contraction. Science, *77:* 219–221 (Feb. 24) 1933.
15. Stetson, R. H., and Throner, G. C.: Training for Flexible Posture and Relaxation Movements. Research Quarterly of Am. Assn. for Health, Phys. Ed. and Rec., *7:* 143–150, 1936.
16. Stetson, R. H., and McDill, J. A.: Mechanism of the Different Types of Movement. Psychological Monographs, *32:* No. 3, 18–40, 1923.
17. Wright, W.: Muscle Function. New York, Paul B. Hoeber, Inc., 1928.

Recommended Readings

Glassow, R. B.: A Laboratory Manual for a Course in Functional Kinesiology. (See 3 above.)
Morehouse, L. E., and Miller, A. T.: Physiology of Exercise. (See 10 above.)
Stetson, R. H., and Throner, G. C.: Training for Flexible Posture and Relaxation Movements. (See 15 above.)

5 · The Spinal Column

If one were faced with the problem of devising a single mechanism that would *simultaneously* (1) give stability to a collapsible cylinder; (2) permit movement in all directions, yet always return to the fundamental starting position; (3) support three structures of considerable weight—a globe, a yoke and a cage; (4) provide attachment for numerous flexible bands and elastic cords; (5) transmit a constantly increasing weight to a rigid basin-like foundation; (6) act as a shock absorber for cushioning jolts and jars; and (7) encase and protect a cord of extreme delicacy, he would be staggered by the immensity of the task. Yet the spinal column fulfills all these requirements with amazing efficiency. It is at the same time an organ of stability and mobility, of support and protection, of resistance and adaptation. It is an instrument of great precision, yet is of robust structure. Its architecture and the manner in which it performs its many functions are worthy of careful study. From the kinesiologic point of view, we are interested in the spine chiefly as a mechanism for maintaining erect posture and for permitting movements of the head, neck and trunk.

In order to understand these functions of the spine, it is necessary to have a clear picture, first of the spinal column as a whole, and secondly of the distinguishing characteristics of the different regions. The spinal column, consisting of seven cervical, twelve thoracic and five lumbar vertebrae, the sacrum and the coccyx, presents four curves as seen from the side. The cervical and lumbar curves are convex forward, the thoracic and sacrococcygeal curves convex to the rear (Fig. 14). The thoracic and sacrococcygeal curves are called primary because they exist before birth. The cervical and lumbar curves develop during infancy and early childhood, hence

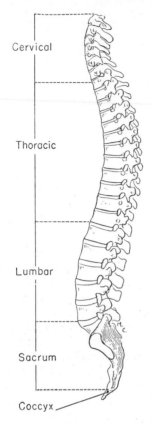

Cervical

Thoracic

Figure 14. Lateral view of the spinal column showing antero-posterior curves.

Lumbar

Sacrum

Coccyx

are called secondary curves. From the first cervical vertebra to the fifth lumbar, the vertebral bodies become increasingly larger, an important factor in the weight-bearing function of the spine.

There are two sets of interspinal articulations, those between the vertebral bodies and those between the vertebral arches. The articulations of the first two vertebrae are atypical and will be described separately.

Articulations of the Vertebral Bodies (Fig. 15).   These joints are classified as synchondroses, or cartilaginous joints. The bodies of the vertebrae are united by means of fibrocartilages, otherwise known as intervertebral disks. These correspond to the surfaces of the adjacent vertebral bodies, except in the cervical region, where they are smaller from side to side. They adhere to the hyaline cartilage both above and below, there being no articular cavity in this type of joint. In thickness they are fairly uniform in the thoracic region, but in the cervical and lumbar regions they are thicker in front than in back. Altogether they constitute one fourth of the

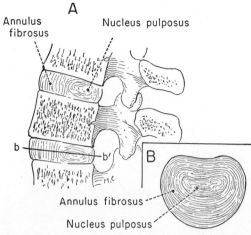

Figure 15. *A,* Sagittal section of lumbar vertebrae and intervertebral fibrocartilage. *B,* Transverse section of intervertebral fibrocartilage.

length of the spinal column. Each disk consists of two parts, an outer fibrous rim and an inner pulpy nucleus, known as the nucleus pulposus. This is a ball of firmly compressed elastic material, not unlike the center of a golf ball. It constitutes a pivot of motion and permits compression in any direction, as well as torsion. The intervertebral disks are also important as shock absorbers.

Ligaments of the Vertebral Bodies. *Anterior Longitudinal Ligament* (Fig. 16). This ligament extends from the inner sur-

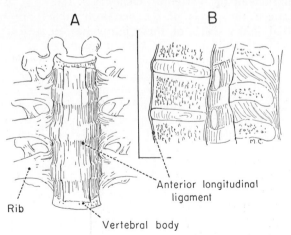

Figure 16. Anterior longitudinal ligament of the spine. *A,* Anterior view; *B,* sagittal section of vertebrae showing lateral view of ligament.

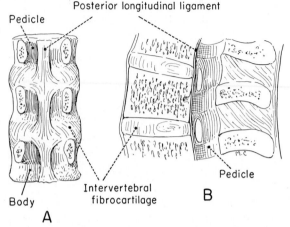

Pedicle

Posterior longitudinal ligament

Body

Intervertebral fibrocartilage

A

Pedicle

B

Figure 17. Posterior longitudinal ligament of spine. *A,* Frontal section of vertebrae showing posterior view of ligament. *B,* Sagittal section of vertebrae showing lateral view of ligament.

face of the occipital bone down the front of the spinal column to the sacrum. It starts as a narrow band and widens as it descends. It is thinnest in the cervical region and thickest in the thoracic.

Posterior Longitudinal Ligament (Fig. 17). This extends from the occipital bone down the back of the vertebral bodies to the coccyx. It is a relatively narrow band with lateral expansions opposite each intervertebral fibrocartilage, especially in the thoracic and lumbar regions.

Articulations of the Vertebral Arches (Fig. 18). The articulations between the facets of the vertebral arches are non-axial diarthrodial joints. Each of these joints has an articular cavity and is enclosed within a capsule. A slight amount of gliding motion is permitted. The resultant movement of each vertebra is determined largely by the direction in which the articular facets face. In the cervical region they slant at about a 45 degree angle, lying halfway between the horizontal and the frontal planes (Fig. 19, *A*). The upper surfaces face partly upward and partly backward; the lower ones partly downward and partly forward. Thus they favor no one motion more than another. In the thoracic region they lie slightly more in the frontal and less in the horizontal plane than the cervical articulations, and they have a slight inward and outward slant (Fig. 19, *B*). The upper facets face backward, slightly upward and lateralward; the lower facets forward, slightly downward and medialward. They are adapted equally well to rotation and to lateral bending. In the lumbar region, except at the lumbosacral articulation, the articular facets lie more nearly in the sagittal plane (Fig. 19, *C*). The upper facets face inward and slightly backward; the lower facets face outward and slightly forward. Furthermore, the upper facets present slightly concave surfaces, and the lower facets convex. By this arrangement of the facets the lumbar vertebrae are virtually locked against rotation. The slight amount of rotation that does occur is made possible by the looseness of the capsules. At the lumbosacral articulation the facets lie somewhat more in the frontal plane than is the case in the other lumbar joints.

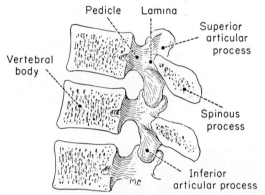

Figure 18. Sagittal section of vertebrae showing articulations of the vertebral arches.

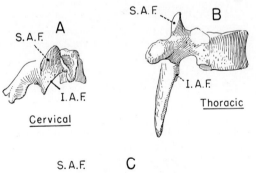

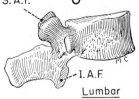

Figure 19. Articular facets of vertebrae. *A*, Cervical; *B*, thoracic; *C*, lumbar. Note: *S.A.F.* = superior articular facet. *I.A.F.* = inferior articular facet.

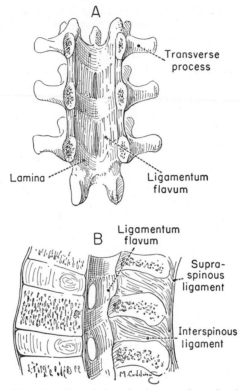

Figure 20. *A,* Frontal section of three lumbar vertebrae showing anterior view
of vertebral arches and ligamenta flava. *B,* Sagittal view of lumbar vertebrae
showing ligaments of vertebral arches.

Ligaments of the Vertebral Arches.   *Ligamenta Flava* (Fig.
20, *A* and *B*).   These are thick elastic plates which connect the
laminae of adjacent vertebrae. They are thickest in the lumbar
region, less thick but fairly strong in the thoracic region, and thin,
broad and membranous in the cervical region.

Interspinous Ligaments (Fig. 20, *B*).   These are thin membranous ligaments, connecting the lower border of each spinous
process with the upper border of the one below it. They are thickest
and broadest in the lumbar region and are but slightly developed
in the cervical region.

Supraspinous Ligament (Fig. 20, *B*).   This is a strong fibrous
cord which connects the tips of the spinous processes, extending
from the seventh cervical vertebra to the sacrum. It is thicker and
broader in the lumbar region than in the thoracic.

Ligamentum Nuchae (Fig. 21).   This is the continuation of

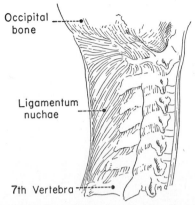

Occipital
bone

Ligamentum
nuchae

7th Vertebra

Figure 21. Side view of cervical spine showing ligamentum nuchae.

the supraspinous ligament in the cervical region. It extends from
the seventh cervical vertebra upward to the occipital bone in the
form of a thin fibrous membrane.

Intertransverse Ligaments. These rather poorly developed
ligaments connect the transverse processes of adjacent vertebrae in
the thoracic and lumbar regions. In the thoracic region they are
round cords; in the lumbar, thin membranous bands.

Atlanto-occipital Articulation (Fig. 22). This is the articulation between the head and the neck. It consists of a pair of joints,
one on each side. Each condyle of the occipital bone of the skull
articulates with the corresponding superior articular fossa of the
first vertebra, known as atlas. Each articulation by itself belongs
to the ovoid (condyloid) classification, but the movement which
occurs in the two joints together is more like that of a hinge joint.
The rigid relationship between the two joints results in a restriction
of the lateral motion that would normally occur in an ovoid joint.
The movements which take place at the atlanto-occipital articulation are chiefly flexion and extension, with a slight amount of
lateral flexion. There is no rotation.

Atlantoaxial Articulation (Fig. 23). This is a perfect example of a pivot joint. The toothlike peg (odontoid process) that
projects upward from the second cervical vertebra, otherwise
known as axis or epistropheus, fits into the ring formed by the inner
surface of the anterior arch of atlas and the transverse ligament
which bridges across the tips of the arch. The only motion permitted at this joint is rotation. Since no rotation occurs at the
atlanto-occipital joint, rotation of atlas on axis will carry the head
with it; thus the movement occurring at the atlantoaxial joint contributes to the movement of the head on the body.

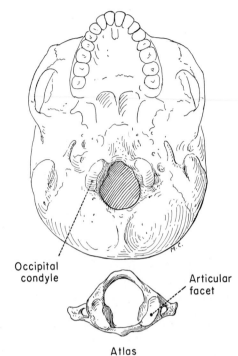

Occipital
condyle

Articular
facet

Atlas

Figure 22. Bones forming atlanto-occipital articulation.

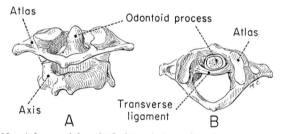

Figure 23. Atlantoaxial articulation. *A,* Posterior view; *B,* superior view.

Movements of the Spine as a Whole. The movements of the spinal column resemble those of a ball-and-socket joint.

Flexion (Fig. 24, *A*). This is forward-downward bending in the sagittal plane about a frontal-horizontal axis. It involves a compression of the anterior parts of the intervertebral disks and a gliding motion of the articular processes. It occurs most freely in the cervical, upper thoracic, and lumbar regions. The cervical curve may be reduced to a straight line, and the lumbar curve, in flexible individuals, may be reversed.

Extension and Hyperextension (Fig. 24, *B*).   Extension is the
return movement from flexion. Hyperextension is a backward-
downward movement in the sagittal plane. It occurs most freely in
the cervical and lumbar regions and particularly at the lumbosacral
junction. In the thoracic region hyperextension is limited by the
overlapping of the spinous processes.

Lateral Flexion (Fig. 24, *C*).   This is a sideward bending in the
frontal plane about a sagittal-horizontal axis. It is freest in the
cervical region and quite free in the lumbar region and at the
dorsolumbar junction. But it is limited in the thoracic region by
the presence of the ribs. Each rib (except the first, tenth, eleventh
and twelfth) articulates with two adjacent vertebrae and the intervening disk, and each rib (except the eleventh and twelfth) articulates with the transverse process of the lower of the two vertebrae (Fig. 25). Thus it is seen that the ribs serve as splints, restricting lateral flexion of the thoracic spine to a marked degree.
It is amazing that any motion can take place there at all. For
several reasons—the slant of the articular processes, the presence
of the anteroposterior curves of the spine, and muscular and ligamentous tensions—lateral flexion is always accompanied by a certain amount of torsion.

Rotation (Fig. 24, *D*).   This is a rotatory movement of the
spine in the horizontal plane about a vertical axis. Spinal rotation
is named by the way the front of the upper spine turns with reference to the lower part. Thus a turning of the head and shoulders to
the right constitutes rotation to the right. A turning of the legs and
pelvis to the left, without turning the upper part of the body,
also constitutes rotation of the spine to the right since the anatomic
relationships are the same as in the former example. The movement
of rotation is most free in the cervical region and next most free in
the thoracic region. Owing to the interlocking of the articular processes, it is extremely limited in the lumbar region, there being only
about 5 degrees of rotation to each side. In the cervical region
there is no rotation between atlas and the skull, but free rotation
at the pivot joint between atlas and axis. Whenever rotation occurs
in the spine, it is accompanied by a slight amount of unavoidable
lateral flexion to the same side.

*Influence of the Starting Position on Lateral Flexion and the
Torsion Accompanying It.*   When lateral flexion is performed
from the erect position, the maximum movement occurs in the
lumbar region and at the dorsolumbar junction, with only a slight
involvement of the lower thoracic spine. (The cervical spine is excluded from this discussion.) The torsion occurs in the same part
of the spine and consists in a turning of the vertebral bodies toward
the side of the lateral flexion. Thus if the spine bends to the right

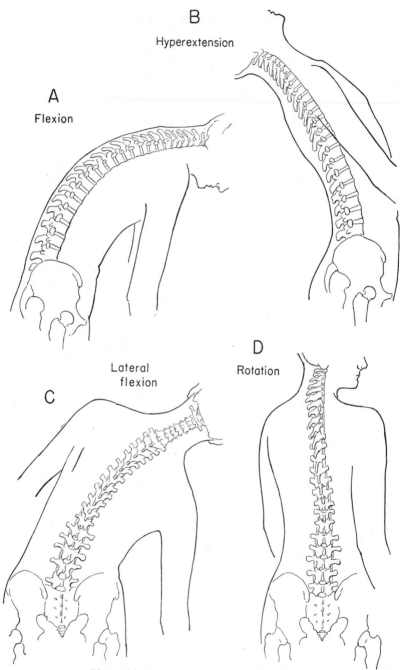

Figure 24. Movements of the spinal column.

(forming a curve concave to the right), the vertebral bodies of the lumbar and lower thoracic vertebrae turn slightly to the right, the spinous processes, therefore, turning to the left.

If the lateral flexion is performed from a position of hyperextension, and the hyperextension is maintained throughout the movement, the lateral flexion moves lower in the spine, occurring almost entirely below the eleventh thoracic vertebra. The torsion occurs in this same region and in the same manner that it does when the lateral flexion is performed from the erect position. The position of hyperextension seems to lock the thoracic spine against lateral movements.

If the lateral flexion is performed from a position of forward flexion, the movement occurs higher in the spine than heretofore, the greatest deviation being at the level of the eighth thoracic vertebra. The torsion in this case reverses itself. Thus in a side bend to the right the vertebral bodies turn to the *left,* and the spinous processes to the right. This reversal is not inconsistent. It is directly related to the anteroposterior curves of the spine. In the first two examples, that is, when the lateral flexion is performed either from the erect or from the hyperextended position, most of the movement takes place in the lower part of the spine, the part that is concave to the rear. The rotation that accompanies the side bend in these two cases is called concave-side rotation because the bodies turn in the direction of the concave or inner side of the laterally curved spine. When the side bend is performed from the flexed position, most of the movement takes place in the thoracic spine, the region that is convex to the rear. The rotation that accompanies the lateral flexion in this case is called convex-side rotation because the vertebral bodies turn in the direction of the convex or outer side of the laterally curved spine.[10]

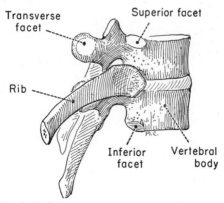

Figure 25. Articulation of a rib with two adjacent vertebrae.

Influence of the Starting Position on Rotation and the Lateral Flexion Accompanying It.   When performed from the erect position, rotation of the spine (below the seventh cervical vertebra) occurs almost entirely in the thoracic region. When performed from the position of hyperextension, the movement shifts lower in the spine, occurring in the vicinity of the dorsolumbar junction. When performed from the flexed position, the rotation is higher than usual, occurring in the upper thoracic spine. Regardless of the position in which the rotation is performed—whether erect, flexed or hyperextended—the slight lateral flexion which accompanies it is always to the same side as the rotation. Thus if the spine rotates to the left, it flexes slightly to the left. This movement is very slight, however, and can scarcely be detected.[10]

Circumduction.   This is a circular movement of the upper trunk on the lower, being a combination of flexion, lateral flexion, and hyperextension, but not including rotation.

Summary of Spinal Movements

Flexion; extension; hyperextension
    Free in all three regions
    Cervical and thoracic curves may be reduced to straight lines
    Lumbar curve may be reversed in flexible subjects
Lateral flexion
    Free in cervical and lumbar regions
    Limited in thoracic region by rib attachments
    Accompanied by torsion
Rotation
    Freest at top, least free at bottom of spine
    Accompanied by slight lateral flexion
Circumduction
    Sequential combination of flexion, lateral flexion, and hyperextension

Regional Classification of Spinal Movements

Occipitoatlantal joint
    Flexion and extension
    Hyperextension
    Slight lateral flexion
Atlantoaxial joint
    Rotation
Remaining cervical joints
    Free flexion and extension
    Free hyperextension
    Free lateral flexion
    Free rotation
Thoracic region
    Moderate flexion and extension
    Slight hyperextension
    Moderate lateral flexion
    Free rotation
Lumbar region
    Moderate to free flexion and extension

Free hyperextension
Free lateral flexion
Slight rotation

Summary of Factors Which Influence the Stability and Mobility of the Spinal Column. Before considering the movements of the spine it is well to review some of the special characteristics which contribute to its stability and which modify its mobility in one way or another.

1. *Pressure and Tension Stresses.* The tendency of the compressed intervertebral disks to push the vertebrae apart, combined with the tendency of the ligaments to press them together, is an important factor in the stability of the spinal column.

2. *Anteroposterior Curves.* The alternating anteroposterior curves of the spinal column influence the nature and the degree of movements that occur in the different regions. Individual variations from the so-called normal curves will make for variations in the movement patterns. The anteroposterior curves are said to serve as a safeguard against the development of abnormal lateral curves (curvature of the spine; scoliosis).

3. *Relative Thickness and Shape of the Intervertebral Disks.* There is a direct relationship between the thickness of the disks and the degree of movement permitted, there being greater freedom of motion where the disks are thicker.

4. *Thickness and Strength of the Ligaments.* These differ in the different regions, and have a corresponding influence on the motions permitted in each region.

5. *Direction and Obliquity of the Articular Facets.* These are characteristic for each region and play an important part in determining the type of motion permitted in each.

6. *Size and Obliquity of the Spinous Processes.* These overlap like shingles in the thoracic region, hence limit hyperextension. In the lumbar region they are horizontal, and, although unusually wide, they do not restrict motion.

7. *Articulations of the Ribs with the Vertebrae.* These limit lateral flexion in the thoracic region.

Muscles. The muscles responsible for the movements of the spine include not only those which have one or both attachments on the vertebrae, but also the abdominal muscles and the hyoids. Both these groups are superficially located on the front of the body; nevertheless they are important muscles of the spinal column. The muscles acting on the spine are as follows:

Muscles of the Head and Neck

Anterior:
Prevertebral muscles
Hyoid muscles

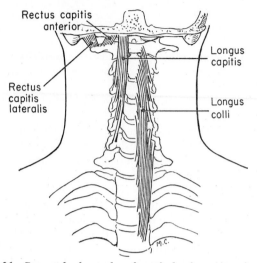

Figure 26. Prevertebral muscles of cervical spine. (Anterior view.)

Lateral:
  Three scaleni
  Sternocleidomastoid
  Levator scapulae
Posterior:
  Splenius
  Suboccipitals
  Capitis and cervicis portions of posterior muscles of spine

Muscles of the Thoracic and Lumbar Spine

Anterior and anterolateral (abdominal muscles):
  Rectus abdominis
  External oblique
  Internal oblique
Lateral:
  Quadratus lumborum
  Psoas
Posterior:
  Sacrospinalis
  Semispinalis
  Deep posterior spinal muscles

Prevertebral Muscles (Fig. 26).   This group of deep anterior muscles of the head and neck consists of longus capitis, longus colli, rectus capitis anterior and rectus capitis lateralis.

LOWER ATTACHMENTS. (o)   Anterior surfaces of various parts of cervical vertebrae and of upper three thoracic vertebrae.

UPPER ATTACHMENTS. (I)   Anterior portions of occipital bone and of cervical vertebrae.

NERVE SUPPLY.   Cervical nerves.

ACTION.   Both: Flexion of head and neck.

One: Lateral flexion of head and neck.

Cannot be palpated.

Hyoid Muscles (Fig. 27).   These include the suprahyoids and the infrahyoids, that is, the muscles above and below the hyoid bone.

ATTACHMENTS.   The suprahyoids are attached to the temporal bone and the mandible above (o) and to the hyoid bone below (i). The infrahyoids are attached to the hyoid bone above (i) and to the sternum and shoulder girdle below (o).

NERVE SUPPLY.   Facial, inferior alveolar, hypoglossi and ansa hypoglossi.

ACTION (AT CERVICAL SPINE).   Flexion.

WHERE TO PALPATE.   The suprahyoids may be palpated just below the jaw bone. The infrahyoids cannot be palpated.

COMMENTS.   These muscles are primarily muscles of some phase of the act of swallowing. They contract in cervical flexion, however, whenever the movement is performed against resistance. By neutralizing one another's pull on the hyoid bone their action is transferred to the skull, and thence to the cervical spine.

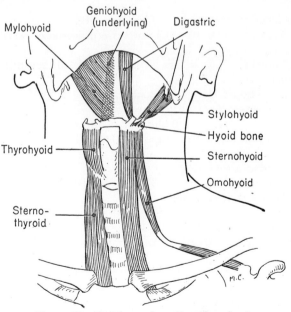

Figure 27. Hyoid muscles. (Anterior view.)

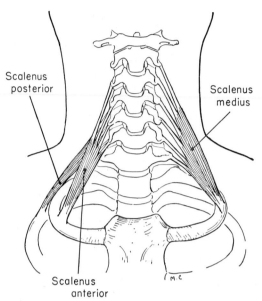

Scalenus posterior

Scalenus medius

Scalenus anterior

Figure 28. The three scaleni muscles. (Anterior view.)

The Three Scaleni (*Scalenus Anterior, Posterior, and Medius*) (Fig. 28)

LOWER ATTACHMENTS. (O)   First two ribs.

UPPER ATTACHMENTS. (I)   Transverse processes of cervical vertebrae.

NERVE SUPPLY.   Branches from second to seventh cervical nerves, inclusive.

ACTION.   Both: Help to flex neck.

One: Lateral flexion of neck.

WHERE TO PALPATE.   On the side of the neck between the sternocleidomastoid and upper trapezius. Difficult to identify.

Sternocleidomastoid (Fig. 29)

LOWER ATTACHMENTS. (O)   By two heads from top of sternum and medial third of clavicle.

UPPER ATTACHMENTS. (I)   Mastoid process of temporal bone and adjacent portion of occipital bone.

NERVE SUPPLY.   Accessory and branches from the second and third cervical.

ACTION.   Both: Flexion of head and neck.

One: Lateral flexion; rotation to opposite side.

WHERE TO PALPATE.   On the side of the neck from just under the ear to the front of the neck at the junction of the clavicle and sternum. It may easily be seen.

COMMENTS.   From the upper attachment of this muscle, one would expect it to hyperextend the head on atlas, regardless of the movement of the cervical vertebrae. In fact, some authors claim this movement for it. The writer, however, has not been able to detect contraction of the sternocleidomastoid when the head was being hyperextended unless the neck was being flexed at the same time. One can only conclude that the pull of the sternocleidomastoid is more nearly in line with the transverse axis of motion than it appears.

Levator Scapulae (see also muscles of the shoulder girdle) (Fig. 30)

UPPER OR PROXIMAL ATTACHMENTS. (O)   Transverse processes of upper four cervical vertebrae.

LOWER OR DISTAL ATTACHMENTS. (I)   Vertebral border of scapula between medial angle and root of spine.

NERVE SUPPLY.   Dorsal scapular and branches from third and fourth cervical.

ACTION (AT CERVICAL SPINE).   Both: None.
                                         One: Lateral flexion.

Cannot be palpated.

COMMENTS.   As the name indicates, the levator scapulae is primarily a muscle of the shoulder girdle. If one scapula is fixed, however, the levator scapulae muscle on that side will flex the cervical spine laterally. If both muscles contract at the same time when both

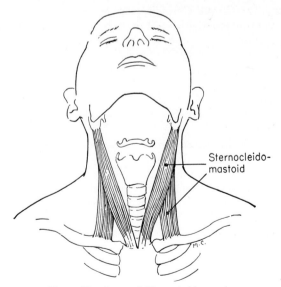

Sternocleido-
mastoid

Figure 29.   Sternocleidomastoid muscle.

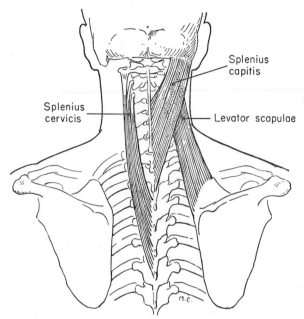

Figure 30. Posterior and lateral muscles of cervical spine.

scapulae are fixed, they neutralize each other without effecting any movement.

Splenius, Capitis and Cervicis (Fig. 30)

LOWER ATTACHMENTS. (O)   Lower half of ligamentum nuchae; spinous processes of seventh cervical and upper six thoracic vertebrae.

UPPER ATTACHMENTS. (I)   Mastoid process of temporal bone and adjacent part of occipital bone; transverse processes of upper three cervical vertebrae.

NERVE SUPPLY.   Branches from the second, third and fourth cervical nerves.

ACTION.   Both: Extension and hyperextension; supports head in erect posture.

One: Lateral flexion; rotation to the same side.

WHERE TO PALPATE.   On the back of the neck just lateral to the trapezius and posterior to the sternocleidomastoid, above the levator scapulae, especially if the head is extended against resistance in the prone position and the shoulders are kept relaxed. It is difficult to identify, however.

COMMENT.   This is an important posture muscle, one of its chief functions being to hold the head erect against the downward pull of gravity. In this it is aided by semispinalis capitis.

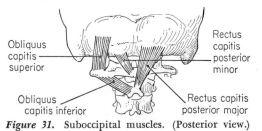

Obliquus capitis superior

Rectus capitis posterior minor

Obliquus capitis inferior

Rectus capitis posterior major

Figure 31. Suboccipital muscles. (Posterior view.)

The Suboccipitals (Fig. 31)

LOWER ATTACHMENTS. (O)   Posterior portions of atlas and axis.

UPPER ATTACHMENTS. (I)   Occipital bone and transverse process of atlas.

NERVE SUPPLY.   Branches from first two cervical nerves.

ACTION.   Both: Extension and hyperextension of head.
One: Lateral flexion; rotation to the same side.
Cannot be palpated.

COMMENTS.   The suboccipitalis consist of the rectus capitis posterior major and minor and the obliquus capitis superior and inferior. They are short muscles, situated deep under the skull.

The remaining posterior muscles of the head and neck consist of the capitis and cervicis portions of sacrospinalis, semispinalis and the deep posterior muscles of the spine.

Sacrospinalis (Erector Spinae) (Fig. 32).

This extensive muscle of the back consists of three branches: namely, iliocostalis, the lateral branch; longissimus, the middle branch; and spinalis, the medial branch. The attachments given here are of necessity very general, since they are for the muscle as a whole, and not for the specific branches.

LOWER ATTACHMENTS. (O)   Lumbodorsal fascia; posterior portions of lumbar, thoracic and lower cervical vertebrae; angles of ribs.

UPPER ATTACHMENTS. (I)   Angles of ribs; posterior portions of cervical and thoracic vertebrae; mastoid process of the temporal bone.

NERVE SUPPLY.   Posterior branches of spinal nerves.

ACTION.   Both: Extension and hyperextension of head and entire spine.
One: Lateral flexion and rotation of head and spine to same side.

WHERE TO PALPATE.   In the lumbar and lower thoracic regions of the back, in two broad ridges on either side of the spine.

COMMENTS.   The muscle commences as a large mass in the lumbosacral region, but soon divides into three branches.

The iliocostalis branch is divided into lumbar, thoracic and cervical portions which are named lumborum, dorsi and cervicis,

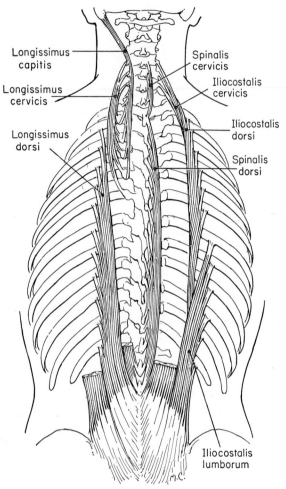

Figure 32.　Sacrospinalis muscle.

respectively. It receives an additional tendon of origin from each rib throughout the thoracic region and gives off small slips to insert into the ribs in the thoracic region and into the transverse processes of the vertebrae in the cervical region.

The longissimus branch consists of three distinct portions which, in fact, appear to be three separate muscles (see Fig. 32). Longissimus dorsi is a broad band lying against the angles of the ribs; longissimus cervicis is narrower and lies slightly closer to the spine, connecting the transverse processes of the upper thoracic vertebrae with those of the lower cervical vertebrae; and longissimus capitis is a thin strand which lies against the vertebrae for its lower two thirds and then slants outward and upward to the mastoid process of the temporal bone.

The spinalis branch lies against the vertebrae and is attached by separate slips to the spinous processes. It is of significance in the thoracic region only.

Semispinalis Dorsi, Cervicis and Capitis (Fig. 33)

LOWER ATTACHMENTS. (O)   Transverse processes of all thoracic and seventh cervical vertebrae; articular processes of lower four cervical vertebrae.

UPPER ATTACHMENTS. (I)   Spinous processes of upper four thoracic and lower five cervical vertebrae; occipital bone.

NERVE SUPPLY.   Posterior branches of cervical and upper six thoracic nerves.

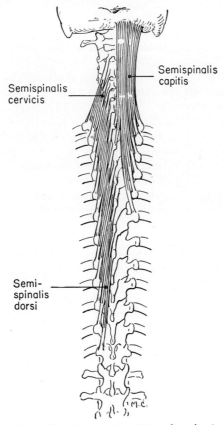

Semispinalis
capitis

Semispinalis
cervicis

Semi-
spinalis
dorsi

Figure 33. Semispinalis. (Posterior view.)

ACTION.   Both: Extension and hyperextension of head, neck and thoracic spine.

One: Lateral flexion of head, neck and thoracic spine; rotation of thoracic spine to opposite side.

Cannot be palpated.

COMMENTS.   The dorsi and cervicis portions consist of tendinous bands which extend obliquely upward and medialward from the transverse processes in the thoracic region and spinous processes in the cervical region to spinous processes of vertebrae above. These portions of the muscle lie beneath the sacrospinalis. Semispinalis capitis is constructed differently from dorsi and cervicis, and is, in fact, frequently described as a separate muscle under the name "complexus." It is a broad band of fibers extending vertically upward from the upper six thoracic and lower four cervical vertebrae to the occipital bone. It lies beneath the splenius capitis and the upper trapezius.

Deep Posterior Muscles of the Spine (Fig. 34).   These include the multifidus, the rotatores, the interspinales, the intertransversales and the levatores costarum.

LOWER ATTACHMENTS. (O)   Posterior surface of sacrum and posterior processes of all the vertebrae.

UPPER ATTACHMENTS. (I)   Spinous and transverse processes and laminae of vertebrae slightly higher than lower attachments.

NERVE SUPPLY.   For first four muscles: Branches of spinal nerves.

For levatores costarum: Intercostal nerves and eighth cervical nerve.

ACTION.   Both: Extension and hyperextension of spine.

One: Rotation to the opposite side; assistance in lateral flexion.

Cannot be palpated.

COMMENTS.   These muscles consist of small slips, in most cases inserting into the vertebrae immediately above their lower attachments. Some of the fibers run vertically, and some slant medially as they ascend. The former are best developed in the cervical and lumbar regions, where their action is that of extension. The latter are best developed in the thoracic region, where they either extend or rotate.

LUMBODORSAL FASCIA (Fig. 37).   The lumbodorsal fascia binds together the sacrospinalis and other deep muscles of the spine, holding them close to the skeletal structure and separating them from the more superficial muscles of the back. In the lumbar region it curves around the lateral margin of the sacrospinalis and folds in front of it to attach to the tips of the transverse processes of the vertebrae and to the intertransverse ligaments. Its lateral portion provides attachment for the transversalis muscle (Fig. 54), and its posterior portion blends with the aponeurosis of the latissimus dorsi (Fig. 61).

Rectus Abdominis (see also muscles of the thorax) (Fig. 35)
LOWER ATTACHMENT. (O)   Crest of pubis.
UPPER ATTACHMENTS. (I)   Cartilages of fifth, sixth and seventh ribs.

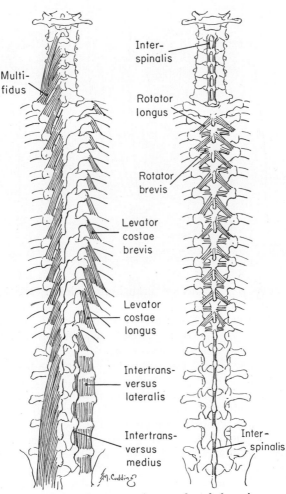

Figure 34. Deep posterior muscles of the spine

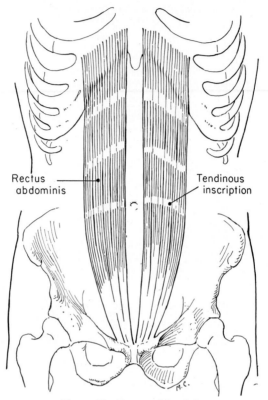

Figure 35. Rectus abdominis.

NERVE SUPPLY.   Anterior branches of lower six intercostal nerves.

ACTION (AT SPINE).   Both: Flexion of thoracic and lumbar spine.
One: Lateral flexion of thoracic and lumbar spine.

WHERE TO PALPATE.   The front of the abdomen, from the pubis to the sternum.

COMMENTS.   The rectus abdominis is situated on the anterior surface of the abdomen on either side of the linea alba. It is a long flat band of muscle fibers extending vertically between the pubis and the lower part of the chest. At three different levels transverse fibrous bands, known as tendinous inscriptions, cross the muscle fibers. The muscle is enclosed in a sheath formed by the aponeuroses of the other muscles making up the abdominal wall.

An electromyographic study made by Walters and Partridge showed that in movements requiring concentric contraction of the rectus abdominis the upper rectus was more active in exercises involving the upper part of the body (e.g., the trunk curl from the supine position), and the lower rectus in movements involving a decrease in the pelvic tilt (e.g., in the supine position, bending the knees and lifting them toward the face until the fifth lumbar vertebra is lifted approximately five inches above the supporting surface).

External Oblique (see also muscles of the thorax) (Fig. 36)

UPPER, LATERAL ATTACHMENTS. (O)   Lower border of lower eight ribs by tendinous slips which interdigitate with those of the serratus anterior.

LOWER, MEDIAL ATTACHMENTS. (I)   Anterior half of crest of ilium; aponeurosis from ribs to crest of pubis.

NERVE SUPPLY.   The lower seven intercostal nerves and the iliohypogastric.

ACTION (AT SPINE).   Both: Flexion of thoracic and lumbar spine.

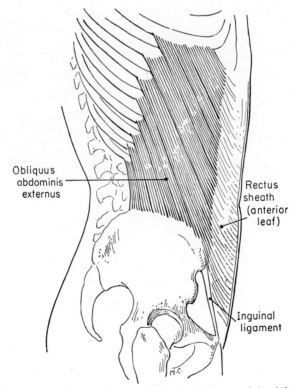

Obliquus
abdominis
externus

Rectus
sheath
(anterior
leaf)

Inguinal
ligament

Figure 36. External oblique abdominal muscle (obliquus abdominis externus)

One: Lateral flexion. Rotation to the opposite side.

WHERE TO PALPATE. At the side of the abdomen.

COMMENTS. The fibers of this muscle run diagonally upward and outward from the lower part of the abdomen, the two muscles together forming an incomplete V, as seen from the front. Walters and Partridge noted that in exercises such as double knee circling in the supine position, the external obliques were the most active of the abdominal muscles.

Internal Oblique (see also muscles of the thorax) (Fig. 37)

LOWER, LATERAL ATTACHMENTS. (O) Inguinal ligament; crest of ilium; lumbodorsal fascia.

UPPER, MEDIAL ATTACHMENTS. (I) Anterior and middle fibers into crest of pubis, linea alba, and aponeurosis on front of body; posterior fibers, by three separate slips, into the cartilages of the lower three ribs.

NERVE SUPPLY. The lower three intercostal nerves, the iliohypogastric and the ilio-inguinal nerves.

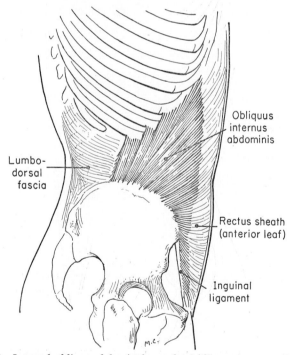

Lumbo-
dorsal
fascia

Obliquus
internus
abdominis

Rectus sheath
(anterior leaf)

Inguinal
ligament

Figure 37. Internal oblique abdominal muscle (obliquus internus abdominis).

ACTION.   Both: Flexion of thoracic and lumbar spine.
One: Lateral flexion. Rotation to the same side.
WHERE TO PALPATE.   The side of the abdomen, beneath the external oblique. It may be palpated through the external oblique when the latter is relaxed, as in rotation.
COMMENTS.   This muscle lies beneath the external oblique. The fibers fan out from the crest of the ilium, most of them passing diagonally forward and upward toward the rib cartilages and sternum, some horizontally forward toward the linea alba, and some diagonally forward and downward toward the crest of the pubis. Walters and Partridge found that the internal oblique, more than any of the other abdominal muscles, was responsible for rotation of the trunk, also that this muscle participated in any activity involving a decrease in the pelvic tilt.

The Abdominal Wall.   The abdominal wall consists of the three abdominal muscles just described and the transversus abdominis (Fig. 54). The latter muscle is a broad sheet of horizontal fibers whose function is to compress the abdomen. It is primarily a muscle of respiration and other physiologic functions. Together, these four muscles form a strong anterior support for the abdominal viscera. They are subject to considerable stress from the pressure of the latter against their inner surface. The more stretched they become, as in the case of a protruding abdomen, the more heavily the organs rest upon the abdominal wall, subjecting it to direct gravitational stress. Thus a vicious circle is set in motion. The pressure against the lower abdominal wall stretches it still more, causing its protrusion to increase and subjecting it to ever increasing gravitational stress. As is so often the case, correction of this postural fault is much more difficult than its prevention. A strong abdominal wall is greatly to be desired.

Quadratus Lumborum (Fig. 38)
LOWER ATTACHMENTS. (o)   Crest of ilium and iliolumbar ligament.
UPPER ATTACHMENTS. (i)   Twelfth rib and tips of transverse processes of upper four lumbar vertebrae.
NERVE SUPPLY.   Branches from the upper three or four lumbar nerves.
ACTION.   Acting singly, it flexes the lumbar spine laterally.
WHERE TO PALPATE.   Just lateral to the sacrospinalis in the lumbar region. It is difficult to palpate and can be felt only on thin, muscular subjects.
COMMENTS.   This is a flat quadrilateral muscle, situated behind the abdominal cavity at the side of the lumbar spine. It prob-

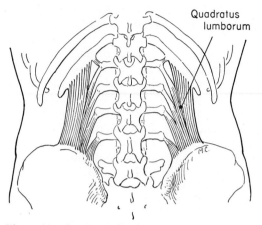

Figure 38. Quadratus lumborum. (Posterior view.)

ably helps to support the weight of the pelvis on the side of the swinging leg in walking.

Psoas (see also muscles of the hip, Fig. 110)

UPPER ATTACHMENTS. (O) Lateral anterior margins of bodies of twelfth thoracic and all lumbar vertebrae, transverse processes of lumbar vertebrae, and intervertebral disks.

LOWER ATTACHMENTS. (I) Lesser trochanter of femur.

NERVE SUPPLY. Upper three lumbar nerves.

ACTION (AT SPINE). When the psoas muscle pulls downward toward its lower attachment, it either flexes the trunk as a whole on the thighs, or it flexes the lumbar spine. If the spine is maintained in a position of extension, the psoas will act with the other hip flexors to flex the trunk on the thighs; but if the hip joint is fixed in extension, the psoas will help the abdominal muscles to flex the lumbar spine. Contraction of one side causes lateral flexion.

WHERE TO PALPATE. See information about the psoas muscle in the chapter on the hip and pelvis. The psoas cannot be palpated when it acts on the spine because of the contraction of the abdominal muscles.

COMMENTS. Like the quadratus lumborum, the psoas is situated at the back of the abdominal cavity. These two muscles may be said to form the posterior abdominal wall. Although the psoas is primarily a muscle of the hip joint, its action on the lower spine and pelvis is of great importance. Ordinarily it causes flexion. Under certain circumstances, however, the psoas muscle appears to reverse its customary function and to participate in hyperextension of the lumbar spine. This is seen when an individual whose abdominal muscles are weak attempts to perform a strenuous abdominal exercise from the supine lying position. For instance, if he lies on his back with both legs extended upward and then slowly lowers his legs, keeping the knees extended, his lumbar spine is seen to hyperextend as his legs approach the floor. Likewise, if he attempts to do a sit-up exercise, keeping his trunk straight, his lower back hyperextends before his upper trunk leaves the floor. It is the weakness of the abdominal muscles and their consequent failure to stabilize the pelvis which is responsible for the hyperextension. Whether or not the psoas actually contributes to the hyperextension is difficult to say. If its line of pull has become shifted to a position behind the axis of motion, it is logical to assume that its customary function has been reversed (p. 27).

Individuals who find that they cannot do the leg lowering or the sit-up exercises without hyperextending the lower back sometimes conclude that since the cause of their difficulty is weak abdominal muscles, the best way to strengthen the muscles is to persist in practicing these exercises. This is a fallacious conclusion. Muscles which are taxed beyond their capacity are more likely to be strained than strengthened.[8, 13] The result may well be a rupture. A better method is to start with less strenuous abdominal exercises and to work up gradually to the more vigorous ones. The criterion whereby one may judge the suitability of an abdominal exercise for his own use is his ability to execute it without hyperextending the lumbar spine.

Muscular Analysis of the Fundamental Movements of the Head and Trunk

CERVICAL SPINE AND ATLANTO-OCCIPITAL JOINT

Flexion

Movers.........
- Principal
  - Sternocleidomastoid
  - Prevertebral muscles
- Assistant.........
  - Three scaleni
  - Hyoid muscles

Neutralizers......................The muscles on the two sides neutralize one another's lateral motions

Stabilizers.......................
- Clavicular portion of pectoralis major
- Subclavius (stabilizes the clavicle for the sternocleidomastoid)
- Lower cervical and upper thoracic extensors (stabilize the spine for the prevertebral muscles and the three scaleni)
- Rectus abdominis (stabilizes the sternum for the sternocleidomastoid)

Extension and Hypertension

Movers
Principal
{
Splenius cervicis and capitis
Sacrospinalis, cervicis and capitis portions
Semispinalis, cervicis and capitis portions
The suboccipitals
The deep posterior spinal muscles, cervicis and capitis portions
}

Assistant.......... Trapezius I

Neutralizers...................... The muscles on the two sides neutralize one another's lateral motions

Stabilizers......................
{
Extensors of the thoracic and lumbar spine
Rhomboid and trapezius IV (stabilize the scapula for trapezius I)
}

Lateral Flexion

Movers
Principal
{
Three scaleni
Splenius, capitis and cervicis
Prevertebral muscles, lateral portion
Sternocleidomastoid
Sacrospinalis, capitis and cervicis portions
Semispinalis, capitis and cervicis portions
}

Assistant
{
Suboccipitals
Deep posterior spinal muscles, cervicis portion
Levator scapulae
}

Neutralizers...................... The anterior and posterior muscles neutralize one another's flexion and extension actions

Stabilizers......................
{
Flexors and extensors of thoracic and lumbar spine
Subclavius (stabilizes the clavicle for the sternocleidomastoid)
Lower trapezius (stabilizes the scapula for the levator scapulae)
}

Rotation (Fig. 39)

Movers
Rotators to the opposite side
{
Sternocleidomastoid
Deep posterior spinal muscles, cervicis portions
}

Rotators to the same side
{
Splenius, capitis and cervicis
Sacrospinalis, capitis and cervicis portions
Suboccipitals
}

Neutralizers...................... The anterior and posterior muscles neutralize one another's flexion and extension tendencies

Stabilizers......................
{
Flexors and extensors of thoracic and lumbar spine
Subclavius (stabilizes the clavicle for the sternocleidomastoid)
}

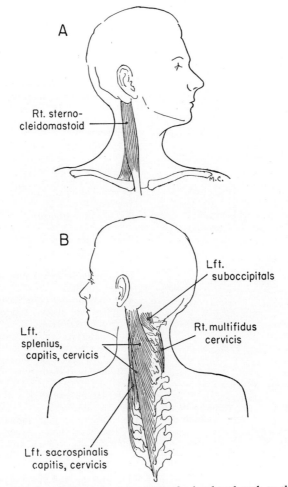

Figure 39. Muscles which contract to rotate the head and neck to the left.

THORACIC AND LUMBAR SPINE

Flexion

Movers........ { Principal........ { Rectus abdominis / External oblique / Internal oblique

Assistant.......... Psoas

Neutralizers...................... The muscles of the left and right sides neutralize one another's lateral flexion and rotational tendencies

Stabilizers......... .... Hip flexors, particularly when the movement is performed in the supine position

Extension

Movers { Principal .... { Sacrospinalis, thoracic and lumbar portions
Semispinalis dorsi

Assistant .... Deep posterior spinal muscles

Neutralizers .... The muscles of the left and right sides neutralize one another's lateral motions

Stabilizers .... Hip extensors, particularly when the movement is performed in the prone position

Lateral Flexion

Movers {

Principal .... { Sacrospinalis, thoracic and lumbar portions
External oblique
Internal oblique
Quadratus lumborum

Assistant .... { Semispinalis dorsi
Rectus abdominis
Psoas
Deep posterior spinal muscles
Latissimus dorsi

Neutralizers .... The anterior and posterior muscles neutralize one another's flexion and extension tendencies

Stabilizers .... Hip abductors on the same side and adductors on the opposite side, particularly when the movement is performed in the side-lying position

Rotation (Fig. 40)

Movers {

Rotators to the opposite side { External oblique
Semispinalis dorsi
Deep posterior spinal muscles

Rotators to the same side { Sacrospinalis, thoracic and lumbar portions, particularly the iliocostalis dorsi
Internal oblique

Neutralizers .... The anterior and posterior muscles neutralize one another's flexion and extension tendencies. The muscles on opposite sides neutralize one another's lateral flexion tendencies

Stabilizers .... The oblique abdominal muscles serve to stabilize the pelvis for the sacrospinalis, and vice versa. The internal intercostals stabilize the ribs for the levatores costarum.

Supplementary Material

The literature contains many observations concerning the contours of the spine, the angulation of the lumbosacral junction, and the shape and posture of the pelvis. The material comes mainly from two sources, notably the original research of investigators in the fields of anatomy, anthropology and physical education, and the clinical observations of orthopedists and other physicians. Because of their significance to the student of kinesiology, a number of these investigations are reported briefly.

Structural Variations in the Lumbosacral and Pelvic Region. In 1933 Howland investigated the position of the sacrum in the adult female pelvis. Measurements made on the x-rays of fifty young women revealed a marked variation in the shape and position of the sacrum and indicated a relationship between these and pelvic obliquity, the slant of the lower lumbar vertebrae, and the position of the line of gravity with reference to the tip of the sacrum. She found, at one extreme, sacra with shallow curves placed high in the pelvis in a relatively vertical position. Sacra of this type were associated with a decreased pelvic inclination and decreased lumbar curve. At the other extreme she found sacra of marked posterior convexity, situated low in the pelvis in a relatively horizontal position. These were associated with an increased pelvic inclination and increased lumbar curve. She suggests that the "normal increase in the curve of the lower lumbar region serves as a compensating factor for the structural component of force set up by the varying position and slope of the sacrum upon

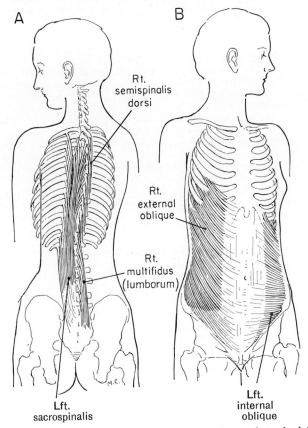

Figure 40. Muscles which contract to rotate the trunk to the left.

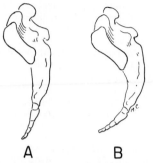

A   **B**

Figure 41. Variations in sacral contour. *A*, Sacrum showing shallow convexity. *B*, Sacrum showing exaggerated convexity.

which the vertebral column must rest." Hence the condition commonly labelled "lordosis" by the correctives instructor may actually be a normal condition for that individual's pelvis and sacrum. It would seem from this investigator's conclusions that she assumes the shape and position of the sacrum to be the primary condition, the increased pelvic inclination and the deep lumbar curve being secondary to it. She suggests a causal relationship.

Brown, on the other hand, believes the sagittal position of the sacrum to be determined by the rotatory movement of the pelvis and lumbar spine. He seems to infer that the shape of the sacrum is the result of its position. In other words, he considers it an example of the modification of structure by function. He condemns the horizontal position of the sacrum as a factor in sacroiliac strain, and he considers that it indicates the need for treatment. His opinion seems to be representative of the orthopedic point of view.

In 1934 Boynton made a study of the pelvis and lumbar spine, using for her subjects fifty college women. Her data consisted both of anthropometric measurements and of measurements taken from lateral x-rays. Like Howland, she found considerable variation in the contour and position of the sacrum, and she observed a close relationship between these and the slope of the lower lumbar vertebrae. In her opinion the slope of the lower lumbar vertebrae is determined by the slope of the top of the sacrum and the position of the sacrum in the pelvis. She also observed that the angle of pelvic obliquity varies with these factors. Furthermore—and this is probably Boynton's most important contribution—she found that the correlation between the measurements on the surface of the body and those on the x-rays was so low that it was impossible to judge accurately the slope of the lower lumbar vertebrae and the angle of pelvic obliquity from the external measurements. The coefficients of correlation which she computed give further emphasis to this revealing observation.

Coefficients of Correlation between Measurements
Made on Surface of Body and Measurements
Made on X-ray

Position of sacrum.................... .0222
Slope of sacrum...................... .2430
Slope of lower lumbar vertebra......... .0465

Bigelow made a study in 1938 on the variations and interrelations of the last lumbar vertebra and the sacrum. Her data were obtained from seventy-nine male and seventy-eight female skeletons, and from seventy-six lateral x-rays of male laborers. She found that the "sacra showed considerable variation, not only in the degree of curvature but in contour." The range of variation in these two aspects of the sacrum are shown in Tables 1 and 2 (Fig. 41). Variations in the size of the lumbosacral angle are recorded in Table 3 and illustrated in Figure 42.

In a very different type of study made on female pelves, Caldwell, Moloy and D'Esopo observed that there were two radically different trends represented in pelvic architecture. On the one hand, they found a range between masculine and feminine types of structures, possibly indicating the presence of a sexual or hormonal factor. On the other hand, they noted an evolutionary trend, a range between the apelike type and the human type of pelvis.

Mitchell[12] discusses the anatomy of the lumbosacral region of the spine in great detail. In regard to variations he says, ". . . the frequency of lumbosacral variations is a good index of the instability of this region and its tendency to evolutionary change."

The significance of these investigations of structural variations in the lumbosacral and pelvic regions would seem to be twofold. In the first place, they enable us to be more intelligent in our body mechanics and corrective programs;

Table 1. Variations in the Contour of the Sacrum (Bigelow)

Degrees of Sacral Curve	Male (N = 79)	Female (N = 78)
95°–104°	3%	0%
105°–114°	22%	16%
115°–124°	28%	26%
125°–134°	24%	26%
135°–144°	14%	26%
145°–154°	9%	6%

Table 2. Variations in the Site of the Apex of the Sacrum (Bigelow)

Site of Apex	Male (N = 79)	Female (N = 78)
Second sacral segment	8%	5%
Third sacral segment	84%	75%
Fourth sacral segment	8%	21%

Table 3. Variations in the Size of the Lumbrosacral Angle (Bigelow)

Size of Lumbosacral Angle	Male X-rays (N = 76)
5°– 9°	7%
10°–14°	28%
15°–19°	43%
20°–24°	14%
25°–29°	5%
30°–34°	3%

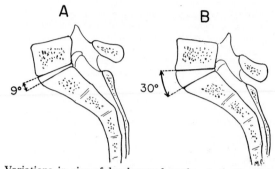

Figure 42. Variations in size of lumbosacral angle. *A*, Angle of 9 degrees; *B*, angle of 30 degrees.

and secondly, they indicate the need for more thorough examinations, preferably by x-ray, before permitting students to participate in strenuous athletics. In fact, Dr. Arthur Steindler, the eminent orthopedic surgeon and kinesiologist, has said that in his opinion x-rays of the lumbar and lumbosacral regions of the spine should be included as part of the routine procedure in examining athletes.* Similarly, although the author is aware of the impracticality of the suggestion, it would be desirable to take x-rays of the lower back of all individuals who contemplate heavy manual labor. If such examinations could be made of athletes and laborers, and if the individuals would be guided by the findings, it is likely that a substantial reduction in the incidence of lower back strains could be effected.

Structural Variations in the Spinal Column.   The literature contains relatively few studies on the nonpathologic human spine as a whole. Physical anthropologists have concerned themselves with evolutionary trends. Sir Arthur Keith has doubtless made the most important contributions in this field. Goldthwait has called attention to variations in the anatomy of the spinal column as representative of variations in body types which he calls "herbivorous" and "carnivorous." Rogers suggests a hereditary factor in determining the postural curves of the spine. McCloy made an x-ray study of the spines of eighteen postadolescents. These fell into two groups, a so-called hereditary group consisting of three individuals who were known to have had round backs from infancy, and three who were known to have had hyperstraight thoracic spines from early youth; and a second group which was subdivided into groups referred to as bent, medium-bent and medium-straight, according to the shape and flexibility of their thoracic spines. Measurements were made of the anterior and posterior thicknesses of each vertebra, of the length of the vertebral body at the lower margin, and of the distances between the articulations. Indices were then computed for each of the subgroups studied. Without giving the actual figures, which are based on too small a number of cases to be of statistical significance, it is interesting to quote the inferences which the investigator considers one is justified in drawing from this study.

1. There is a wide range of individual difference in bony structure. Many of the differences are undoubtedly hereditary.

2. There is no one standard of curvature to which all individuals should conform.

3. There is need for discovering accurate methods of determining what is the correct standard of posture for each type and for each individual.

* Statement made in Advanced Kinesiology class, State University of Iowa, November, 1945. Quoted by permission of Dr. Steindler.

The present author investigated the spinal contours of 100 college women as recorded in routine anteroposterior posture photographs in which the MacEwan pointers were used to show the location of the tips of the spinous processes. These 100 photographs were selected from 1200, fifty of them on the basis of a predominantly convex spine, that is, a spine in which the convexity involves a portion, possibly all, of the lumbar region; and fifty on the basis of a predominantly concave spine, that is, a spine in which the concavity extends well up into the thoracic region. Because the convex spine is characteristic of the anthropoid apes, this group was called the "anthropoid spine" group; and because a lumbar curve is characteristic of the human spine, the second group was called the "humanoid spine" group (Fig. 43). Measurements made on the photographs revealed that significant measurable differences existed between the two types of spine. The mean values of these measurements are presented in Table 4.

An interesting study of the flexibility of the spinal column of four individuals was made by Wiles. Two of the subjects were normally active women; two were acrobatic dancers, one of them a child and the other a man. While too small in scope to be of any real significance, this study is interesting because it suggests the wide variation in flexibility found in the human spine. Although attention

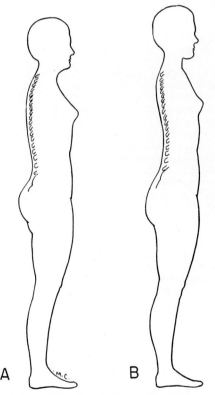

Figure 43. Lateral views of two female figures illustrating variations in spinal type. *A,* Convex or "anthropoid" type of spine. *B,* Concave or "humanoid" type of spine.

Table 4. Comparison of "Anthropoid" and "Humanoid" Types of Spines with Reference to the Depth and Length of the Antero-posterior Curves of the Thoracic and Lumbar Portions of the Spine (Wells)

(Mean values of measurements taken from the posture photographs of 100 college women, 50 representing the "anthropoid" type, and 50 the "humanoid" type.)

Aspect of Spine Measured	"Anthropoid" Spine	"Humanoid" Spine
Total length of thoracic and lumbar portion of spine...................	3.54 cm.	3.54 cm
Length of posterior convexity..........	2.79 cm. (79%)	1.48 cm. (42%)
Length of posterior concavity..........	0.75 cm. (21%)	2.06 cm. (58%)
Depth of posterior convexity...........	0.22 cm.	0.08 cm.
Depth of posterior concavity...........	0.06 cm.	0.16 cm.

was not called to the fact, the present writer noticed that the photograph of Miss P. showed a spine of "normal" contours; that of Miss R. showed a long convexity or "anthropoid type" of spine; that of the child showed a marked lordosis; and that of the man showed a shallow but long concavity or "humanoid type" of spine. The range of motion in each spine, as measured on x-rays, is recorded in Table 5. The relationship between the type of spine and the degree of flexibility should be noted. The Wiles study, although it involves only four individuals, two of whom were highly atypical from the point of view of agility, nevertheless suggests a relationship between structure and function. It is interesting to note that Miss R., whose spine seemed to be of the "anthropoid type," showed a marked limitation in hyperextension, whereas the adult male acrobat, who seemed to represent the extreme "humanoid type," had excessive hyperextension, but limited flexion. A study of the flexibility of a large sampling of these two spinal types might prove to be of value to the physical educator and the athletic coach.

The significance of studies such as these to physical educators and therapists lies in their implication for posture education and for recommendations regarding activity. Such studies are valuable to the degree that they give (1) a broad concept of the "normal," (2) an appreciation of the relatedness between structural type and physical skills, and (3) an awareness of the limitations characteristic of each type. Physical educators and therapists should realize that identical goals of posture, flexibility and function cannot be laid down for all

Table 5. Anteroposterior Spinal Flexibility of Four Selected Cases (Wiles)

Subject	Flexion	Hypertension	Total
Miss P.............................	64°	35°	99°
Miss R.............................	62°	19°	81°
Child..............................	76°	39°	115°
Man...............................	50°	71°	121°

types of body build. Just what the specific abilities and limitations of each type are, and just what the goals for each type should be, are problems that are still wide open for investigation.

Demonstrations and Laboratory Exercises

Joint Structure

1. Study the bones of the spinal column, then fill out an outline like the one on page 88 for each of the following joints, including the articulations of both the bodies and the arches.
   a. Atlanto-occipital
   b. Atlantoaxial
   c. A middle cervical joint
   d. The joint between the seventh cervical and the first thoracic vertebrae
   e. A middle thoracic joint
   f. The joint between the twelfth thoracic and the first lumbar vertebrae
   g. A middle lumbar joint
   h. The lumbosacral joint

Joint Action

2. Have a subject sit tailor-fashion on a table and flex his spine as completely as possible. Observe the shape of the spine as seen from the side. Compare the three regions of the spine as to forward flexibility. Make a line drawing of the side view of the spine.

3. Have a subject sit astride a chair, facing its back, and hyperextend the spine as completely as possible. Observe and record the shape of the spine as in 2.

4. Have a subject sit astride a bench and bend sideward as far as possible, first to one side and then to the other. Observe from the rear and draw a line representing the spine in maximum lateral flexion, both left and right.

5. Have a subject sit astride a bench with the hands at the neck, then rotate the trunk as far as possible, first to one side, then to the other. Observe and compare the regions of the spine as to rotating ability.

6. Observe flexion, hyperextension, lateral flexion and rotation of the spine in several subjects, preferably subjects representing different body builds, and note individual differences.

7. Have a subject lie face down on a table with the legs and pelvis supported on the table, the trunk extending forward beyond the table, and the hands clasped behind the neck.
   a. Have the subject bend laterally. Compare the thoracic and lumbar regions. Note the torsion accompanying the lateral flexion.
   b. Have the subject flex the spine and then flex it laterally. Observe as in a.
   c. Have the subject hyperextend the spine (with someone helping to support the elbows) and then flex laterally. Observe as in a.
   d. Have the subject rotate the trunk to one side as far as possible. Compare the thoracic and lumbar regions. Is any lateral bending apparent in the spine?
   e. Have the subject flex the spine and then rotate it. Observe as in d.
   f. Have the subject hyperextend the spine and then rotate it. Observe as in d.

Muscular Action

The purpose of these exercises is not to test the strength of the muscles, but to enable the observer to study the action of the muscles in simple movements of the body. The procedure, therefore, is quite different from that followed by the physical therapist in testing muscle strength. It is suggested that students work in groups of three, one acting as the subject, one as an assistant helping to support or steady the stationary part of the body and giving resistance to the moving part,

OUTLINE FOR STUDYING THE JOINTS OF THE SPINE

Region of spine:_____Name of joint:_____

Check the correct item:

Type of Joint

_____ Diarthrosis   _____ Synarthrosis
          _____ Irregular   _____ Cartilaginous (synchondrosis)
          _____ Hinge
          _____ Pivot
          _____Ovoid   _____ Ligamentous (syndesmosis)
          _____ Saddle
          _____ Ball-and-socket   _____ Fibrous (sutures)

Type of Movement   *Axis of Motion*
          _____ Gliding   _____ Non-axial
                                      _____ Uniaxial
          _____ Axial or rotatory _____ Biaxial
                                      _____ Triaxial

Enumerate and describe briefly:

Articular surfaces

Ligaments

Fibrocartilage

Special characteristics of joint

Movements

and one palpating the muscles and recording the results. The check lists on pages 89 and 90 may be used for this purpose. They may also be used for the analysis of other movements.

8. Flexion of the neck

a. Subject: Lie on the back and lift the head, bringing the chin toward the chest.

Observer: Palpate and identify as many of the contracting muscles as possible.

b. Subject: Lie on the back and lift the head, leading with the chin.

Observer: Compare the action of the sternocleidomastoid in *b* with its action in *a*.

9. Extension and hyperextension of the neck

a. Subject: Lie face down on a table with the head over the edge. Raise the head as far as possible, hyperextending both the head and the neck.

Assistant: May resist the movement if stronger muscular action is desired.

Observer: Palpate and identify as many of the contracting muscles as possible.

b. Subject: Lie face down on a table with the head over the edge. Raise the head as far as possible with the chin tucked in.

Assistant: Resist the retraction of the chin.

Observer: Compare the muscular action in (*b*) with that in (*a*).

10. Lateral flexion of the head and neck
    Subject: Lie on one side and raise the head toward the shoulder without turning the head or tensing the shoulder.
    Assistant: Give slight resistance at the temple.
    Observer: Palpate and identify as many muscles as possible.
11. Rotation of the head and neck
    Subject: Sit erect and turn the head to the left as far as possible.
    Assistant: Give fairly strong resistance to the side of the jaw.
    Observer: Palpate the sternocleidomastoid. Which one contracts?
12. Flexion of the thoracic and lumbar spine
    Subject: Lie on the back with the arms folded across the chest. Raise the head, shoulders and upper back from the table, keeping the chin in. There is no need to come to a sitting position, since this is intended as a movement of spinal, not hip, flexion.
    Assistant: Hold the thighs down.
    Observer: Palpate the rectus abdominis and the external oblique abdominal muscle.

CHECK LIST FOR THE MUSCULAR ANALYSIS OF MOVEMENTS OF THE HEAD AND NECK

	Flexion	Extension	Lateral Flexion	Rotation Same Side	Rotation Opposite Side
ANTERIOR:					
Prevertebral muscles					
Hyoid muscles					
LATERAL:					
Three scaleni					
Sternocleidomastoid					
Levator scapulae					
POSTERIOR:					
Splenius					
Suboccipitals					
Sacrospinalis					
Semispinalis					
Deep poster. muscles					
OTHER:					

13. Extension and hyperextension of the thoracic and lumbar spine

Subject: Lie face down with the hands on the hips. Raise the head and trunk as far as possible.

Assistant: Hold the feet down.

Observer: Palpate the sacrospinalis and the gluteus maximus (the large hip extensor muscle located in the buttocks). What is the function of the latter muscle in this movement?

14. Lateral flexion of the thoracic and lumbar spine

Subject: Lie on one side with the under arm placed across the chest and the hand resting on the opposite shoulder, and with the hand of the top arm resting on the hip. Raise the trunk sideways.

Assistant: Hold the legs down. If necessary, help the subject by pulling at the elbow.

Observer: Palpate the rectus abdominis, external oblique abdominal muscle, sacrospinalis and latissimus dorsi (the large superficial muscle of the lower back whose tendon of insertion forms the posterior margin of the arm pit).

CHECK LIST FOR THE MUSCULAR ANALYSIS OF MOVEMENTS OF THE THORACIC AND LUMBAR SPINE

	Flexion	Extension	Lateral Flexion	Rotation Same Side	Rotation Opposite Side
ANTERIOR:					
Rectus abdominis					
Ext. oblique abd.					
Int. oblique abd.					
LATERAL:					
Quad. lumborum					
Psoas					
POSTERIOR:					
Sacrospinalis					
Semispinalis dorsi					
Deep. post. muscles					
OTHER:					

15. Rotation of the thoracic and lumbar spine

Subject: Sit astride a bench with the hands placed behind the neck. Twist to one side as far as possible without leaving the bench.

Assistant: Resist the movement by grasping the subject's arms close to his shoulders and pushing (or pulling) in the opposite direction.

Observer: Palpate as many of the spinal and abdominal muscles as possible. Disregard the muscles of the scapula and arm.

Action of the Muscles Other Than the Movers

16. The sit-up

Subject: Lie on the back and come to a sitting position, keeping the spine as rigid as possible.

Assistant: Hold the feet down.

Observer: Palpate the abdominal muscles, the sacrospinalis and the sternocleidomastoid. Explain the function of each.

17. Double leg lowering

Subject: Lie on the back. Raise both legs, then slowly lower them.

Observer: Palpate the abdominal muscles and the sacrospinalis. Explain the function of each.

18. Trunk bending forward

Subject: Stand with the feet slightly separated. Bend forward from the hips, keeping the back flat.

Observer: Palpate the sacrospinalis. Explain its function.

19. Push-up

Subject: Assume a front-leaning-rest position on the hands and toes with the body straight. Let the elbows bend until the chest almost touches the floor, then push up again, keeping the body straight the entire time. Do not let it sag or hump.

Observer: Palpate the abdominal muscles. Explain their function.

Bibliography

1. Bigelow, M. D.: The Variations and Interrelations of the Last Lumbar Vertebra and Sacrum. Research Quarterly of Am. Assn. for Health and Phys. Ed., *9:* 15–29, 1938.
2. Boynton, B.: Individual Differences in the Structure of Pelvis and Lumbar Spine as a Factor in Body Mechanics. Thesis, State University of Iowa, 1934.
3. Brown, L. T.: The Mechanics of the Lumbosacral and Sacroiliac Joints. J. Bone & Joint Surg., *19:* 770–775, 1937.
4. Caldwell, W. E., Moloy, H. C., and D'Esopo, D. A.: Further Studies on the Pelvic Architecture. Am. J. Obst. & Gynec., *28:* 482–487, 1934.
5. Duvall, E. N.: Kinesiology; The Anatomy of Motion. Englewood Cliffs, N. J., Prentice-Hall, 1959.
6. Goldthwait, J. E., Brown, L. T., Swaim, L. T., and Kuhns, J. G.: Essentials of Body Mechanics in Health and Disease. 5th ed. Philadelphia, J. B. Lippincott Company, 1952, Chap. 2.
7. Howland, I. S.: A Study of the Position of the Sacrum in the Adult Female Pelvis and Its Relationship to Body Mechanics. Thesis, State University of Iowa, 1933.
8. Kendall, H. O., and Kendall, F. P.: The Role of Abdominal Exercises in a Program of Physical Fitness. J. Health and Phys. Educ., *14:* 480, 481, 504–506, 1943.
9. Keith, A.: Man's Posture—Its Evolution and Disorders. Brit. M. J., *1:* 451, 454, 499, 502, 545, 548, 587, 590, 624, 628, 669, 672 (March 17, 24, 31, April 7, 14, 21), 1923.

10. Lovett, R. W.: Lateral Curvature of the Spine and Round Shoulders. 5th ed. Philadelphia P. Blakiston's Son and Co., Inc., 1931, Chap. 3.
11. McCloy, C. H.: X-ray Studies of Innate Differences in Straight and Curved Spines. Research Quarterly of Am. Assn. for Health and Phys. Ed., *9:* 50–57, 1938.
12. Mitchell, G. A. G.: The Lumbosacral Junction. J. Bone & Joint Surg., *16:* 233–254, 1934.
13. Rathbone, J. L.: Corrective Physical Education. 6th ed. Philadelphia, W. B. Saunders Company, 1959, pp. 94–95.
14. Rogers, J. F.: The Long and Short of the Carriage Business. J. Health and Phys. Ed., *3:* 11–13, 1932.
15. Walters, C. E., and Partridge, M. J.: Electromyographic Study of the Differential Action of the Abdominal Muscles during Exercise. Am. J. Phys. Med., *36:* 259–268, 1957.
16. Wells, K. F.: An Investigation of Certain Evolutionary Tendencies in the Female Human Structure. Research Quarterly of Am. Assn. for Health, Phys. Ed. and Recreation, *18:* 260–270, 1947.
17. Wiles, P.: Movements of the Lumbar Vertebrae during Flexion and Extension. Proc. Roy. Soc. Med., *28:* 647–651, 1935.

Recommended Readings

Kendall, H. O. and Kendall, F. P.: The Role of Abdominal Exercises in a Program of Physical Fitness. (See 8 above.)
Mitchell, G. A. G.: The Lumbosacral Junction. (See 12 above.)

6 · The Movements of the Thorax in Respiration

THE THORAX is a bony-cartilaginous cage, shaped considerably like a beehive, with an inverted V-shaped doorway in the front (Fig. 44). It is formed mainly by the ribs and their cartilages, but also includes the sternum, which constitutes the anterior base of attachment for the ribs, and the thoracic portion of the spine, which constitutes the posterior base of attachment. The upper seven ribs are called true ribs because their cartilages articulate directly with the sternum. The remaining five ribs are called false ribs. This is a misleading term, since the ribs themselves are just as real as the others, the only "false" thing about them being that they do not articulate with the sternum. In the case of the eighth, ninth and tenth ribs, the cartilages of each unite with the cartilage above, but in the case of the eleventh and twelfth ribs, known as the "floating ribs," there is no anterior attachment. These ribs, shorter than those immediately above, have only short tips of cartilages and, except for their muscular attachments, are free at their anterior ends.

The angle formed between the margins of the lower rib cartilages at the front of the chest (the "door" to the "beehive") is called the subcostal angle. This is characteristically wider in individuals of stocky build than in those of slender build. The thorax is wider from side to side than it is from front to back, and is slightly flattened in front. An infant or young child has a more "barrel-shaped" chest than does an adult, that is, a thorax whose anteroposterior diameter more nearly approaches its transverse diameter than it does in the adult.

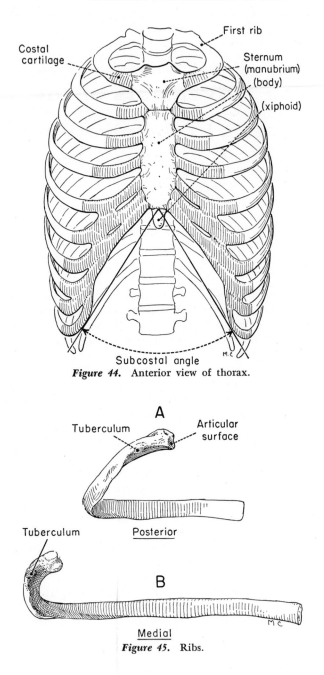

Figure 44. Anterior view of thorax.

Figure 45. Ribs.

Before studying the articulations and the movements of the thorax the student should review the ribs by observing them on a skeleton, noting particularly their shape and the way in which they twist. If no skeleton is available, he should look carefully at pictures of the ribs such as those shown in Figure 45.

Articulations and Ligaments. The majority of the articulations of the thorax belong to the non-axial, diarthrodial classification. They permit a very slight amount of gliding.

Costovertebral. CAPITULAR (COSTOCENTRAL). The head of the rib articulates with the costal facets of two adjacent vertebrae and the intervertebral disk between them (Fig. 25). The first, tenth, eleventh and twelfth ribs each articulate with a single vertebra.

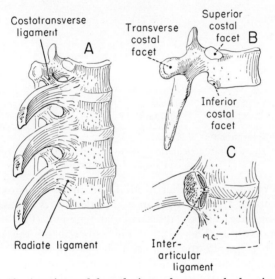

Figure 46. Anterior and lateral views of costovertebral articulations.

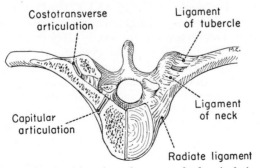

Figure 47. Superior view of costovertebral articulations.

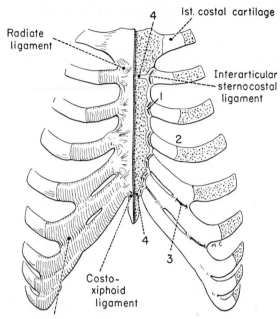

Figure 48. Sternocostal articulations. Key: *1,* Sternocostal; *2,* costochondral; *3,* interchondral; *4,* intersternal.

The joint is a non-axial, diarthrodial one and permits only a slight gliding motion. It is enclosed in a capsule and is strengthened by a radiate ligament and an interarticular ligament (Fig. 46).

COSTOTRANSVERSE (Fig. 47).   The tubercle on the under side of each rib (Figs. 45 and 47), with the exception of the eleventh and twelfth, articulates with the adjacent transverse process. This is a non-axial, diarthrodial joint. The articular capsule, which is thin and membranous, is reinforced by the anterior and posterior costotransverse ligaments (Figs. 46 and 47) and the strong little ligaments of the neck and tubercle of the rib, respectively.

Sternocostal Articulations (Fig. 48).   There are four groups of articulations in the sternocostal region: (1) the sternocostal joints between the costal cartilages and the sternum; (2) the joints between each rib and its cartilage, known as the costochondral joints; (3) the joints between one costal cartilage and another, called the interchondral joints; and (4) the two intersternal joints, one between the manubrium and body of the sternum, the other between the body and the xiphoid process. The reinforcing ligaments in this region include the radiate sternocostal, the interarticular sternocostal, and the costoxiphoid.

Movements. Because most of the ribs are attached both posteriorly and anteriorly, their movement is extremely limited. In
the thoracic expansion associated with inhalation the anterior ends
of the ribs are elevated in a flexion type of movement. This is accompanied by a slight eversion in which the lower margin of the
central portion of the rib turns upward and lateralward, the inner
surface being made to face somewhat downward. As the anterior
ends of the upper ribs move upward they also push forward, carrying the sternum forward and upward with them. In the case of the
lower ribs, the anterior ends move laterally, thus "opening" the
chest and widening the subcostal angle.

The expansion of the thorax is associated not only with inhalation, but also with all movements of the body requiring effort. If
one were to push or lift a heavy piece of furniture, for instance, he
would first inhale, then hold his breath while making the effort to
move the object. The inhalation that occurs may be considered a
secondary function of the thorax in this case. The primary function
is the stabilization of the ribs and sternum for the purpose of providing firm anchorage for the muscles which attach to them, namely,
the abdominal muscles, the pectoralis major and minor, and the
serratus anterior.

In inhalation the thorax is enlarged in three diameters—transverse, anteroposterior and vertical.

Increase in the Transverse Diameter (Fig. 49). This is due
to the elevation and eversion of the lateral portion of the ribs. The
shape and twist of the ribs, together with their anterior and posterior attachments, are responsible for what has so aptly been called
"bucket-handle inspiratory movement" (Cates). The elevation of
the lower ribs is accompanied by a lateral movement of their anterior
ends. This widening of the lower part of the thorax increases the
power of the diaphragm by putting it on a stretch.

Increase in the Anteroposterior Diameter (Fig. 49, *A*). This

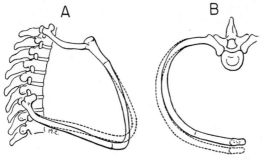

Figure 49. Expansion of thorax during inhalation. *A,* Lateral view; *B,* superior
view.

is due to elevation of the anterior ends of the obliquely placed ribs
and to elevation of the body of the sternum, caused by the elevation of the ribs. The elevation of the anterior ends of the ribs causes
the ribs to assume a more horizontal position and results in a
straightening of the costal cartilages. The movements of the thorax
in the anteroposterior and transverse diameters are inseparable.
The expansion in both directions when the ribs are elevated is the
natural result of their shape and of the oblique direction of their
axes of motion.

Increase in the Vertical Diameter.   This is due partly to the
elevation of the first two ribs, but even more to the depression of
the central tendon of the diaphragm. If inhalation is forced, expansion of the thorax is aided by complete extension of the thoracic
spine.

Muscles.   Muscular action is required for all inhalation, no
matter how shallow, but ordinary exhalation is brought about by
the recoil of the elastic structures of the thorax and by the weight
of the chest. In vigorous or resisted exhalation, however, and in all
forms of vocalization, muscular action is required.

Muscles of normal inhalation
  Diaphragm
  External intercostals
  Internal intercostals, anterior cartilaginous region
Additional muscles of vigorous inhalation
  Sternocleidomastoid*
  The three scaleni*
  Levatores costarum
  Serratus posterior superior
  Pectoralis minor*
  Trapezius I*
  Levator scapulae*
  The thoracic spine extensors*
Muscles of vigorous exhalation
  Internal intercostals, posterior and lateral portions
  Transversalis
  Rectus abdominis*
  Oblique abdominal muscles*
  Transversus thoracis
  Serratus posterior inferior

Diaphragm (Fig. 50)

PERIPHERAL ATTACHMENT. (O)   Circumference of thoracic outlet.

CENTRAL ATTACHMENT. (I)   Central tendon, a clover leaf-shaped
aponeurosis.

NERVE SUPPLY.   Phrenic.

ACTION.   Depression of the central tendon, hence an increase

* These are primarily muscles of either the spine or the shoulder girdle.

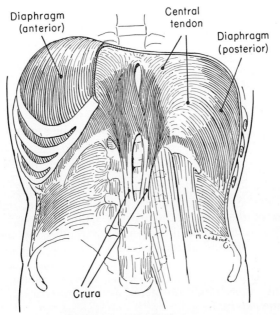

Diaphragm (anterior)

Central tendon

Diaphragm (posterior)

Crura

Figure 50. The diaphragm.

in the vertical diameter of the thorax; a tendency to lift the lower ribs to which it is attached.

Cannot be palpated.

COMMENTS. The diaphragm is a dome-shaped muscular sheet which separates the thoracic and abdominal cavities. When it contracts, it pulls down at its central tendon, thus increasing the vertical diameter of the thorax. In doing this, it presses against the abdominal organs, which in turn push forward against the relaxed abdominal wall. By increasing the intra-abdominal pressure it helps in defecation, vomiting and other forms of expulsion. Although primarily a muscle of inhalation, it assists indirectly in exhalation by means of its elastic recoil when it relaxes.

External Intercostals (Fig. 51)

ATTACHMENTS. Lower border of one rib and upper border of rib beneath.

NERVE SUPPLY. Branches from corresponding intercostal nerves.

ACTION. Elevation of the ribs.

WHERE TO PALPATE. On thin subjects, between the ribs anterior to the serratus anterior.

COMMENTS. These muscles lie between the ribs, from the spine in back to the costal cartilages in front. They consist of short parallel fibers which slant downward and forward in the same direction as the fibers of the external oblique abdominal muscle. They lift the ribs, thus increasing the thoracic cavity in both the transverse and anteroposterior diameters.

Internal Intercostals (Fig. 51)

ATTACHMENTS.   Inner surface and costal cartilage of one rib and upper border of rib immediately below.

NERVE SUPPLY.   Branches from corresponding intercostal nerves.

ACTION.   Anterior portion: Elevation of ribs.
Lateral and posterior portions: Depression of ribs. Cannot be palpated.

COMMENTS.   Like the external intercostals, these consist of short parallel fibers which lie between the ribs, but, unlike them, the fibers of the internal intercostals slant downward and backward. This is the same direction as that taken by the fibers of the internal oblique abdominal muscle. They extend from the sternum in front, to the angles of the ribs in back. Since the external intercostals extend only as far forward as the costal cartilages, the anterior portion of the internal intercostals is not covered by the external.

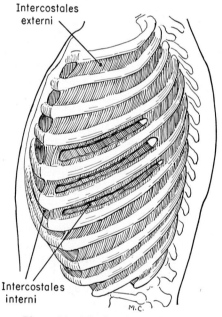

Intercostales
externi

Intercostales
interni

M. C.

Figure 51. The intercostal muscles.

Sternocleidomastoid (see also muscles of the spine) (Fig. 29)

LOWER ATTACHMENTS. (O)   By two heads from top of sternum and medial third of clavicle.

UPPER ATTACHMENTS. (I)   Mastoid process of temporal bone and adjacent portion of occipital bone.

NERVE SUPPLY.   Accessory and branches from the second and third cervical.

ACTION (ON THORAX).   Helps to elevate the sternum and clavicle.

WHERE TO PALPATE.   On the side of the neck just under the ear and on the front of the neck at the junction of the clavicle and sternum.

COMMENTS.   In vigorous inhalation the head is held firmly erect and the sternocleidomastoid, instead of flexing the head and neck, pulls up on the sternum and sternal end of the clavicles, lifting them slightly.

The Three Scaleni (see also muscles of the spine) (Fig. 28)

UPPER ATTACHMENTS. (O)   Transverse processes of cervical vertebrae.

LOWER ATTACHMENTS. (I)   First two ribs.

NERVE SUPPLY.   Branches from second to seventh cervical nerves, inclusive.

ACTION (AT THORAX).   Help to elevate first two ribs.

WHERE TO PALPATE.   On the side of the neck between the sternocleidomastoid and the upper trapezius. They are difficult to identify.

COMMENTS.   In vigorous inhalation the head and neck are held firmly erect. This makes it possible for the scaleni muscles to lift the first two ribs.

Levatores Costarum (Levator Costae) (Fig. 52)

UPPER ATTACHMENTS. (O)   Ends of transverse processes of seventh cervical and upper eleven thoracic vertebrae.

LOWER ATTACHMENTS. (I)   The two ribs below, between the tubercles and the angles.

NERVE SUPPLY.   Branches from corresponding intercostal nerves.

ACTION (AT THORAX).   Elevation of ribs.

Cannot be palpated.

COMMENTS.   The levatores costarum are sometimes called the posterior portions of the external intercostals. They have two functions, extension of the spine and elevation of the ribs. Which of these movements they will cause depends upon which attachment is stabilized. According to the principle of muscular tension, one would expect them to be more effective in lifting the ribs

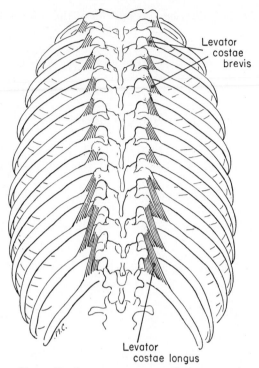

Figure 52. Levatores costarum (levator costae).

if the spine were maintained in a position of flexion. Yet this does not seem to be the case, since we know that elevation of the ribs is usually accompanied by extension of the spine. This is an interesting point, but one which cannot be easily settled, since it is impossible to palpate the levatores costarum.

Serratus Posterior Superior (Fig. 53)

UPPER ATTACHMENTS. (O)   Spinous processes and ligaments of lower two or three cervical and upper two thoracic vertebrae.

LOWER ATTACHMENTS. (I)   Upper borders of second, third, fourth and fifth ribs.

NERVE SUPPLY.   Branches from the first four intercostal nerves.

ACTION.   Elevation of second, third, fourth and fifth ribs. Cannot be palpated.

COMMENTS.   This is a flat quadrilateral muscle whose parallel fibers slant upward and backward from the upper ribs to the spine.

Pectoralis Minor (see also muscles of the shoulder girdle) (Fig. 67)

LOWER ATTACHMENTS. (O)   Anterior surface of third, fourth and fifth ribs near their cartilages.

UPPER ATTACHMENT. (I)   Tip of coracoid process of scapula.
NERVE SUPPLY.   Medial anterior thoracic.
ACTION (AT THORAX).   Elevation of third, fourth and fifth ribs.
WHERE TO PALPATE.   Halfway between the clavicle and the
nipple, or between this point and the tip of the shoulder.

COMMENTS.   The pectoralis minor can reverse the direction
of its pull and lift the ribs only if the thoracic spine is extended and
the scapula is stabilized. The most favorable position for the
latter is one of elevation and adduction.

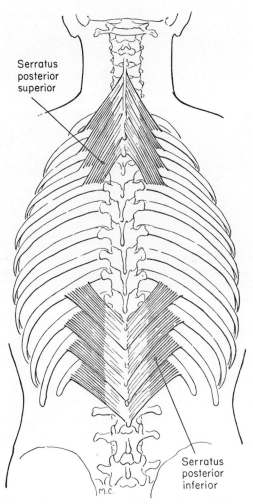

Serratus
posterior
superior

Serratus
posterior
inferior

Figure 53. Serratus posterior superior and inferior.

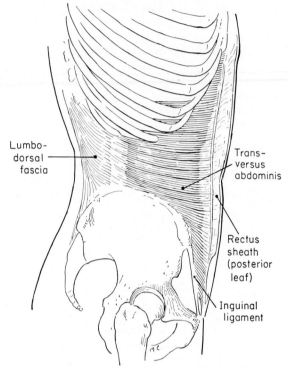

Figure 54.   Transversus abdominis.

Transversalis (Transversus Abdominis) (Fig. 54)

LATERAL ATTACHMENTS. (O)   Inguinal ligament, crest of ilium, lumbodorsal fascia, and cartilages of lower six ribs.

MEDIAL ATTACHMENTS. (I)   Linea alba and crest of pubis.

NERVE SUPPLY.   Branches of lower six intercostal nerves, ilio-hypogastric and ilio-inguinal nerves.

ACTION.   Compression of the abdomen and depression of the lower ribs.

Cannot be palpated.

COMMENTS.   This is one of the four muscles forming the abdominal wall. Its fibers run horizontally from the lumbodorsal fascia and cartilages of the lower ribs forward to the linea alba. Its pull is inward against the abdominal viscera; hence it is a strong muscle of exhalation and expulsion.

Rectus Abdominis, External and Internal Obliques (see also muscles of the spine) (Figs. 35, 36, 37)

ATTACHMENTS.   Lower ribs and rib cartilages, lumbodorsal fascia, upper portions of pelvis, and linea alba. (For exact attachments, see muscles of the spine.)

NERVE SUPPLY.   Intercostal iliohypogastric, and ilio-inguinal.

ACTION (AT THORAX).   Depression of the lower ribs and sternum; compression of the abdomen.

WHERE TO PALPATE.   Front and sides of the abdomen.

COMMENTS.   When the spine is fixed in extension, these muscles contract in vigorous exhalation. By compressing the abdominal viscera they indirectly exert an upward pressure against the diaphragm, causing it to be pushed up into the thorax.

Transversus Thoracis (Triangularis Sterni) (Fig. 55)

MEDIAL ATTACHMENTS. (O)   Lower half of inner surface of sternum and adjoining costal cartilages.

LATERAL ATTACHMENTS. (I)   Lower borders and inner surfaces of costal cartilages of second, third, fourth, fifth and sixth ribs.

NERVE SUPPLY.   Branches from upper six thoracic intercostal nerves.

ACTION.   Depression of the ribs to which it is attached. Cannot be palpated.

COMMENTS.   This muscle consists of flat bands and is located

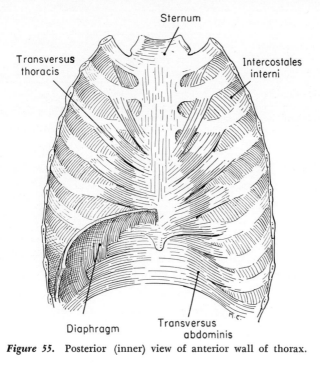

Figure 55.   Posterior (inner) view of anterior wall of thorax.

CHECK LIST FOR THE MUSCULAR ANALYSIS OF THE MOVEMENT
INVOLVED IN RESPIRATION

	Normal Inhalation	Vigorous Inhalation	Vigorous Exhalation
MUSCLES OF RESPIRATION:			
Diaphragm			
External intercostals			
Internal intercostals, anterior			
Internal intercostals, posterior and lateral			
Levatores costarum			
Serratus posterior superior			
Serratus posterior inferior			
Transversus thoracis			
Transversalis			
MUSCLES OF THE SPINE:			
Sternocleidomastoid			
Three scaleni			
Thoracic extensors			
Rectus abdominis			
External oblique			
Internal oblique			
MUSCLES OF THE SHOULDER GIRDLE AND JOINT:			
Pectoralis minor			
Trapezius I			
Levator scapulae			
OTHERS:			

on the inner surface of the front wall of the thorax. The bands radiate upward and outward from the sternum to the ribs, the lowest fibers being continuous with those of the transversus abdominis.

Serratus Posterior Inferior (Fig. 53)

LOWER, MEDIAL ATTACHMENTS. (O)   Spinous processes and ligaments of lower two thoracic and upper two or three lumbar vertebrae.

UPPER LATERAL ATTACHMENTS. (I)   Lower borders of lower four ribs.

NERVE SUPPLY.   Branches from ninth, tenth and eleventh intercostal nerves.

ACTION.   Depression of the lower four ribs.

Cannot be palpated.

COMMENTS.   Like the superior, this is a flat quadrilateral muscle. The fibers slant downward and medialward from the lower ribs to the spine.

Muscles, Other Than the Principal or Assistant Movers, Acting in Respiration.   Since the muscles which act as the movers in inhalation and exhalation have already been listed (p. 98), it seems unnecessary to repeat them here. The principal movers are the muscles which belong primarily to the thorax; the assistant movers, those which are primarily muscles of the spine or shoulder girdle. Some of the latter muscles also serve as stabilizers in respiration.

Stabilizers in Inhalation.   QUADRATUS LUMBORUM.   This anchors the last rib against the pull of the diaphragm.

THE THREE SCALENI.   These hold the upper two ribs against the pull of the external intercostals.

CERVICAL AND THORACIC EXTENSORS.   These stabilize the head and neck against the pull of the sternocleidomastoid and scaleni.

ABDOMINAL MUSCLES.   By their normal tension these muscles stabilize the lower ribs against the pull of the diaphragm.

UPPER TRAPEZIUS AND LEVATOR SCAPULAE.   These stabilize the scapula against the pull of the pectoralis minor.

Stabilizers in Exhalation.   SACROSPINALIS.   Stabilizes the spine and pelvis against the pull of the abdominal muscles.

Demonstrations and Laboratory Exercises

1. Movements of the thorax in respiration.

Subject: Breathe naturally for a while, then as deeply as possible.

Observer: a. Place the hands on the sides of the thorax and note the movement in the lateral diameter.

b. Place one hand on the ribs at the subcostal angle (just below the sternum) and the other hand against the back at the same level. Note the movement in the anteroposterior diameter.

    c. Place the fingers on the sternum. Can you detect any movement in normal respiration? In deep respiration?

    2. Muscular action in forced inhalation.

    a. Subject: Inhale through a small rubber tube, pinching it slightly in order to furnish resistance.

    Observer: Note the action of the sternocleidomastoid, cervical and thoracic extensors, and upper trapezius. Can any other musclar action be detected? If so, explain.

    b. Subject: Run in place or around the room until short of breath. Hang from a horizontal bar.

    Observer: Can you detect any action of the pectoralis major accompanying inhalation? (By stabilizing the arms, the pectoralis major is made to act on the ribs.)

    3. Muscular action in vigorous exhalation.

    Subject: Blow through a small rubber tube, pinching it slightly or holding a finger loosely over the end. (Or blow into a spirometer, flarimeter or toy balloon.)

    Observer: Note the action of the abdominal muscles and of the sacrospinalis.

Bibliography

1. Cates, H. A., and Basmajian, J. V.: Primary Anatomy. 3rd ed. Baltimore, Williams & Wilkins Company, 1955, p. 45.
2. Morris' Human Anatomy. 11th ed. New York, McGraw-Hill Book Company, Inc., 1953.
3. Steindler, A.: Kinesiology of the Human Body. Springfield, Ill., Charles C Thomas, 1955, Lecture 13.

Recommended Reading

Steindler, A.: Kinesiology of the Human Body. (See 3 above.) For advanced students.

7 · Movements of the Upper Extremity: The Shoulder Region

Nowhere in the body is anatomic cooperation more beautifully illustrated than in the movements of the arm on the trunk. The arm travels through a wide range of movements. In each of these the scapula contributes to the movement by placing the glenoid fossa in the most favorable position for the head of the humerus. For instance, when the arm is elevated sideways, the scapula rotates upward, making the glenoid fossa face somewhat upward. When the arm is raised forward, the scapula not only rotates upward, but, unless deliberately prevented from so doing, also revolves on its vertical axis in such a way that the glenoid fossa faces somewhat forward. In certain artificial movements, such as the arm flingings and placings of formal gymnastics, the forward movement of the scapula is deliberately inhibited. In all natural movements, however, the scapula shares with the humerus in the movements of the arm on the trunk.

These movements of the scapula occur not in one joint, but in two. The scapula articulates with the clavicle, and the clavicle, in turn, articulates with the sternum (Fig. 56). All movements of the scapula involve motion in both these joints. Thus, just as the scapula cooperates with the humerus, the clavicle cooperates with the scapula. This is but one of the many illustrations of teamwork found in the human mechanism.

In order to understand the movements of the arm as a whole,

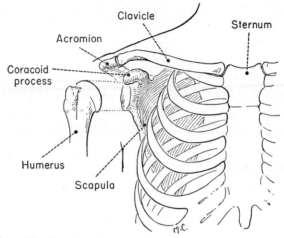

Figure 56. Anterior view of shoulder joint and shoulder girdle.

each joint which participates in these movements should be studied separately.

The Shoulder Joint (Scapulohumeral Articulation)

Structure.   The shoulder joint is formed by the articulation of the spherical head of the humerus with the small, shallow, somewhat pear-shaped glenoid fossa of the scapula (Fig. 56). It is a ball-and-socket joint. The structure of the joint and the looseness of the capsule (permitting between 1 and 2 inches of separation between the two bones) account for the remarkable mobility of the shoulder

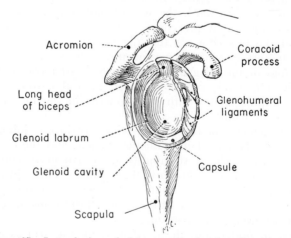

Figure 57. Lateral view of right scapula showing glenoid cavity.

joint. Both the humeral head and the glenoid fossa are covered with hyaline cartilage. The cartilage on the head is thicker at the center; that which lines the cavity is thicker around the circumference. The glenoid fossa is further protected by a flat rim of white fibrocartilage, likewise thicker around the circumference. This cartilage, called the glenoid labrum, serves both to deepen the fossa and to cushion it against the impact of the humeral head in forceful movements (Fig. 57).

The joint is completely enveloped in a loose sleevelike articular capsule which is attached proximally to the circumference of the glenoid cavity, and distally to the anatomic neck of the humerus. The capsule is reinforced both by ligaments and by muscle tendons. The latter are particularly important in preserving the stability of the joint.

Ligamentous Reinforcements.   CORACOHUMERAL   LIGAMENT (Fig. 58).   This is a broad band connecting the lateral border of the coracoid process with the anterior border of the greater tubercle of the humerus. It reinforces the upper anterior portion of the capsule.

GLENOHUMERAL LIGAMENTS (Fig. 57).   These are three adjacent bands of fibers which blend with and strengthen the inner fibers of the front and lower part of the capsule. They attach along the anterior edge of the glenoid fossa from the apex to the inferior rim. From here they pass in front of and beneath the shoulder joint, to attach to the anterior and inferior portions of the anatomic neck of the humerus.

CORACOACROMIAL LIGAMENT (Fig. 58).   Structurally, this ligament should be classed with those of the scapula, since both its

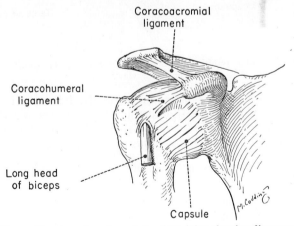

Figure 58. Anterior view of shoulder joint showing ligaments.

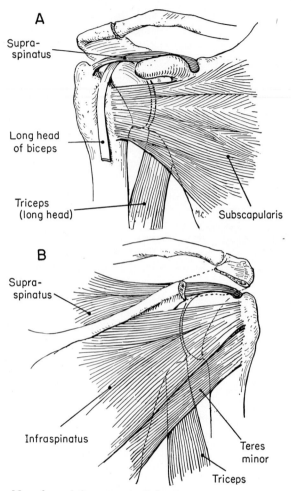

Figure 59. Muscular reinforcements of shoulder joint. *A,* Anterior view; *B,* posterior view.

attachments are on this bone. Functionally, however, it belongs with the ligaments of the shoulder joint. By connecting the acromion and coracoid processes, it forms a bridge over the top of the shoulder joint, thus serving to protect this structure.

Muscular Reinforcements (Fig. 59)

1. Superior
   Supraspinatus
   Long head of biceps
   The relation of this tendon to the joint is unique in that it origi-

nates from within the joint capsule. It arises from the upper margin of the glenoid fossa as a continuation of the glenoid labrum, penetrates the capsule, and passes through the intertubercular groove, which has been converted into a tunnel by the transverse humeral ligament. Its passage through the capsule, over the humeral head and between the two tubercles is facilitated by a tubular sheath of synovial membrane.

2. Inferior
>   Long head of triceps
3. Posterior
>   Infraspinatus
>   Teres minor
4. Anterior
>   Subscapularis
>   Fibrous prolongations of pectoralis major and teres major
>   These blend with the transverse humeral ligament.

The synovial membrane lines the capsule, folds back over the glenoid labrum, covers all but the upper portion of the anatomic neck of the humerus, and extends through the intertubercular groove in the form of a sheath for the tendon of the long head of the biceps. There are several bursae in the region of the shoulder joint. Among the larger are the one between the deltoid and the capsule, and the one on top of the acromion process.

Movements.   The movements of the shoulder joint are as follows:

Flexion and Hyperflexion.   A forward upward movement of the humerus in a plane at right angles to the plane of the scapula. If the movement exceeds 180 degrees, it is hyperflexion.

Extension.   Return movement from flexion.

Hyperextension.   A backward movement of the humerus in a plane at right angles to the plane of the scapula.

Abduction.   A sideward upward movement of the humerus in a plane parallel with the plane of the scapula.

Adduction.   Return movement from abduction.

Outward Rotation.   A rotation of the humerus around its mechanical axis so that, when the arm is in its normal resting position, the anterior aspect turns laterally.

Inward Rotation.   A rotation of the humerus around its mechanical axis so that when the arm is in its normal resting position, the anterior aspect turns medially.

Horizontal Flexion-Adduction.   A forward movement of the sideward-elevated humerus in a horizontal plane (i.e., from a plane parallel to the plane of the scapula to a plane at right angles to it).

Horizontal Extension-Abduction.   A backward movement of

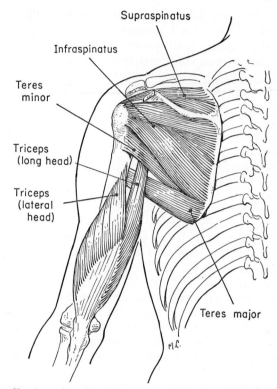

Supraspinatus

Infraspinatus

Teres
minor

Triceps
(long head)

Triceps
(lateral
head)

Teres major

M.C.

Figure 60. Posterior view of muscles of shoulder joint, deep layer.

the forward-elevated humerus in a horizontal plane (i.e., from a plane at right angles to the plane of the scapula to a plane parallel to it).

Circumduction.   A combination of flexion, abduction, extension, hyperextension and adduction, performed sequentially in either direction, so that the arm as a whole describes a cone, and the finger tips a circle.

Muscles.   The muscles of the shoulder joint may be classified according to their position in relation to the joint. Some of them are situated above the joint, some in front of it, and some behind it.

Superior:
  Middle deltoid
  Supraspinatus
Anterior:
  Pectoralis major
  Coracobrachialis
  Anterior deltoid
  Subscapularis
  Biceps (primarily a muscle of the elbow joint)

Posterior:
    Posterior deltoid
    Latissimus dorsi
    Teres major
    Infraspinatus
    Teres minor
    Long head of triceps (primarily a muscle of the elbow joint)

Deltoid (Figs. 61 and 62)

PROXIMAL ATTACHMENTS (O):
    Anterior: Anterior border of outer third of clavicle.
    Middle: Acromion process and outer end of clavicle.
    Posterior: Lower margin of spine of scapula.

DISTAL ATTACHMENT. (I)   Lateral aspect of humerus, near midpoint.

NERVE SUPPLY.   Axillary (circumflex)

ACTION:
    Anterior: Flexion; horizontal flexion-adduction; inward rotation.
    Middle: Abduction; horizontal extension-abduction.
    Posterior: Horizontal extension-abduction; outward rotation; extension; adduction.

WHERE TO PALPATE:
    Anterior: In front of the head of the humerus and for a space of 2 or 3 inches below this.
    Middle: Lateral surface of upper third of upper arm.
    Posterior: Upper and lateral portion of posterior surface of scapula below scapular spine.

COMMENTS.   The deltoid muscle is complex in structure, consisting of several bundles of fibers. The extreme anterior and posterior bundles are of spindle or fusiform construction; the bundles comprising the middle portion are multipenniform. This arrangement of the middle portion makes for great strength without resulting in too much bulk. The muscle is a powerful abductor of the humerus. In addition to raising the arm it is frequently called upon to hold the arm in an elevated position for long periods of time, making it possible for the hand to work at a height. The multipenniform arrangement of fibers also serves to compensate for the middle deltoid's poor angle of pull. This poor angle of pull, on the other hand, means that the muscle has a strong stabilizing component of force. This is fortunate, since the shoulder joint depends more on its muscles than on its ligaments for holding the head of the humerus in the glenoid fossa.

The anterior portion of the deltoid aids in all forward movements of the arm and in inward rotation of the humerus. The posterior portion aids in backward movements of the arm and in outward rotation of the humerus. The most posterior fibers, being

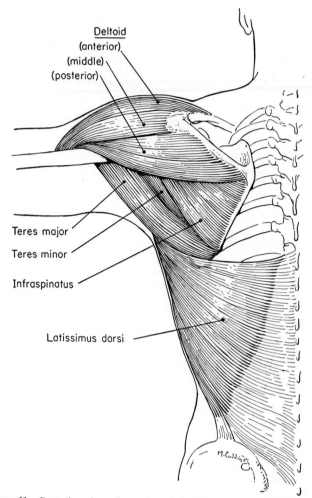

Deltoid
(anterior)
(middle)
(posterior)

Teres major
Teres minor
Infraspinatus

Latissimus dorsi

M.Coddin

Figure 61. Posterior view of muscles of shoulder joint, superficial layer.

situated below the axis of motion, assist in depressing the arm from an elevated position. In this movement they serve as either extensors or adductors of the humerus, depending upon whether the arm is in a position of forward or sideward elevation. When the arm is raised overhead, the posterior deltoid, in whole or in part, may shift its relationship to the axis of motion in such a way that it will contribute to the abduction. This is an example of the reversal of a muscle's customary function (see p. 27). It cannot perform its usual function of adducting or extending until the arm has been lowered to the point where the fibers are again below the center of motion in the shoulder joint.

Supraspinatus (Fig. 60)

PROXIMAL ATTACHMENT. (O)   Medial two thirds of supraspinatus fossa above spine of scapula.

DISTAL ATTACHMENT. (I)   Top of greater tuberosity of humerus.

NERVE SUPPLY.   Suprascapular.

ACTION.   Abduction; lifts capsule out of way.

WHERE TO PALPATE.   Above spine of scapula, provided scapula is supported, e.g., when armpit rests over back of chair.

COMMENTS.   Besides assisting the middle deltoid in abducting the humerus and in holding the head of the humerus in the glenoid fossa, this muscle is credited with the task of lifting the capsule out of the way when the humerus is raised. Some authorities also say that it rotates the humerus outward.

Pectoralis Major (Fig. 62)

PROXIMAL ATTACHMENTS. (O)   Medial two thirds of clavicle; anterior surface of sternum; cartilages of first six ribs; slip from aponeurosis of external oblique abdominal muscle.

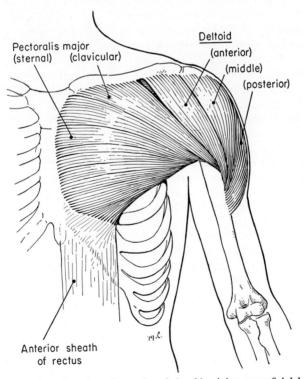

Figure 62.   Anterior view of muscles of shoulder joint, superficial layer.

DISTAL ATTACHMENT. (I)   Lateral surface of humerus just below head by a flat tendon 2 to 3 inches wide.

NERVE SUPPLY.   Medial and lateral anterior thoracic.

ACTION:

Upper or clavicular portion: Flexion; horizontal flexion-adduction; inward rotation; abduction when arm is above the horizontal.

Lower or sternal portion: Adduction; horizontal flexion-adduction; inward rotation; extension.

WHERE TO PALPATE:

Clavicular: Just below the medial two thirds of the clavicle.

Sternal: Lateral to the sternum, below clavicular portion.

Both: Anterior border of axilla.

COMMENTS.   This large fan-shaped muscle of the chest converges to a flat tendon of insertion which twists on itself in such a way that the fibers coming from the lower portion terminate in the higher insertion, and vice versa. The muscle is divided into three parts, the clavicular, the sternal and the abdominal, corresponding to its proximal attachments. Since the abdominal portion is relatively small and since it does not seem to have any unique function of its own, the common practice is to include it with the sternal portion. The clavicular portion lies close to the anterior deltoid muscle and works with it in the flexion, inward rotation and horizontal flexion-adduction of the humerus. Ordinarily the line of pull of the clavicular portion of the pectoralis major lies below the axis of the shoulder joint. When the arm is raised sideward well above the horizontal, however, this muscle's line of pull shifts above the shoulder joint axis. It is then in a position to aid in further abduction of the humerus. This is another instance of the reversal of a muscle's customary function (see p. 27). The sternal portion acts only in downward and forward movements of the arm. The pectoralis major as a whole is particularly important in all pushing, throwing and punching activities.

Coracobrachialis (Fig. 63)

PROXIMAL ATTACHMENT. (O)   Coracoid process of scapula.

DISTAL ATTACHMENT. (I)   Inner surface of humerus opposite deltoid attachment.

NERVE SUPPLY.   Musculocutaneous.

ACTION.   Horizontal flexion-adduction; stabilization of shoulder joint; aids in flexion, adduction, inward rotation, and in extension when the arm is raised overhead.

WHERE TO PALPATE.   Anterior surface of upper arm, medial to short head of biceps. Forearm must be supported in flexed position and resistance given to lower end of humerus. Difficult to palpate.

COMMENTS.   Because the line of pull is so nearly parallel with the long axis of the humerus, the chief function of this muscle would seem to be stabilization of the shoulder joint.

Subscapularis (Fig. 63)

PROXIMAL ATTACTMENT. (O)   Entire anterior surface of scapula.
DISTAL ATTACHMENT. (I)   Lesser tuberosity of humerus.
NERVE SUPPLY.   Subscapular.
ACTION.   Inward rotation; horizontal flexion-adduction; lower fibers aid in adduction when the arm is above the horizontal.
Cannot be palpated.
COMMENTS.   Inward rotation is the chief action of the subscapularis. It performs this movement best when the arm is at the side or elevated backward.

Biceps (see also muscles of elbow) (Fig. 63)

PROXIMAL ATTACHMENTS. (O)   Long head from upper margin of glenoid fossa; short head from apex of coracoid process of scapula.

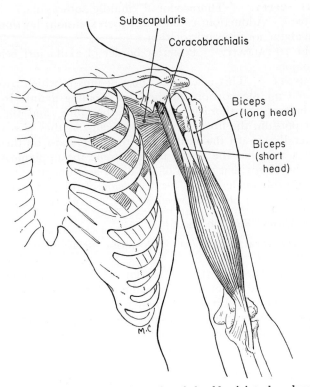

Figure 63. Anterior view of muscles of shoulder joint, deep layer.

DISTAL ATTACHMENT. (I) Bicipital tuberosity of radius.

NERVE SUPPLY. Musculocutaneous.

ACTION (AT SHOULDER JOINT). Long head: Stabilization of shoulder joint; may aid slightly in abduction and horizontal flexion-adduction. Short head: Flexion; horizontal flexion-adduction; adduction.

WHERE TO PALPATE. Medial-anterior surface of upper arm, 3 or 4 inches above elbow.

COMMENTS. The biceps can contribute effectively to movements of the humerus only when the elbow joint is extended.

Latissimus Dorsi (Fig. 61)

PROXIMAL ATTACHMENTS. (O) Spinous processes of lower six thoracic and all lumbar vertebrae; posterior surface of sacrum; crest of ilium; and lower three ribs.

DISTAL ATTACHMENT. (I) Anterior surface of humerus below head, by a flat tendon, just anterior to and parallel with tendon of pectoralis major.

NERVE SUPPLY. Thoracodorsal (middle subscapular).

ACTION. Adduction; extension; hyperextension; horizontal extension-abduction; inward rotation.

WHERE TO PALPATE. Posterior border of axilla just below the teres major.

COMMENTS. This is a broad sheet of muscle which covers the lower and middle portions of the back. Coming mainly from the lower half of the thoracic portion of the spine, and the entire lumbar portion, the fibers gradually converge as they pass upward and laterally toward the axilla. Here the fibers twist on themselves in such a way that the lowest fibers become the uppermost. They end in the narrow flat tendon of the distal attachment. The muscle has a favorable angle of pull for depression of the arm, particularly when the latter is raised between 30 and 90 degrees.

Teres Major (Figs. 60 and 61)

PROXIMAL ATTACHMENT. (O) Posterior surface of inferior angle of scapula.

DISTAL ATTACHMENT. (I) Anterior surface of humerus below head, just medial to tendon of latissimus dorsi.

NERVE SUPPLY. Lower subscapular.

ACTION. Adduction; extension; hyperextension; inward rotation; horizontal extension-abduction.

WHERE TO PALPATE. Posterior border of axilla just above latissimus dorsi.

COMMENTS. This muscle is the latissimus dorsi's "little helper." Although it is a much smaller muscle than the latissimus, its action on the humerus is the same. Like the latissimus, it has a good angle of pull when the arm is raised between 30 and 90 degrees.

Infraspinatus and Teres Minor (Figs. 59, 60 and 61)

PROXIMAL ATTACHMENT. (O)   Axillary border and posterior surface of scapula below scapular spine.

DISTAL ATTACHMENT. (I)   Posterior aspect of greater tuberosity of humerus.

NERVE SUPPLY.   Suprascapular and axillary.

ACTION.   Outward rotation; horizontal extension-abduction.

WHERE TO PALPATE.   Posterior surface of scapula, medial and inferior to posterior deltoid muscle.

COMMENTS.   From the point of view of the kinesiologist there is no reason why these muscles should have separate names. They are as truly one muscle as are the two parts of the pectoralis major, or the three parts of the deltoid, in fact even more so because there is no difference in their function. Besides their powerful outward rotatory action, these muscles aid materially in holding the head of the humerus in the glenoid fossa. These two muscles, like all the muscles uniting the scapula with the humerus, act effectively to move the humerus only when the scapula is stabilized.

Long Head of Triceps (see also muscles of elbow) (Figs. 59 and 60)

PROXIMAL ATTACHMENT. (O)   Just below glenoid fossa of scapula.

DISTAL ATTACHMENT (I)   Olecranon process of ulna.

NERVE SUPPLY.   Musculospiral.

ACTION (AT SHOULDER JOINT).   Assists in adduction, extension and hyperextension.

WHERE TO PALPATE.   Posterior surface of arm close to shoulder joint.

The Shoulder Girdle (Acromioclavicular and Sternoclavicular Articulations)

Structure of Acromioclavicular Articulation (Fig. 64).   The articulation between the acromion process of the scapula and the outer end of the clavicle belongs to the diarthrodial classification. Within this group it is further classified as an irregular (arthrodial) joint. A small wedge-shaped disk may be found between the upper part of the joint surfaces, but this is frequently absent. The articular capsule is strengthened above by the acromioclavicular ligament, and behind by the aponeurosis of the trapezius and deltoid muscles. The clavicle is further stabilized by means of the coraco-

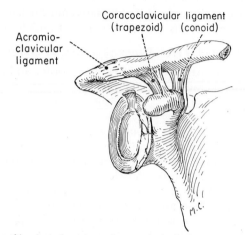

Figure 64. Anterior view of acromioclavicular articulation.

clavicular ligament, which, as the name suggests, binds the clavicle to the coracoid process.

Ligaments.   ACROMIOCLAVICULAR.   This passes from the upper part of the outer end of the clavicle to the upper surface of the acromion process.

CORACOCLAVICULAR.   This is really two ligaments, the conoid and the trapezoid. The conoid ligament passes from the base of the coracoid process to the conoid tubercle on the under side of the clavicle. The trapezoid ligament extends from the top of the coracoid process to the trapezoid ridge on the under side of the clavicle.

Structure of Sternoclavicular Articulation (Fig. 65).   The sternal end of the clavicle articulates with both the sternum and the cartilage of the first rib. It is classified as a double arthrodial joint because there are two joint cavities, one on either side of the articular disk. This round flat disk of white fibrocartilage is attached above to the upper and posterior border of the articular surface of the clavicle, and below to the cartilage of the first rib near its junction with the sternum. The articular capsule is thin above and below, but is thickened in front and behind by bands of fibers called the anterior and posterior sternoclavicular ligaments.

Ligaments.   ANTERIOR STERNOCLAVICULAR.   This is a band of fibers blending with the anterior fibers of the articular capsule.

POSTERIOR STERNOCLAVICULAR.   The fibers forming this ligament blend with the posterior fibers of the articular capsule.

INTERCLAVICULAR.   This ligament consists of a flat band which passes across the upper margin of the sternum and attaches to the sternal end of each clavicle.

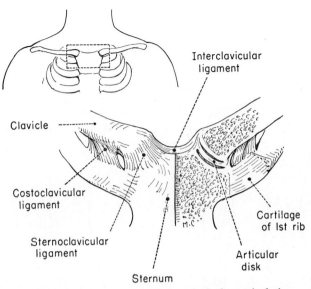

Clavicle

Interclavicular
ligament

Costoclavicular
ligament

Sternoclavicular
ligament

Cartilage
of 1st rib

Articular
disk

Sternum

Figure 65.   Anterior view of sternoclavicular articulation.

COSTOCLAVICULAR.   This is a short strong band of fibers which
connects the upper border of the first costal cartilage with the
costal tuberosity on the under side of the clavicle.

The sternoclavicular articulation is of great importance in the
movements of the shoulder girdle, in fact of the whole upper
extremity. It is the only point at which the shoulder girdle and the
upper extremity articulate with the trunk.

Movements (Fig. 66).   It is customary to define the movements of the shoulder girdle in terms of the movements of the scapulae. In doing this, there is some danger that the reader will visualize the movement as taking place solely in the joint between the
scapula and the clavicle. It is well to emphasize the fact that *every
movement of the scapula involves motion in both joints.*

The movements of the shoulder girdle, expressed in terms of the
composite movements of the scapula, are as follows:

Elevation (Fig. 66, *A*).   An upward movement of the scapula
with the vertebral border remaining approximately parallel to the
spinal column. Elevation is always accompanied by slight adduction and occasionally by slight upward tilt.

Depression.   The return from the position of elevation. There
is no depression below the normal resting position.

Abduction (Fig. 66, *B*).   A lateral movement of the scapula
away from the spinal column, with the vertebral border remaining
approximately parallel to it. Abduction is usually accompanied by
a slight lateral tilt, that is, a turning of the scapula on its vertical

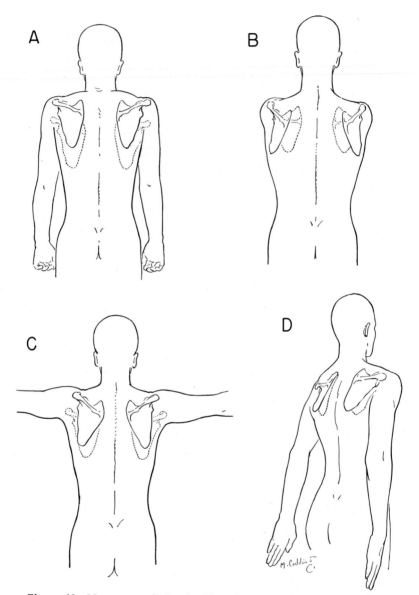

Figure 66. Movements of the shoulder girdle. *A,* Elevation; *B,* abduction (combined with lateral tilt and upward rotation); *C,* upward rotation; *D,* upward tilt.

axis so that the vertebral border protrudes from the back and the glenoid fossa faces slightly forward. This is necessitated by the rounded contour of the back and by the forward movement of the outer end of the clavicle, to which the scapula is attached.

Adduction. A medial movement of the scapula toward the spinal column, with the vertebral border remaining approximately parallel to it. Adduction is usually accompanied by a reduction of lateral tilt.

Upward Tilt (Fig. 66, *D*). A turning of the scapula on its frontal-horizontal axis so that the posterior surface faces upward and the inferior angle protrudes from the back.

Reduction of Upward Tilt. The return from upward tilt.

Upward Rotation (Fig. 66, *C*). A rotation of the scapula in the frontal plane so that the glenoid fossa faces somewhat upward.

Downward Rotation. The return from the position of upward rotation. There may be slight downward rotation beyond the normal resting position, so that the glenoid fossa faces slightly downward.

Muscles. The muscles of the shoulder girdle are classified as anterior or posterior muscles, according to their location on the trunk.

Anterior:
  Subclavius
  Pectoralis minor
  Serratus anterior

Posterior:
  Levator scapulae
  Trapezius
  Rhomboids

Subclavius (Fig. 67)

PROXIMAL ATTACHMENT. (O)   Upper surface of first rib at junction with cartilage.

DISTAL ATTACHMENT. (I)   Under side of middle half of clavicle.

NERVE SUPPLY.   Branches from fifth and sixth cervical.

ACTION.   Depression of clavicle; stabilization of sternoclavicular joint.

Cannot be palpated.

COMMENTS.   The fibers of the subclavius run almost parallel with the long axis of the clavicle. They have a slight downward and strong medialward pull. This would seem to indicate that, although the muscle is in a position to depress the outer end of the clavicle when necessary, its real function is to protect and stabilize the sternoclavicular articulation. When the clavicle is fixed in elevation, the subclavius can aid slightly in lifting the first rib in forced inspiration.

Pectoralis Minor (Fig. 67)

PROXIMAL ATTACHMENTS. (O)   Anterior surface of third, fourth and fifth ribs near cartilages.

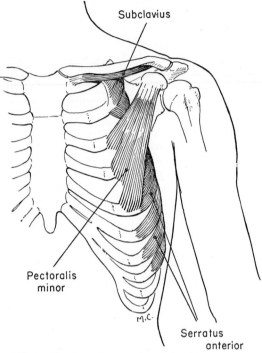

Figure 67. Anterior muscles of shoulder girdle.

DISTAL ATTACHMENT. (I)   Tip of coracoid process of scapula.

NERVE SUPPLY.   Medial anterior thoracic.

ACTION.   Downward rotation; abduction and lateral tilt; upward tilt; depression.

WHERE TO PALPATE.   Cannot be palpated when pectoralis major is contracting. May be palpated halfway between clavicle and nipple when arm is elevated backward as far as possible or against resistance. May also be palpated if subject sits with forearm resting on table at side of body and pushes both downward and laterally at the same time.

COMMENTS.   Besides its action on the scapula, an important function of the pectoralis minor is its lifting effect on the ribs, both in forced inspiration and in maintaining good chest posture. When the scapulae are stabilized by the adductors, contraction of the pectoralis minor elevates the third, fourth and fifth ribs. Even without contracting, it exerts a slight upward and outward pull on these ribs if its tonus is good. Thus the pectoralis minor can contribute either to good posture or to poor, depending upon whether its more effective pull is on the ribs or on the scapula. The key to its function as a muscle of good posture is stabilization of the scapulae by the adductors—the rhomboids and the middle trapezius.

Serratus Anterior (Fig. 67)

PROXIMAL ATTACHMENTS. (O)   Outer surfaces of upper nine ribs at side of chest.

DISTAL ATTACHMENT. (I)   Anterior surface of vertebral border and inferior angle of scapula.

NERVE SUPPLY.   Long thoracic.

ACTION:

Upper: Abduction and lateral tilt.

Lower: Upward rotation.

Both: A combination of the above plus a tendency to pull the vertebral border of the scapula inward toward the ribs.

WHERE TO PALPATE.   Anterior-lateral surface of upper thorax, especially on a thin, muscular subject.

COMMENTS.   The serratus anterior is made up of separate bands or bundles attached to the ribs, as the name suggests, in a saw-tooth arrangement. The first band, coming from the first two ribs, attaches to the uppermost portion of the vertebral border. The next two or three bands, coming from the second, third, and occasionally fourth ribs, fan out to attach along almost the entire length of the vertebral border. These first four or five bands comprise the upper serratus anterior, whose chief function is abduction of the scapula.

The lower portion consists of bands which come from the next four or five ribs and converge to attach to the anterior surface of the inferior angle of the scapula. Their function is to rotate the scapula upward.

Levator Scapulae (see also muscles of neck) (Fig. 68)

PROXIMAL ATTACHMENTS. (O)   Transverse processes of first four cervical vertebrae.

DISTAL ATTACHMENT. (I)   Vertebral border of scapula between medial angle and scapular spine.

NERVE SUPPLY.   Dorsal scapular and branches from third and fourth cervical.

ACTION (AT SCAPULA).   Elevation; downward rotation.

Cannot be palpated.

COMMENTS.   Bowen has pointed out that, although one would expect the levator scapulae to elevate and adduct the scapula, actually it causes elevation and downward rotation. His explanation of this action is that the weight of the arm at the acromial end of the scapula pulls that end down at the same time that the levator is pulling up on the medial angle. Thus these two forces act as a couple to rotate the scapula. (A couple, in physics, is a pair of equal and opposite forces acting on either side of the fulcrum of

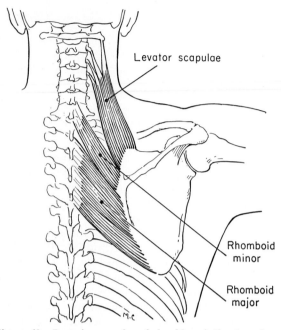

Figure 68. Posterior muscles of shoulder girdle, deep layer.

a lever. A common example is the action of the two hands in turning the steering wheel of a car, particularly when the hands are placed opposite each other.) If it is true that the weight of the arm changes the levator's action from adduction to downward rotation, then this would only be the case when the body is in such a position that the force of gravity pulls the arm down. In other positions, as when a person is swimming, one would expect the levator to adduct, as well as elevate, the scapula. Unfortunately the muscle's location makes experimentation difficult.

Trapezius (Fig. 69)

PROXIMAL ATTACHMENTS. (O)   Occipital bone; ligamentum nuchae; spinous processes of seventh cervical and all thoracic vertebrae.

DISTAL ATTACHMENTS (I):

Part I: Posterior border of lateral third of clavicle.

Part II: Top of acromion process.

Part III: Upper border of spine of scapula.

Part IV: Root of spine of scapula.

NERVE SUPPLY.   Spinal accessory and branches from third and fourth cervical.

ACTION:
Part I: Elevation.
Part II: Elevation; upward rotation; assists in adduction.
Part III: Adduction.
Part IV: Upward rotation; depression; assists in adduction.

WHERE TO PALPATE. Kite-shaped area in upper back and neck (Fig. 69).

COMMENTS. The trapezius is a fascinating muscle to study. Since its location directly under the skin makes it easy to palpate, the student should investigate all its actions for himself. While some anatomists treat the muscle in three parts, it is more accurate to consider separately the four parts listed above. Parts I and II comprise the upper trapezius, part III the middle, and part IV the lower. The relation of the trapezius to the rhomboids and ser-

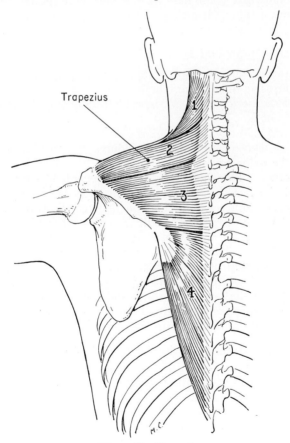

Trapezius

Figure 69. Trapezius.

ratus is interesting. The rhomboids and part III of the trapezius both adduct the scapulae. In this action they are partners. Parts II and IV, however, rotate the scapulae upward; the rhomboids rotate them downward. In this respect, then, they are antagonists. Trapezius II and IV are partners with the lower serratus with respect to upward rotation, but trapezius III and the upper serratus are antagonistic, the former adducting, and the latter abducting, the scapulae. Parts II and IV of the trapezius act on the scapula as a couple (see p. 127) to rotate the scapula upward, part II pulling up on the acromial end of the scapular spine, and part IV pulling down on the medial end or root.

These various combinations of function illustrate one of the major characteristics of muscular action, namely, a teamwork that surpasses the most ingenious invention of man. It is this amazing variety of muscular combinations, together with similar combinations of joint action, that makes the human structure such an astonishingly versatile mechanism.

Rhomboid, Major and Minor (Fig. 68)

PROXIMAL ATTACHMENTS. (O)   Spinous processes of seventh cervical and first five thoracic vertebrae.

DISTAL ATTACHMENT. (I)   Vertebral border of scapula from spine to inferior angle.

NERVE SUPPLY.   Dorsal scapular.

ACTION.   Downward rotation; adduction; elevation. Cannot be palpated.

COMMENTS.   The rhomboids may be regarded as one muscle, in spite of the fact that they are usually described as two. There is no important difference in function between the two parts. The rhomboids' cooperative action with trapezius III, which has been discussed above, is an important factor in the maintenance of good shoulder posture. When the tonus of these two muscles is deficient, the unbalanced pull of the pectoralis minor and the serratus anterior results in habitually abducted and tilted scapulae. This in turn means that the pectoralis minor and the serratus anterior fail to hold the chest in good posture. Thus one weak link in the chain of postural relationships leads to another.

Movements of the Arm on the Trunk

It has already been stated that the movements of the arm on the trunk do not take place at the shoulder joint alone, but that they also involve movement of the shoulder girdle at the acromioclavicular and sternoclavicular joints. In order to analyze correctly the movements of the upper extremity, it is necessary to understand the cooperative action of the shoulder joint and shoulder girdle. The fundamental movements of the arm are given below, together with the analysis of each in terms of shoulder joint and shoulder girdle action.

Sideward Elevation (Fig. 70)

Shoulder Joint.   Abduction; outward rotation if the palms are turned to face each other in the overhead position.

Shoulder Girdle.   Upward rotation, particularly after arm passes above the horizontal.

Sideward Depression

Shoulder Joint.   Adduction; reduction of outward rotation.

Shoulder Girdle.   Downward rotation.

Forward Elevation (to the horizontal)

Shoulder Joint.   Flexion; slight outward rotation; abduction if scapula is laterally tilted (in which case glenoid fossa will be facing partly forward).

Shoulder Girdle.   Slight upward rotation; abduction and lateral tilt, unless inhibited.

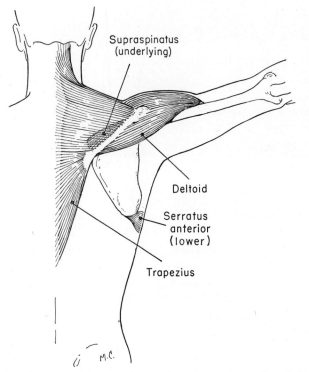

Supraspinatus
(underlying)

Deltoid

Serratus
anterior
(lower)

Trapezius

M.C.

Figure 70.   Muscles which contract to produce sideward elevation of the arm.

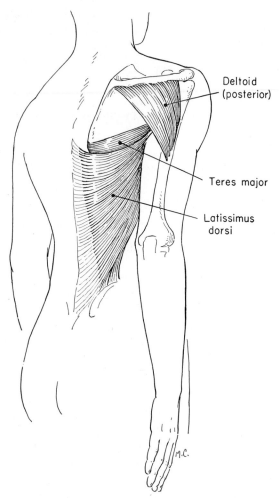

Deltoid
(posterior)

Teres major

Latissimus
dorsi

Figure 71. Muscles which contract to produce backward elevation of the arm.

Forward-Upward Elevation (from the horizontal to the vertical and beyond)

Shoulder Joint.   Flexion and hyperflexion; slight outward rotation.
Shoulder Girdle.   Upward rotation; reduction of abduction and lateral tilt.

Forward-Downward Depression (from the vertical to the starting position)

Shoulder Joint.   Extension; adduction; reduction of outward rotation.
Shoulder Girdle.   Downward rotation; passes through position of abduction and lateral tilt, unless prevented by strong action of the scapular adductors.

Backward Elevation (Fig. 71)

Shoulder Joint.   Hyperextension.
Shoulder Girdle.   Upward tilt; elevation if movement is carried to extreme.

Outward Rotation (Fig. 72)

Shoulder Joint.   Outward rotation.
Shoulder Girdle.   Adduction; reduction of any lateral tilt which may have been present.

Inward Rotation

Shoulder Joint.   Inward rotation.
Shoulder Girdle.   Abduction and lateral tilt; tendency toward elevation.

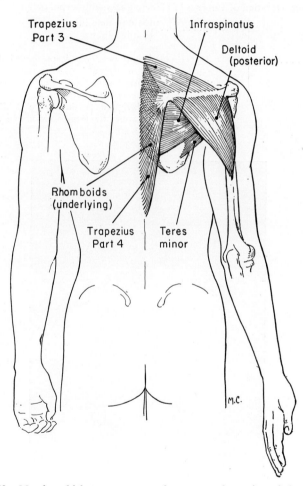

Figure 72.   Muscles which contract to produce outward rotation of the arm and accompanying adduction of the scapula.

Horizontal Forward Swing from Position of Sideward Elevation

Shoulder Joint. Horizontal flexion-adduction; slight inward rotation.
Shoulder Girdle. Abduction and lateral tilt, unless inhibited.

Horizontal Sideward-Backward Swing from Position of Forward Elevation

Shoulder Joint. Horizontal extension-abduction; slight outward rotation.
Shoulder Girdle. Adduction and reduction of lateral tilt.

Muscular Analysis of the Fundamental Movements of the Arm at the Shoulder Joint

Abduction (elevation of humerus in plane parallel with scapula)

Movers
- Principal
  - Middle deltoid
  - Supraspinatus
- Assistant
  - Long head of biceps, especially if the movement is resisted
  - Anterior deltoid, after the arm passes above the horizontal
  - Clavicular portion of pectoralis major, after the arm passes above the horizontal

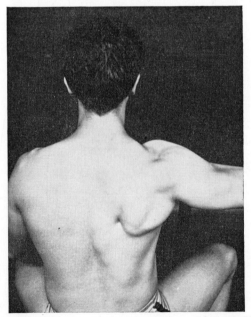

Figure 73. Sideward depression of the arm against resistance. The latissimus dorsi, teres major and rhomboids are in strong contraction.

Neutralizers......................The infraspinatus and teres minor neutralize the flexion tendencies of the
anterior deltoid and upper pectoralis
major after the arm passes above the
horizontal

Stabilizers....................... $\begin{cases} \text{Trapezius} \\ \text{Subclavius} \end{cases}$

Note: 1. Extreme abduction of the humerus is usually accompanied by outward rotation, since a greater range of abduction is possible in this position.
2. In a sense, all the muscles which attach the scapulae to the trunk
may be looked upon as stabilizing or supporting muscles in all movements of the
upper extremity. These include the subclavius, pectoralis minor, serratus anterior,
levator scapulae, rhomboids and trapezius.

Adduction (return from abduction) (Fig. 73)

Note: If performed when the body is erect, the movement could be produced
by gravitational force alone, without muscular action. If performed more slowly
than this, the abductors work in lenthening contraction in order to control the movement, and the adductors are relaxed. If performed more quickly than by the force
of gravity, or if performed against resistance, the muscular action is as given below.

Movers........ $\begin{cases} \text{Principal} \dots \dots \begin{cases} \text{Latissimus dorsi} \\ \text{Teres major} \\ \text{Pectoralis major, sternal portion} \end{cases} \\ \\ \text{Assistant} \dots \dots \begin{cases} \text{Posterior deltoid} \\ \text{Coracobrachialis, when the arm is above} \\ \quad \text{the horizontal} \\ \text{Subscapularis, when the arm is above} \\ \quad \text{the horizontal} \\ \text{Short head of biceps, when the arm is} \\ \quad \text{above the horizontal} \\ \text{Long head of triceps, if the elbow is in} \\ \quad \text{flexed position} \end{cases} \end{cases}$

Neutralizers......................The anterior and posterior muscles
neutralize one another's flexion and
hyperextension tendencies

Stabilizers........................The coracobrachialis, the short head of
the biceps and the long head of the
triceps are all shoulder stabilizers as
well as movers. Each has a relatively
large nonrotatory or stabilizing component of force pulling lengthwise
through the humerus toward the
glenoid fossa. The rhomboids stabilize
the scapula. The abdominal muscles
and spinal extensors stabilize the
trunk if the adduction is forceful

Flexion (forward elevation of humerus in plane perpendicular to scapula) (Fig. 74)

Movers........ $\begin{cases} \text{Principal} \dots \dots \begin{cases} \text{Anterior deltoid} \\ \text{Pectoralis major, clavicular portion} \end{cases} \\ \\ \text{Assistant} \dots \dots \begin{cases} \text{Coracobrachialis} \\ \text{Short head of biceps, especially if elbow} \\ \quad \text{is in extended position} \end{cases} \end{cases}$

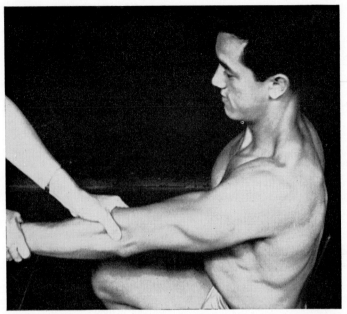

Figure 74.   Forward elevation of the arm against resistance. The anterior and middle deltoid, upper trapezius and serratus anterior are in strong contraction.

Neutralizers	The infraspinatus and teres minor neutralize the inward rotatory components of the anterior deltoid and pectoralis major
Stabilizers	{Trapezius {Subclavius

Extension (return from flexion) (Fig. 75)

Note: See note under Adduction, regarding the effect of the force of gravity.

Movers . . . .
    Principal . . . .
{ Latissimus dorsi, especially during the lower 60 degrees of motion
Pectoralis major, sternal portion, diminishing as the movement progresses
Teres major }

    Assistant . . . .
{ Posterior deltoid
Long head of triceps, especially if elbow is in flexed position }

Neutralizers . . . . The posterior deltoid neutralizes the inward rotatory tendency of the pectoralis major and latissimus dorsi. If the movement is performed with force, the infraspinatus and teres minor also contract to prevent inward rotation

Stabilizers........................The long head of triceps and the coracobrachialis stabilize the shoulder
joint; the rhomboids stabilize the
scapula; the abdominal muscles and
internal intercostals stabilize the ribs;
and the sacrospinalis stabilizes the
spine. The degree to which these muscles contract depends upon the forcefulness of the act

Hyperextension (backward elevation of humerus in a plane perpendicular to
scapula)

Movers........................ $\begin{cases} \text{Posterior deltoid} \\ \text{Latissimus dorsi} \\ \text{Teres major} \end{cases}$

Neutralizers......................The posterior deltoid, on the one hand,
and the latissimus dorsi and teres
major, on the other, are mutual neutralizers with respect to outward and
inward rotation

Stabilizers........................The levator, trapezius and rhomboids
stabilize the scapulae. The sacro-
spinalis stabilizes the spine

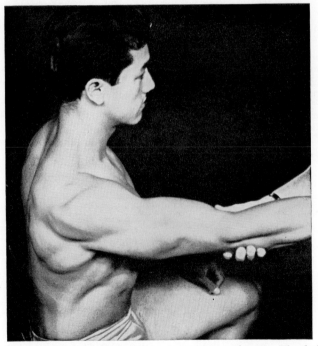

Figure 75. Forward depression of the arm against resistance. The latissimus
dorsi and teres major are in strong contraction.

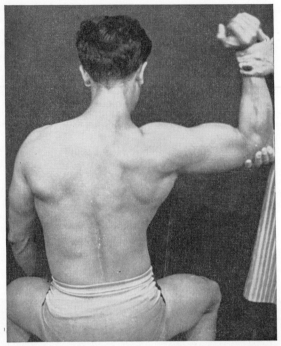

Figure 76. Outward rotation of the arm against resistance. The posterior deltoid, infraspinatus and teres minor are in strong contraction. (The hyperextension and lateral flexion of the trunk are due to the extreme effort. The latissimus is contracting because he is pushing his elbow down.)

Outward Rotation (a lateral rotation of humerus around its longitudinal axis) (Fig. 76)

Movers . . . .
- Principal . . . . Infraspinatus and teres minor
- Assistant . . . . Posterior deltoid, when the humerus is adducted and extended

Neutralizers . . . . None in the movement of the humerus. Trapezius IV neutralizes the tendency of the rhomboids to elevate the scapula

Stabilizers . . . . The middle trapezius and rhomboids stabilize the scapulae

Inward Rotation (medial rotation of humerus around its longitudinal axis)

Movers . . . .
- Principal . . . .
  - Subscapularis
  - Teres major
- Assistant . . . .
  - Latissimus dorsi
  - Anterior deltoid
  - Pectoralis major
  - Coracobrachialis (helps to reduce outward rotation)
  - Short head of biceps (helps to reduce outward rotation)

Neutralizers........................The anterior deltoid, coracobrachialis and clavicular portion of pectoralis major neutralize the extension function of the latissimus dorsi and teres major

Stabilizers........................The pectoralis minor and serratus anterior stabilize the scapulae

Horizontal Flexion-Adduction (a forward movement of the humerus in the horizontal plane)

Movers........ { *Principal*........ { Subscapularis / Pectoralis major / Anterior deltoid / Coracobrachialis / *Assistant*........ Short head of biceps when forearm is extended

Neutralizers........................None

Supporters and Stabilizers..............The middle deltoid and supraspinatus support the humerus against the downward pull of gravity. The pectoralis major on the opposite side stabilizes the sternum; the first part of trapezius and possibly the subclavius stabilize the clavicle; and the serratus anterior and second part of trapezius stabilize the scapula

Horizontal Extension-Abduction (a sideward-backward movement of the humerus in the horizontal plane)

Movers........ { *Principal*........ { Posterior deltoid and posterior portion of middle deltoid / Infraspinatus and teres minor, especially if the movement is combined with outward rotation

Assistant........ { Latissimus dorsi / Teres major, especially if the movement is combined with inward rotation

Neutralizers........................The middle deltoid and supraspinatus neutralize the tendency of the latissimus dorsi and teres major to adduct the humerus. The infraspinatus and teres minor, on the one hand, and the latissimus dorsi and teres major, on the other hand, are mutual neutralizers with respect to outward and inward rotation

Supporters and Stabilizers..............The middle deltoid and supraspinatus support the humerus against the downward pull of gravity. The lower three parts of the trapezius and the rhomboids stabilize the scapula, and the abdominal muscles stabilize the trunk

Muscular Analysis of the Fundamental Movements of the Shoulder Girdle

Elevation

Movers.........
- Principal........ { Levator scapulae / Trapezius, parts I and II / Rhomboids }
- Assistant........ { Sternocleidomastoid, clavicular portion, if the movement is performed against resistance }

Neutralizers....................... The trapezius and rhomboids are mutually neutralizing with respect to upward and downward rotation. The serratus anterior neutralizes the adduction motions of the rhomboids and trapezius

Stabilizers........................ If the movement is performed on one side only, the lateral cervical flexors on the opposite side stabilize the cervical spine

Depression (return from elevation)

Note: No muscular action is required in the erect position if the shoulders are simply allowed to drop from the elevated position. If lowered slowly, the movement is controlled by means of lengthening contraction of the elevators. If performed against resistance, or in a position other than the vertical, the muscular action is as given below.

Movers......................... { Trapezius, part IV / Pectoralis minor / Subclavius }

Neutralizers...................... The lower trapezius and pectoralis minor are mutually neutralizing with respect to adduction and abduction; also with respect to upward and downward rotation

Stabilizers........................ The sacrospinalis and abdominal muscles stabilize the spine, and the internal intercostals and abdominal muscles stabilize the ribs when the movement is performed against resistance

Abduction and Lateral Tilt (protraction of scapulae)

Movers......................... { Serratus anterior / Pectoralis minor }

Neutralizers...................... The serratus anterior and pectoralis minor mutually neutralize one another's tendency to rotate the scapula

Stabilizers........................ The abdominal muscles, and possibly the internal intercostals, stabilize the ribs if the movement is forceful. The levator scapulae helps to support the scapula

Adduction and Reduction of Lateral Tilt (retraction of scapulae)

Movers .... {Principal .... {Rhomboids / Middle trapezius, part III / Assistant .... Trapezius II and IV

Neutralizers .... The rhomboids and lower trapezius are mutually neutralizing with respect to elevation and depression of the scapula, also with respect to downward and upward rotation

Stabilizers .... The abdominal muscles and the sacrospinalis stabilize the spine. This is particularly true if the movement is performed unilaterally because of the tendency of the spine to rotate

Upward Tilt (a backward projection of the inferior angle of the scapula)

Mover .... Pectoralis minor

Neutralizers .... It is doubtful whether there is any neutralizing action in this movement

Stabilizers .... Possibly the internal intercostals contract to stabilize the ribs

Note: This is an uncommon movement which occurs only in conjunction with extreme hyperextension of the humerus.

Reduction of Upward Tilt

Note: Ordinarily no muscular action is needed.

Movers .... Trapezius IV and the lower serratus anterior are in a position to reduce an upward tilt of the scapula, but they do not need to contract unless the movement of the arm is resisted

Neutralizers and Stabilizers .... Impossible to tell

Upward Rotation (occurs only in conjunction with abduction and flexion of the humerus)

Movers .... {Trapezius II and IV / Serratus anterior

Neutralizers .... Trapezius II and IV are mutually neutralizing with respect to elevation and depression

Stabilizers .... The abdominal muscles, and possibly the internal intercostals, help to stabilize the ribs if the movement is forceful

Downward Rotation (occurs only in conjunction with adduction, inward rotation and hyperextension of the humerus)

Note: No muscular action is necessary if the arm is allowed to drop to the side. If the arm is lowered slowly, the movement is controlled by means of lengthening contraction of the upward rotators. When the arm movement is performed forcefully, quickly, or against gravity (i.e., when the body is inverted), the muscular analysis of the shoulder girdle movement is as given below.

Movers........ {
    Principal........ { Rhomboids / Pectoralis minor

    Assistant........ { Levator scapulae (it tends to pull the scapula upward and inward, but the weight of the arm causes the scapula to rotate downward)

Neutralizers........................The rhomboids and pectoralis minor are mutually neutralizing with respect to elevation and depression, also with respect to adduction and abduction. Trapezius IV helps to prevent elevation of scapula when movement of arm is resisted

Stabilizers.........................The abdominal muscles, and possibly the internal intercostals, help to stabilize the ribs if the movement is forceful

Supplementary Material

INDIVIDUAL VARIATIONS IN STRUCTURE

Upper extremity variations which have been observed, and in some cases measured, include the degree of torsion in the humerus, the contour of the vertebral border of the scapula, and the length of the clavicle.

Humeral Torsion. The distal and proximal ends of the humerus do not lie in the same plane, but in planes which form a slight angle with each other. The twist in the humeral shaft which is responsible for this deviation of planes is known as humeral torsion. Although there is a pathologic condition of torsion occasionally found in the long bones of the body, the torsion referred to here is a normal characteristic of the humerus which, like other characteristics, shows considerable individual variation. From the point of view of the physical educator, variations in humeral torsion are significant because of their relation to the use of the arm. A relatively small degree of torsion results in limited motion of the arm in movements such as those used preparatory to throwing a baseball or serving a tennis ball. The effect is similar to that of limited outward rotation in the shoulder joint, with this difference: whereas joint flexibility can be increased, bony torsion cannot be changed.

The amount of torsion in the humerus has been investigated by Krahl and Evans. They noted the following variations in their study of 57 pairs of male and 32 pairs of female humeri:

Sex	Number	Range	Mean	S.D.	Stand. Error of Mean
M	114	56–87 }	74.8	± 8.3	± 0.6
F	64	51–81 }			

Contour of Vertebral Border of Scapula. The contour of the vertebral border of the scapula has been studied by several investigators—among them, Graves, Gray, Hrdlička and Kuhns. They classified the scapulae according to the shape of the vertebral border, i.e., whether it was convex, straight or concave. Gray reported that his examination of 1151 human scapulae revealed the following distribution of types:

Per Cent

Convex vertebral border.............. 61.3
Straight vertebral border.............. 26.6
Concave vertebral border 9.9

Graves claimed that scapular types are not influenced by sex, age, body build, or occupation. Kuhns, on the other hand, in a ten-year longitudinal study of the scapulae of 1000 individuals, observed that the concave vertebral border was almost twice as common in the first decade of life as in the second. He also observed that a concave border was three times as frequent in children of slender body type as in those of stocky build, and that concave borders tended to be associated with poor musculature and poor posture. His comparison of scapular types in childhood and early adulthood is significant.

Vertebral Border in Childhood Per Cent		*Vertebral Border in Early Adulthood* Per Cent	
Convex........	0	Convex........	10
Straight........	61	Straight........	81
Concave........	39	Concave........	9

Kuhns also investigated the scapulae of seventy-two cadavers. The findings of these investigations suggest a tendency for the vertebral borders of scapulae to become progressively more convex with age.

Vertebral Border of Scapulae of 72 Cadavers Per Cent	
Convex..........	30
Straight..........	61
Concave.........	9

Hrdlička, like Kuhns, recognized the influence of age and muscular development on the shape of the scapula.

The kinesiologist is interested in variations of scapular shape chiefly because of the way in which they influence his interpretation of his observations. If the degree of scapular abduction is judged by the space between the vertebral borders of the two scapulae, or between the vertebral border of one scapula and the spinal column, scapulae whose vertebral borders are concave will appear to be abducted further than those whose borders are convex.

Length of Clavicle.   Although the author has not heard of any studies made of clavicular length, she has occasionally heard orthopedists and kinesiologists suggest that short clavicles may be a cause of poor shoulder posture, a cause which obviously cannot be remedied by corrective exercise. A study of the relationship of clavicular length to shoulder posture, and perhaps to the range of motion in the shoulder, would doubtless be of interest to physical educators, physical therapists and occupational therapists. There are certain hazards in such a study, however. By itself, the length measurement of a clavicle is meaningless. It would be necessary to relate the clavicular measurement to some other skeletal measurement, such as chest width, humeral length or trunk length, in order to correlate it with posture or range of motion. For it is the *relative* length of the clavicle which makes it a factor for "good" or for "bad" in an individual's build.

SCAPULAR MOVEMENTS

An Electromyographic Study of the Trapezius Muscle.   Wiedenbauer and Mortensen investigated the activity of the trapezius muscle in various movements of the scapula and arm. Eleven men served as subjects, and the tests were made with the subject seated. The trapezius showed definite activity during both elevation and retraction (adduction) of the scapula. In elevation, the upper portion showed the greatest activity, and in retraction, the middle and lower portions. During abduction of the humerus and the accompanying upward rotation of the scapula, the lower two-thirds of the trapezius were most active, and during

Measurement of
upward rotation

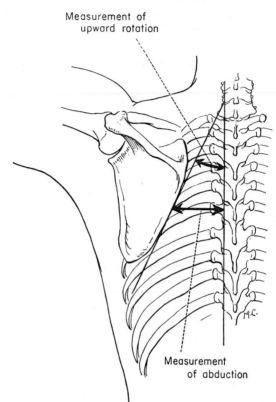

Measurement
of abduction

Figure 77. Measurements of the scapular movements accompanying sideward elevation of the arm. (The sketch is based on an x-ray.)

flexion of the humerus, the lower third. The greatest activity of the trapezius as a whole was seen in abduction of the humerus.

These findings are more or less what one would expect, with possibly two exceptions. In the first place, since the scapula rotates upward in both flexion and abduction of the humerus, why is the trapezius more active in abduction? Is it possibly because the lower serratus anterior is relatively more active in flexion and the trapezius less so? An electromyographic study of the serratus anterior might give the answer. In the second place, one might have expected the second and fourth parts of the trapezius to show more nearly equal activity in upward rotation of the scapula. At least this would seem to be the case if it is true that these two portions of the muscle turn the scapula like two forces in a couple. Can the explanation perhaps be that the distal attachment of part IV is farther from the acromioclavicular joint than is that of part II, and therefore has greater torque? It will doubtless take further research to give us conclusive answers to these and other questions that arise from the findings of electromyographic studies.

Scapular Movements Accompanying Elevation of the Arm.   The author investigated the movements of the scapula accompanying forward and sideward elevation of the arm, using a series of x-rays of one subject. Each x-ray was traced, and measurements were then made on the tracings. Abduction of the scapula was measured in terms of the horizontal distance between the midpoint of the vertebral border of the scapula and the near margin of the spinal column. (A line connecting the spinous processes would have been the logical reference line, but it could not be used, since many of the spinous processes did not show in the x-ray.) Rotation was measured, by means of a protractor, in terms of the angle formed between a continuation of the vertebral border and the margin of the spinal column (Fig. 77). The results were as follows:

Position of Arm	Amount of Abduction	Degrees of Rotation
At rest	5.5 cm	−3° (downward rot.)
Sideward elev. about 45°	4.6 cm	0 (parallel)
Sideward elev. about 90°	5.6 cm	11° (upward rot.)
Sideward elev. about 135°	6.5 cm	36° (upward rot.)
Sideward elev. about 180°	7.3 cm	36° (upward rot.)
At rest	5.5 cm	−3° (downward rot.)
Forward elev. about 45°	7.2 cm	3.5° (upward rot.)
Forward elev. about 90°	10.1 cm	8° (upward rot.)
Forward elev. about 135°	9.3 cm	21° (upward rot.)
Forward elev. about 180°	8.2 cm	31.5° (upward rot.)

The reader should not make any generalizations from a study such as this which uses only one subject. In order to make a study from which generalizations can safely be made it would be necessary to standardize the methods of measurement and to use a large number of subjects selected at random. Even then, use of this type of measurement technique is a precarious practice because of the distortion present in x-rays.

Demonstrations and Laboratory Exercises

Joint Structure and Function

1. Take a humerus and a scapula of the same side and "construct" a shoulder joint, using felt for the fibrocartilage and adhesive tape for the ligaments. Be accurate in the attachment of these structures. Two or three may work together on this project.

2. Using a form like that on page 150, record the essential information regarding the glenohumeral, acromioclavicular and sternoclavicular articulations. Study the movements of these joints both on the skeleton and on the living body.

3. In five different subjects measure the amount of abduction that occurs in the shoulder girdle (i.e., the separation of the scapulae) when the arms are raised to the forward-horizontal position. How much can this vary in one individual? In measuring the distance between the scapulae measure the horizontal distance between the midpoint of the vertebral border of each scapula.

4. Using a Lufkin rule or a protractor-goniometer, measure the amount of upward rotation of the scapula which occurs when the arm is raised sideward-upward to the overhead position. To make this measurement, center the instrument over the medial angle of the scapula, and adjust one of its arms in line with the normal resting position of the inferior angle and the other in line with the inferior angle after maximum upward rotation of the scapula has taken place

Muscular Action (record the results on the chart found on pages 148 and 149)

Directions. Work in groups of three, one person serving as the subject, the second as an assistant, helping to support or steady the stationary part of the body and giving resistance to the moving part, and the third palpating the muscles and recording the results on the check list.

5. Sideward elevation of the arm (shoulder joint: abduction and possibly outward rotation; shoulder girdle: upward rotation)

SUBJECT: In erect position, raise arm sideward to shoulder level, keeping elbow straight.

ASSISTANT: Resist movement by exerting pressure downward on subject's elbow. See to it that subject does not elevate shoulder.

OBSERVER: Palpate the three portions of the deltoid and tell which portions contract. Palpate the four parts of the trapezius. Which parts contract? Does the pectoralis major contract during any part of the movement?

6. Sideward depression of the arm (shoulder joint: adduction and possibly reduction of outward rotation; shoulder girdle: downward rotation)

SUBJECT: In erect position with arm raised sideward to shoulder level, lower arm to side.

ASSISTANT: Place hand under subject's elbow and resist movement (If no resistance is given, the muscle action will be the same as in elevation, except that the contraction will be eccentric instead of concentric.)

OBSERVER: Palpate the latissimus dorsi, teres major, pectoralis major and posterior deltoid. Do they each contract, and, if so, during which part of the movement?

7. Forward elevation of the arm (shoulder joint: flexion and abduction; shoulder girdle: upward rotation and probably abduction)

SUBJECT: In erect position, raise arm forward to shoulder level, keeping elbow straight.

ASSISTANT: Resist movement by exerting pressure downward on the subject's elbow. See that subject does not elevate shoulder.

OBSERVER: Palpate the anterior deltoid and the pectoralis major. Do both the sternal and clavicular portions of the latter muscle contract?

8. Forward depression of the arm (shoulder joint: adduction and extension; shoulder girdle: downward rotation and probably adduction).

SUBJECT: In erect position with arm raised forward to shoulder level, lower it to the side.

ASSISTANT: Resist movement at under side of elbow.

OBSERVER: Palpate the latissimus dorsi and the pectoralis major. Do they contract with equal force throughout the movement?

9. Backward elevation of the arm (shoulder joint: hyperextension; shoulder girdle: upward tilt)

SUBJECT: Either in erect position or lying face down, raise arm backward, keeping elbow straight.

ASSISTANT: Place hand over subject's elbow and resist movement.

OBSERVER: Palpate the posterior deltoid, latissimus dorsi and teres major.

10. Horizontal sideward-backward swing of the arm from forward-horizontal position (shoulder joint: horizontal extension-abduction and slight outward rotation; shoulder girdle: adduction and reduction of lateral tilt)

a. SUBJECT: In erect position with arms raised forward to shoulder level, palms down, swing arms sideward in horizontal plane as far as possible.

ASSISTANT: Stand facing subject between his arms and resist movement by grasping his elbows.

OBSERVER: Palpate the posterior deltoid and latissimus dorsi. What other muscles can be palpated?

b. SUBJECT: Lying face down on narrow plinth, or on table close to edge with arm hanging straight down, raise arm sideward as far above the horizontal as possible.

ASSISTANT: Resistance may be given at elbow, but is not necessary, since gravity furnishes sufficient resistance.

OBSERVER: Same as in *a*.

11. Horizontal sideward-forward swing of the arm from side-horizontal position (shoulder joint: horizontal flexion-adduction and slight inward rotation; shoulder girdle: abduction and lateral tilt)

a. SUBJECT: In erect position with arm raised sideward to shoulder level, palm down. Swing arm forward in horizontal plane.

ASSISTANT: Stand behind subject's arm and resist movement by holding elbow.

OBSERVER: Palpate pectoralis major and anterior deltoid.

b. SUBJECT: Lie on back on table with arm extended sideward, palm up. Raise arm to vertical position, keeping elbow straight.

ASSISTANT: Resistance may be given at elbow, but is not necessary, since gravity furnishes sufficient resistance.

OBSERVER: Same as in *a*.

12. Outward rotation of arm (shoulder joint: outward rotation; shoulder girdle: possibly adduction and reduction of lateral tilt)

SUBJECT: Lie face down on table with upper arm at shoulder level, resting on table, and forearm hanging down off edge of table. Raise forearm forward-upward to limit of motion, without allowing upper arm to leave table.

ASSISTANT: Steady upper arm and resist movement of forearm by holding wrist.

OBSERVER: Palpate infraspinatus and teres minor.

13. Inward rotation of arm (shoulder joint: inward rotation; shoulder girdle: abduction and lateral tilt, and tendency toward elevation)

a. SUBJECT: Same position as in 12. Raise forearm backward-upward.

ASSISTANT: Steady upper arm and resist movement of forearm by holding wrist.

OBSERVER: Palpate teres major and latissimus dorsi.

b. SUBJECT: Lie on back on table with upper arm at shoulder level resting on table and forearm raised to vertical position. Lower forearm forward-downward to the limit of motion.

ASSISTANT: Steady upper arm and resist forearm motion by holding wrist.

OBSERVER: Palpate anterior deltoid and clavicular portion of pectoralis major.

14. Elevation of shoulder

SUBJECT: In erect position, lift shoulder toward ear, keeping arm muscles relaxed.

ASSISTANT: Resist movement by pressing down on shoulder.

OBSERVER: Palpate trapezius I and II.

15. Depression of shoulder

a. SUBJECT: In erect position with shoulder raised and elbow flexed. Push down with elbow, lowering shoulder to normal position.

ASSISTANT: Resist movement by holding hand under elbow.

OBSERVER: Palpate trapezius IV.

b. SUBJECT: Take cross rest position between two chairs or parallel bars.

OBSERVER: Palpate trapezius IV.

16. Adduction of shoulder girdle (retraction)

SUBJECT: In erect position with arms raised sideward, elbows flexed and fingers resting on shoulders, push elbows backward, keeping them at shoulder level.

ASSISTANT: Stand facing subject and resist movement by pulling elbows forward.

OBSERVER: Palpate middle and lower trapezius (parts III and IV). (This movement is somewhat similar to the one in 10, but here the emphasis is on the shoulder girdle rather than on the arm.)

17. Abduction of shoulder girdle (protraction)

SUBJECT: In erect position with arms raised sideward, elbows flexed and fingers

CHECK LIST FOR MUSCULAR ANALYSIS OF MOVEMENTS OF THE ARM ON THE BODY

	Side-ward Elev. of Arm	Side-ward Depr. of Arm	Fwd. Elev. of Arm	Fwd. Depr. of Arm	Bkwd. Elev. of Arm	Hor. Bkwd. Swing of Arm	Hor. Side-ward Fwd. Swing	Outwd. Rot'n of Arm	Inwd. Rot'n of Arm	Elev. of Shoul. Gird.	Depr. of Shoul. Gird.	Abd. of Scap.	Add. of Scap.
SHOULDER JOINT													
Deltoid: middle													
Deltoid: anterior													
Deltoid: posterior													
Supraspinatus													
Pect. major: clavicular													
Pect. major: sternal													
Coracobrachialis													
Subscapularis													
Latissimus dorsi													
Teres major													
Infrasp. & teres minor													

CHECK LIST FOR MUSCULAR ANALYSIS OF MOVEMENTS OF THE ARM ON THE BODY (Continued)

	Sideward Elev. of Arm	Sideward Depr. of Arm	Fwd. Elev. of Arm	Fwd. Depr. of Arm	Bkwd. Elev. of Arm	Hor. Bkwd. Swing of Arm	Hor. Sideward Fwd. Swing	Outwd. Rot'n of Arm	Inwd. Rot'n of Arm	Elev. of Shoul. Gird.	Depr. of Shoul. Gird.	Abd. of Scap.	Add. of Scap.
SHOULDER GIRDLE													
Subclavius													
Pectoralis minor													
Serratus anterior													
Levator scapulae													
Trapezius I													
Trapezius II													
Trapezius III													
Trapezius IV													
Rhomboids													

resting on shoulders, pull elbows forward, attempting to touch them in front of chest.

ASSISTANT: Stand behind subject and resist movement by pulling elbows back.

OBSERVER: Palpate serratus anterior.

Action of the Muscles Other Than the Movers

18. Stabilization of the scapula during depression of the arm

SUBJECT: In erect position with arm raised sideward above shoulder level, lower arm against strong resistance.

ASSISTANT: Resist the arm movement by placing hand under the arm just above the subject's elbow.

OBSERVER: Palpate trapezius IV. Explain.

19. Stabilization of scapula during outward rotation of humerus

SUBJECT: Rotate the arm outward as it hangs at the side.

OBSERVER: Palpate the scapular adductors. Explain.

20. Rotation of arm in position of side elevation

SUBJECT: With one arm raised sideward to shoulder level, rotate it first outward, then inward.

OBSERVER: Palpate middle deltoid. Explain its action.

21. Vigorous arm-flinging sideward to the horizontal

SUBJECT: Fling arm vigorously to the side horizontal position.

OBSERVER: Palpate the adductors of the shoulder joint. Do they contact momentarily at the very end of the movement? Explain.

22. Vigorous arm-flinging downward

SUBJECT: From an overhead position, fling arm vigorously forward-downward, stopping it at the body.

OBSERVER: Palpate the flexors of the shoulder joint. Do they contract momentarily at the end of the movement? Explain.

23. Repeat exercise 9

OBSERVER: Palpate pectoralis major. Explain.

OUTLINE FOR STUDYING THE JOINTS OF THE EXTREMITIES

Name of joint: _____

Type of joint (check appropriate items):

_____ Diarthrodial	_____ Synarthrodial
_____ Irregular	_____ Cartilaginous (synchondrosis)
_____ Hinge	_____ Ligamentous (syndesmosis)
_____ Pivot	_____ Fibrous (sutures)
_____ Ovoid	
_____ Saddle	
_____ Ball-and-socket	

Articular processes and surfaces (describe briefly): _____

Ligaments and cartilages (enumerate and state location): _____

Special characteristics, if any (describe briefly): _____

Movements (check):	Comments on movements:
_____ Flexion and extension	_____
_____ Hyperextension	_____
_____ Abduction and adduction	_____
_____ Inward and outward rotation	_____
_____ Upward and downward rotation	_____
_____ Pronation and supination	_____
_____ Elevation and depression	_____

Bibliography

1. Bowen, W. P., and Stone, H. A.: Applied Anatomy and Kinesiology, 7th ed. Philadelphia, Lea & Febiger, 1953.
2. Duvall, E. N.: Kinesiology; The Anatomy of Motion. Englewood Cliffs, N. J., Prentice-Hall, 1959.
3. Graves, W. W.: Observations on Age Changes in the Scapula: A Preliminary Note. Am. J. Phys. Anthrop., *5:* 21–39, 1922.
4. Graves, W. W.: The Relations of Scapular Types to Problems of Human Heredity, Longevity, Morbidity and Adaptability in General. Arch. Int. Med., *34:* 1–26, 1924.
5. Graves, W. W.: A Note on the Biological and Clinical Significance of Inherited Variations. I. The Types of Scapulae. South. M. J., *32:* 740–742, 1939.
6. Gray, D. J.: Variations in Human Scapulae. Am. J. Phys. Anthrop., *29:* 57–72, 1942.
7. Hrdlička, A.: The Adult Scapula. Am. J. Phys. Anthrop., *29:* 363–415, 1942.
8. Krahl, V. E., and Evans, F. G.: Humeral Torsion in Man. Am. J. Phys. Anthrop., *3* (new series): 229–251, 1945.
9. Kuhns, J. G.: Variations in the Vertebral Border of the Scapula: Their Relation to Muscular Function. Physiotherapy Rev., *25:* 207–210, 1945.
10. Wiedenbauer, M. M., and Mortensen, O. A.: An Electromyographic Study of the Trapezius Muscle. Am. J. Phys. Med., *31:* 363–372, 1952.

8 · Movements of the Upper Extremity: The Elbow Joint and Radioulnar Articulations

THE ELBOW and the radioulnar joints work together to serve the hand in much the same way that the two joints of the shoulder girdle work together to serve the shoulder joint. Man's hand owes its usefulness to the variety of positions made possible by the joints of the elbow, the forearm and the shoulder. If, for instance, man were to lose the ability to rotate his forearm, the use of his hand would be so limited that he would have to change his whole mode of living. The shape of his tools, eating implements, door knobs, and similar items, would have to be changed. Furthermore, his method of handling them would seem crude and clumsy compared with his present dexterity.

Structure of the Elbow Joint

The elbow joint consists of the articulation of the lower end of the humerus with the upper ends of the ulna and radius. Together they comprise a hinge joint whose only motions are flexion and extension. The rotatory movements of the forearm occur at the articulations between the radius and the ulna, not at the elbow joint. The semicircular structure at the upper end of the ulna is cupped around the back and under side of the spool-like process, known as the trochlea, at the lower end of the humerus (Fig. 78). The inner surface of this semicircular structure is known as the semilunar notch. It terminates above and behind in the olecranon process, and below and in front in the coronoid process. Just lateral to the trochlea, on the lower end of the humerus, is the capitulum, the small spherical structure that articulates with the saucer-like surface of the radial head.

The two articulations of the elbow joint, as well as the proximal radioulnar articulation, are completely enveloped in an extensive capsule. The capsule is strengthened on all four sides by bands of fibers which are usually described respectively as the anterior, posterior, ulnar collateral and radial collateral ligaments (Figs. 79

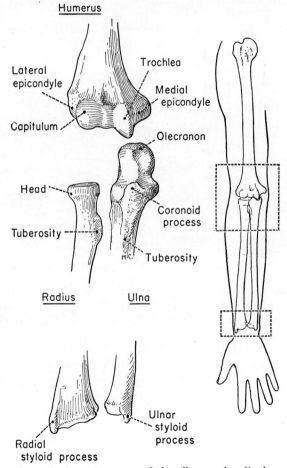

Figure 78. The bony structures of the elbow and radioulnar joints.

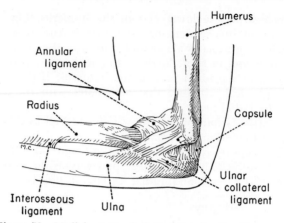

Figure 79. Medial aspect of elbow joint showing ligaments.

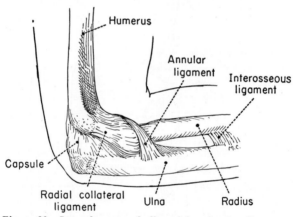

Figure 80. Lateral aspect of elbow joint showing ligaments.

and 80). Synovial membrane not only lines the capsule, but it also extends into the proximal radioulnar articulation, covers the olecranon, coronoid and radial fossae, and lines the annular ligament.

Ligaments. *Anterior.* This is a broad, thin layer of fibers which blend with and thicken the anterior portion of the capsule.

Posterior. This is a thin, membranous layer of fibers which blend with and strengthen the posterior portion of the capsule.

Ulnar Collateral (Fig. 79). This is a strong, thick triangular band, attached above by its apex to the medial epicondyle of the humerus, and below by its base to the medial margins of the coronoid and olecranon processes of the ulna, and the ridge between them.

Radial Collateral (Fig. 80).   This is a short fibrous band, attached above to the lower part of the lateral epicondyle of the humerus, and below to the lateral side of the annular ligament which encircles the head of the radius.

Structure of the Radioulnar Joints

Proximal (Fig. 78).   The disk-shaped head of the radius fits against the radial notch of the ulna and is encircled by the annular ligament. The notch and the annular ligament together form a complete ring within which the radial head rotates. The articulation is classified as a pivot joint. It has no capsule of its own, but is enclosed within the capsule of the elbow joint.

Annular Ligament (Figs. 79 and 80).   This is a strong band of fibers forming three quarters of the ring which encircles the radial head. It holds the radial head in close contact with the radial notch of the ulna. It is lined with a synovial membrane which is continuous with that of the elbow joint.

Distal (Fig. 78).   At the distal end of the forearm the radius articulates, by means of a small notch, with the head of the ulna. A triangular shaped fibrocartilaginous disk lies between the head of the ulna and the carpal bones. It is attached by its apex to the styloid process of the ulna, and by its base to the medial margin of the lower end of the radius. It serves to reinforce the distal radioulnar joint and to separate this joint from the wrist. A loose articular capsule surrounds the joint.

Ligaments.   VOLAR RADIOULNAR.   This is situated on the volar (anterior) surface of the joint and is attached to the edge of the notch on the radius, the articular disk and the ulnar head.

DORSAL RADIOULNAR.   This lies behind the joint and is attached to the margin of the notch on the radius, the articular disk and the ulnar head.

Mid-Radioulnar Union.   The shafts of the radius and ulna are united by means of the oblique cord and the interosseous membrane (Figs. 79 and 80).

Movements.   *Elbow Joint.*   FLEXION.   From the anatomic position (Fig. 1, *B*) this is a forward-upward movement of the forearm in the sagittal plane.

EXTENSION.   Return movement from flexion. A few individuals are able to hyperextend at the elbow joint. This ability is probably due to a short olecranon process, rather than to loose ligaments.

Radioulnar Joints.   PRONATION.   This is a rotation of the forearm around its longitudinal axis, corresponding to inward rotation of the humerus. It usually accompanies the latter when the elbow is in extension.

SUPINATION.   This is a rotation of the forearm around its longitudinal axis, corresponding to outward rotation of the humerus. It usually accompanies the latter when the elbow is in extension.

Pronation and supination of the forearm involve a rotation of the radial head within the ring formed by the ulnar notch and annular ligament at the proximal joint, and, at the distal joint, a rotation of the lower end of the radius around the outside of the ulnar head. Neither bone rotates about its own mechanical axis, as does the humerus, but each rotates about the mechanical axis of the forearm as a whole.

Muscles.　　The muscles of the elbow and radioulnar joints are classified below in two ways, first, according to their action, and, secondly, according to their location.

Muscles Listed According to Action

Elbow Joint	Radioulnar Joints
Flexors	Pronators
Biceps	Pronator teres
Brachialis	Pronator quadratus
Brachioradialis	
Pronator teres	Supinators
Extensors	Supinator
Triceps	Biceps
Anconeus	

Muscles Listed According to Location

Anterior (elbow region)	Anterior (wrist region)
Biceps	Pronator quadratus
Brachialis	Posterior
Brachioradialis	Triceps
Pronator teres	Anconeus
	Supinator

Biceps (Fig. 81)

PROXIMAL ATTACHMENTS (O):
Long head: Upper margin of glenoid fossa.
Short head: Apex of coracoid process of scapula.
DISTAL ATTACHMENT. (I)　　Bicipital tuberosity of radius.
NERVE SUPPLY.　　Musculocutaneous.
ACTION.　　Flexion at elbow joint; supination of forearm. (See also shoulder joint.)
WHERE TO PALPATE.　　Anterior surface of lower two thirds of upper arm.
COMMENTS.　　The biceps is a two-headed or twin spindle type of muscle. It is primarily a muscle of the elbow joint and of the proximal radioulnar articulation, but it also acts at the shoulder joint.

The short head lies parallel to the coracobrachialis and acts with it in moving the humerus at the shoulder joint. The tendon of the long head passes through the intertubercular groove, over the top of the humeral head, and through the joint capsule to its attachment on the apex of the glenoid fossa. Since the two heads converge to a common tendon of insertion, they have a common action at the elbow joint, likewise at the proximal radioulnar joint. Unless prevented from doing so (by the action of neutralizers), the biceps simultaneously supinates the forearm and flexes it at the elbow. Basmajian and Latif found, in their electromyographic study, that the biceps would not supinate the fully extended forearm

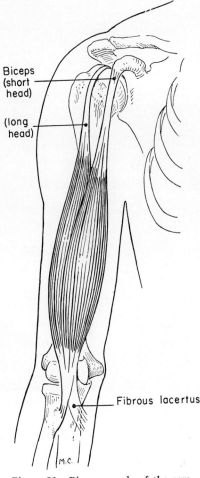

Biceps
(short
head)

(long
head)

Fibrous lacertus

M.C.

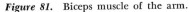

Figure 81. Biceps muscle of the arm.

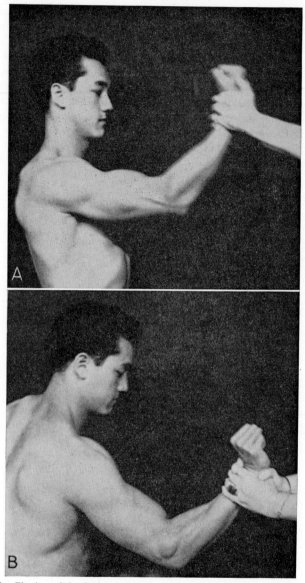

Figure 82. Flexion of the forearm. *A*, In a position of supination; *B*, in a position of pronation.

unless the movement were strongly resisted. Some kinesiologists have been interested in the question as to whether the forcefulness of elbow flexion was related to the position of the forearm. Neither Beevor nor Wright could find any appreciable difference. Three fairly recent investigations, reported briefly in the supplementary material at the end of this chapter, throw a little light on this matter, although the findings are not in complete agreement.

Brachialis (Fig. 83)

PROXIMAL ATTACHMENT. (O)   Anterior surface of lower half of humerus.

DISTAL ATTACHMENT. (I)   Anterior surface of coronoid process of ulna.

NERVE SUPPLY.   Musculocutaneous and branch from radial.

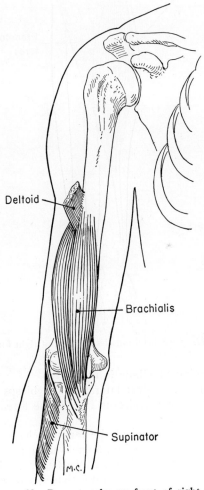

Figure 83. Deep muscles on front of right arm.

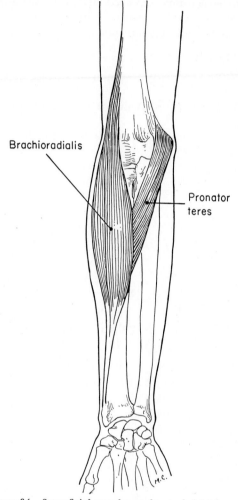

Figure 84. Superficial muscles on front of right forearm.

ACTION.   Flexion at elbow joint.

WHERE TO PALPATE.   Just lateral to the biceps if the contraction is sufficiently strong, and especially if the forearm is flexed in the pronated position.

COMMENTS.   This is one of the few muscles of the upper extremity that have but one action. Some anatomists[5] claim that the brachialis, rather than the biceps, is *the* flexor of the forearm. Be that as it may, any schoolboy knows that his biceps muscle will bulge in a hard mass when he chins himself or flexes his forearm vigorously. As for objective evidence regarding the comparative strength of the two muscles in flexing the forearm, Steindler quotes Fick as stating that the biceps perform 4.58 kg. of work, and the brachialis 3.84 kg.

Brachioradialis (Fig. 84)

PROXIMAL ATTACHMENT. (O)   Upper two thirds of lateral supracondylar ridge of humerus.

DISTAL ATTACHMENT. (I)   Lateral side of base of styloid process of radius.

NERVE SUPPLY.   Radial.

ACTION.   Flexion at elbow joint; tends to reduce pronation or supination of forearm during flexion.

WHERE TO PALPATE.   On anterior-radial aspect of upper half of forearm.

COMMENTS.   The brachioradialis is primarily a flexor of the forearm. If the forearm is either pronated or supinated, however, it will tend to "de-rotate" the forearm at the same time that it flexes it. According to Basmajian and Latif, the brachioradialis neither supinates nor pronates the fully extended forearm unless the movement is strongly resisted.

Pronator Teres (Fig. 84)

PROXIMAL ATTACHMENTS. (O)   Medial epicondyle of humerus and medial side of coronoid process of ulna.

DISTAL ATTACHMENT. (I)   Lateral surface of radius near middle.

NERVE SUPPLY.   Median.

ACTION.   Pronation of forearm; assists in flexing forearm. Cannot be palpated.

COMMENTS.   Although the pronator teres is listed both with the pronators and with the flexors of the forearm, it is first and fore-

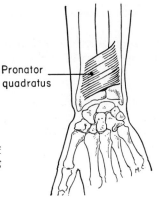

Pronator quadratus

Figure 85. Anterior view of distal end of forearm showing pronator quadratus.

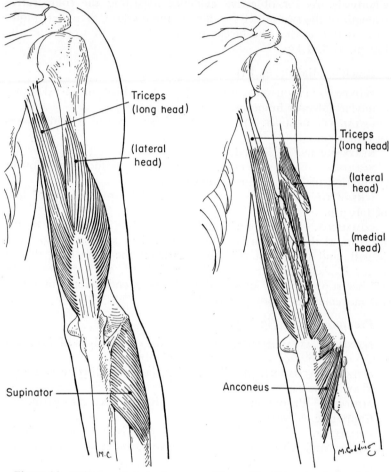

Figure 86. Triceps and supinator.   **Figure 87.** Triceps and anconeus.

most a pronator. It assists in forearm flexion only when the movement is meeting with resistance.

Pronator Quadratus (Fig. 85)

MEDIAL ATTACHMENT. (O)   Anterior surface of lower fourth of
ulna.

LATERAL ATTACHMENT. (I)   Anterior surface of lower fourth of
radius.

NERVE SUPPLY.   Branch from median nerve.

ACTION.   Pronation of forearm.

Cannot be palpated.

COMMENTS. All the essential information about the pronator quadratus is contained in its name. It is quadrilateral in shape, and its sole function is to pronate the forearm.

Triceps (Figs. 86 and 87)

PROXIMAL ATTACHMENTS (O):

Long head: Infraglenoid tuberosity.

Lateral head: Posterior surface of upper half of humerus.

Medial head: Posterior surface of lower two thirds of humerus.

DISTAL ATTACHMENT. (I)   Olecranon process of ulna.

NERVE SUPPLY.   Radial.

ACTION.   Extension of forearm at elbow joint.

WHERE TO PALPATE.   Posterior surface of upper arm.

COMMENTS.   The triceps, virtually three muscles in one, covers the entire posterior surface of the upper arm. Only its long middle head crosses the shoulder joint. Its fibers are for the most part longitudinal, running parallel with the long axis of the humerus. The medial and lateral portions run parallel to the middle portion at first, then turn toward it obliquely downward to unite with its broad flat tendon of attachment. The triceps is a forceful extensor of the forearm. Two factors contributing to its effectiveness are its large physiologic cross section (p. 307) and its good angle of pull (p. 25).

Anconeus (Fig. 87)

PROXIMAL ATTACHMENT. (O)   Posterior surface of lateral epicondyle of humerus.

DISTAL ATTACHMENT. (I)   Lateral side of olecranon process and posterior surface of upper part of ulna.

NERVE SUPPLY.   Branch from radial nerve.

ACTION.   Extension of forearm.

WHERE TO PALPATE.   Lateral margin of olecranon process on back of elbow.

COMMENTS.   The anconeus is the triceps' "little helper."

Supinator (Figs. 83 and 86)

PROXIMAL ATTACHMENT. (O)   Lateral condyle of humerus; adjacent portion of ulna; radial collateral and annular ligaments.

DISTAL ATTACHMENT. (I)   Lateral surface of upper third of radius.

NERVE SUPPLY.   Branch from deep radial nerve.

ACTION.   Supination of forearm.

Cannot be palpated.

COMMENTS.   According to Steindler, the supinator is most effective in supinating the forearm when it is extended.

Muscular Analysis of the Fundamental Movements of the Forearm at the Elbow and Radioulnar Joints

Flexion

Movers
- Principal........ {Biceps, Brachialis, Brachioradialis}
- Assistant........ {Pronator teres, Flexors of the hand and fingers (probably unimportant as forearm flexors)}

Neutralizers......................The pronator teres and the biceps are mutually neutralizing with respect to pronation and supination of the forearm. The pronator quadratus helps to counteract the supinatory function of the biceps when flexion is resisted or when flexion is performed with the forearm in a pronated position

Stabilizers........................If not prevented from so doing, flexion of the forearm will cause slight hyperextension of the arm at the shoulder joint, expecially if a weight is held in the hand. If this is not desired, the pectoralis major, anterior deltoid and coracobrachialis will contract to stabilize the humerus. In many instances, as in pulling, the cooperative action of the forearm flexors and upper arm extensors is necessary. In such cases the humerus will not need to be stabilized, but it will require the stabilization of the scapula or of the trunk itself

Extension

Movers........
- Principal..........Triceps
- Assistant..........Anconeus

Neutralizers.......................None

Stabilizers (when forearm is extended forcefully).............. {Pectoralis major, sternal portion, Latissimus dorsi, Teres major}

Pronation

Movers........
- Principal........ {Pronator quadratus, Pronator teres}
- Assistant........ {Brachioradialis (reduction of supination to neutral position)}

Neutralizers......................The triceps and anconeus counteract the flexion tendency of the pronator teres

Stabilizers........................The contraction of the triceps, anconeus and pronator teres serves to stabilize the elbow joint

Supination

Movers........
- Principal........ {Supinator, Biceps}
- Assistant..........Brachioradialis (reduction of pronation to neutral position)

Neutralizers...................... If flexion is not desired, the triceps and anconeus counteract the flexion tendency of the biceps

Stabilizers......................... The contraction of the triceps, anconeus and biceps serves to stabilize the elbow joint

Supplementary Material

Comparison of Force of Elbow Flexors in the Midposition, in Supination and in Pronation. *Investigation by Wells.* In order to discover whether one position seemed more favorable than another for elbow flexion, the author conducted a small experiment on ten subjects, all women majoring in physical education. A grip dynamometer in a regulation holder used for testing shoulder retraction was fastened securely to the wall facing a typical classroom chair, 20 inches higher than the arm rest of the chair. The subject sat with both feet resting on the floor, her right elbow supported on the arm rest with the forearm vertical. A 2-inch web strap was passed through the handle of the dynamometer holder and around the subject's wrist (to eliminate the use of the finger flexors). The subject was instructed to flex her forearm at the elbow joint as forcefully as possible, first with her thumb turned toward her shoulder, second with her palm facing her shoulder, and third with the back of her hand toward her shoulder. A full minute's rest was required before each trial. The mean score for each position was as follows:

Midposition.............36.4 lbs.
Supination..............39.5 lbs.
Pronation...............31.6 lbs.

Investigation by Downer. In 1952 Downer investigated the same problem in a study which included other aspects of elbow flexion. One of her four objectives was "to determine the position of the forearm (supination, pronation, or midposition) in which maximum strength is obtained when the elbow is flexed to 90 degrees." Thirty adult women were tested with a Beasley myodynemeter (an electronic instrument) both in a breaking point test and in an isometric test. Downer found that the strongest contraction of the elbow flexors was obtained when the forearm was in the midposition, and the least strong when the forearm was pronated.

A comparison of Downer's study with that of the author reveals a lack of agreement with respect to the relative influence of the midposition and the supinated position on the degree of contraction of the elbow flexors. The results of both studies agree, however, with respect to the unfavorable influence of the position of pronation. In making a comparison of the two investigations, the differences in technique, in instrument, and in the number of subjects should not be overlooked. The lack of agreement in the results of these studies would seem to indicate the need for further investigation in which a standardized procedure is used with a large number of subjects of both sexes.

Electromyographic Study of the Elbow Flexors. Basmajian and Latif made an electromyographic study in 1957 of the actions of the biceps, brachialis and brachioradialis muscles. They found that the biceps acted to flex the forearm when the latter was supinated. It also flexed the forearm in a "semiprone" (mid ?) position when acting against resistance. When the forearm was pronated, however, the part played by the biceps was negligible, even when a two-pound weight was lifted.

The brachialis, they found, contracted to flex the forearm under all conditions. They termed it the "flexor *par excellence*" and "the workhorse of the elbow joint."

The brachioradialis was found to act in rapid flexion of the forearm, also in slow movements performed against resistance. The investigators concluded that this muscle was a reserve flexor which acts when either quick or forceful movements are required. They noted that all three muscles acted simultaneously and with the greatest activity when the forearm was flexed against resistance in the "semiprone" (mid ?) position. This appears to lend support to Downer's findings about the influence of the position of the forearm on the force exerted by the elbow flexors.

Demonstrations and Laboratory Exercises
Joint Structure and Function

1. Using a form like the one on page 150, record the essential information regarding the two articulations of the elbow joint, likewise the two radioulnar articulations. Study the movements of these joints both on the skeleton and on the living body.

2. With a humerus, radius and ulna, "construct" an elbow joint, using felt for fibrocartilage and adhesive tape for ligaments. Attach these structures accurately. It is suggested that two or three students work together on this project.

3. Using a Lufkin rule or a protractor, measure the range of motion in flexion, pronation and supination of the forearm on five different subjects.

CHECK LIST FOR MUSCULAR ANALYSIS OF MOVEMENTS OF FOREARM AT ELBOW AND RADIOULNAR JOINTS

	Flexion	Extension	Supination	Pronation
MUSCLES OF ELBOW AND FOREARM:				
Biceps				
Brachialis				
Brachioradialis				
Pronator teres				
Pronator quadratus				
Supinator				
Triceps				
Anconeus				
MUSCLES OF WRIST:				
Flexor carpi radialis				
Flexor carpi ulnaris				
Palmaris longus				
Extensor carpi radialis longus				
Extensor carpi radialis brevis				
Extensor carpi ulnaris				

Muscular Action (record the results on the chart found on page 166).

4. Flexion

Subject: Sit with entire arm resting on table. Flex forearm (*a*) with palm up (forearm supinated), (*b*) with thumb up (forearm in neutral position), and (*c*) with palm down (forearm pronated).

Assistant: Resist movement by holding wrist. Steady upper arm if necessary.

Observer: Palpate as many of the forearm flexors as possible. Do you notice any difference in the muscular action in *a, b* and *c?*

5. Extension

a. Subject: Lie face down on table with arm raised to shoulder level, with upper arm resting on table, and with forearm hanging down. Extend forearm without moving upper arm.

Assistant: Steady upper arm and resist forearm by holding wrist.

Observer: Palpate the triceps.

b. Subject: On hands and knees, bend and extend at the elbows in a push-up exercise.

Observer: Palpate the triceps.

6. Supination

Subject: Assume hand-shaking position with assistant and turn forearm outward.

Assistant: Assume same position with subject and resist his movement.

Observer: Palpate and identify the muscles which contract.

7. Pronation

Subject: Assume hand-shaking position with assistant and turn forearm inward.

Assistant: Assume same position with subject and resist movement.

Observer: Palpate and identify the muscles which contract.

Action of Muscles Other Than Movers

8. Supination without flexion

Subject: Sit with arm supported, elbow in slightly flexed position and relaxed. Supinate forearm without increasing or decreasing flexion at elbow.

Observer: Palpate the triceps. Explain.

9. Vigorous flexion of forearm

Subject: Flex forearm vigorously, then check movement suddenly before completing full range of motion.

Observer: Palpate the triceps. Does it contract during any part of the movement? Explain.

10. Perform a movement in which the supinator acts as a neutralizer.

Bibliography

1. Basmajian, J. V., and Latif, A.: Integrated Actions and Functions of the Chief Flexors of the Elbow. J. Bone & Joint Surg., *39A:* 1106–1118, 1957.
2. Beevor, C.: The Croonian Lectures on Muscular Movements. Reprint. New York, Macmillan Company, 1951.
3. Downer, A. H.: Strength of the Elbow Flexor Muscles. Physical Therapy Rev., *33:* 68–70, 1953.
4. Duvall, E. N.: Kinesiology; The Anatomy of Motion. Englewood Cliffs, N. J., Prentice-Hall, 1959.
5. Smout, C. F. V., and McDowall, R. J. S.: Anatomy and Physiology for Students of Physiotherapy, Occupational Therapy and Gymnastics. 3rd ed. Baltimore, Williams & Wilkins Company, 1956.
6. Steindler, A.: Kinesiology of the Human Body. Springfield, Ill., Charles C Thomas, 1955.
7. Wright, W. G.: Muscle Function. New York, Hoeber, 1928.

9 · The Wrist and Hand

PHILOSOPHERS and scientists alike have paid tribute to man's hand for the part it has played in human culture. Even the psalmist was indirectly honoring man's hand when he praised God's creations as "the work of thy fingers." With such an appreciation of the significance of the human hand as a background the student of kinesiology will find his study of the structure and movements of the hand to be more meaningful. No piece of modern machinery is more delicately constructed or more perfectly coordinated than the human hand. The extraordinary versatility of the hand is due largely to the thumb's ability to separate widely from the rest of the hand, to swing around in front of the palm, and to press with equal force against any one of the four fingers. Its action is like that of a crane which revolves on its base and then swings down and up to perform its task.

In a sense, the wrist is simply a mechanism for contributing to the usefulness of the hand, for it adds to the variety of positions in which the hand may be used. The same is true of the elbow joint and the radioulnar articulations, in fact, even of the shoulder. As a matter of fact, all the joints of the upper extremity may be thought of as servants of the hand.

The hand and wrist owe their unusual mobility to their generous supply of joints (Fig. 88). The most proximal of these is the radiocarpal or wrist joint. Just beyond this are the two rows of carpal bones, each row consisting of four bones. The carpal joints include the articulations within each of these rows, as well as the articulations between the two rows. The carpometacarpal joints are located at the base of the hand. Closely associated with them are the intermetacarpal joints, those points of contact between the base of each metacarpal bone—except that of the thumb—and its neighbor. The fingers unite with the hand at the metacarpophalangeal joints. In the fingers themselves are the two sets of interphalangeal joints, the first between the proximal and middle rows of phalanges, and the second between the middle and distal rows. The thumb differs from the four fingers by having a more freely movable metacarpal bone and by having only two phalanges instead of three. The metacarpal bone of the thumb is so similar to a phalanx that it might well be described as a cross between a phalanx and a metacarpal.

Structure of the Wrist Joint.   The wrist joint is an ovoid (condyloid) joint formed by the union of the slightly concave, oval-shaped surface of the radius and articular disk with the slightly convex, oval-shaped surface of the proximal row of carpal bones (i.e., the navicular, lunate and triquetral bones, but not the pisiform). The distal radioulnar joint is in close proximity to the wrist joint and shares with it the articular disk which lies between the head of the ulna and the triquetral bone of the wrist. Yet it is not a part of the wrist joint, for each joint has its own articular capsule. The capsule of the wrist consists of four ligaments which merge to form a continuous cover for the joint.

Capsular Ligaments.   VOLAR RADIOCARPAL (Fig. 89).   A strong ligament, attached above to the anterior margin of the radius

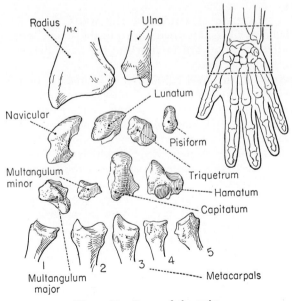

Figure 88.   Bones of the wrist.

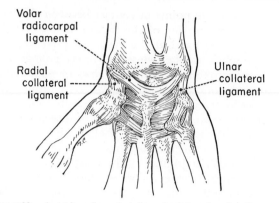

Figure 89.   Anterior view of right wrist joint showing ligaments.

and articular disk, and below to both rows of carpal bones and to the volar intercarpal ligament.

DORSAL RADIOCARPAL (Fig. 90).   A thin, membranous ligament, attached above to the posterior margin of the radius and articular disk, and below to the proximal row of carpal bones.

ULNAR COLLATERAL LIGAMENT OF THE WRIST (Figs. 89 and 90). A small fan-shaped ligament, attached above by its apex to the styloid process of the ulna and to the articular disk, and below by its base to the pisiform bone and the transverse carpal ligament (Fig. 101).

RADIAL COLLATERAL LIGAMENT OF THE WRIST (Figs. 89 and 90). A small band of fibers, attached above to the styloid process of the radius, radiating downward to attach to the navicular, capitate and greater multangular bones.

Movements of the Wrist Joint.   *Flexion.*   From the anatomic position (Fig. 1, *B*) this is a forward-upward movement in the sagittal plane, whereby the palmar surface of the hand approaches the anterior surface of the forearm.

Extension.   Return movement from flexion.

Hyperextension.   A movement in which the dorsal surface of the hand approaches the posterior surface of the forearm—the exact opposite of flexion.

Radial Flexion (Abduction).   From the anatomic position this is a sideward movement in the frontal plane, whereby the hand moves away from the body and the thumb side of the hand approaches the radial side of the forearm.

Ulnar Flexion (Adduction).   From the anatomic position this is a sideward movement in the frontal plane, whereby the hand moves toward the body and the little finger side of the hand approaches the ulnar side of the forearm.

Circumduction.   A movement of the hand at the wrist whereby the finger tips describe a circle, and the hand as a whole describes a cone. It consists of flexion, radial flexion, hyperextension and ulnar flexion, taking place in sequence in either direction.

Structure and Movements of the Midcarpal and Intercarpal Joints.   The articulation between the four carpal bones in the proximal row with the four in the distal row is known as the midcarpal articulation.* The joints between the bones within either row are known as the intercarpal joints of the proximal and distal rows, respectively.* All these joints are diarthrodial in structure, since they all have joint cavities. Within this classification they belong to the non-axial group. This means that they permit only a slight gliding motion between the bones. Although this is the only type of motion that takes place in the individual joints comprising the midcarpal articulation, these movements add up to a modified hinge type of movement for the midcarpal joint as a whole.

A further characteristic of the carpal region is that the bones are shaped and arranged in such a way that the anterior surface of the carpal region is slightly concave from side to side. This provides a protected passageway for the tendons, nerves and blood vessels going to the hand. Among the many carpal ligaments, the radiate is the strongest. Its fibers radiate from the capitate to the navicular, lunate and triquetral bones on the anterior surface of the wrist.

Structure of the Carpometacarpal and Intermetacarpal Joints (Fig. 91).   In many anatomy books the difference between the carpometacarpal joint of the thumb and that of the four fingers is emphasized. The former is described as a saddle joint, the latter as irregular (non-axial) joints. Morris, however, quotes Fick as describing the carpometacarpal joints of all the fingers as modified

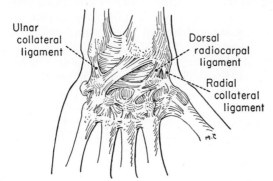

Ulnar
collateral
ligament

Dorsal
radiocarpal
ligament

Radial
collateral
ligament

Figure 90.   Posterior view of right wrist joint showing ligaments.

* Anatomists differ in regard to these definitions. See Gray, Edwards and Morris.

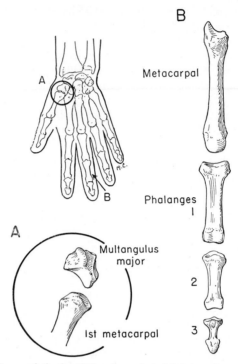

Figure 91. Bones of the hand showing selected joint surfaces. *A,* Carpometa-carpal joint of thumb (a saddle joint). *B,* Metacarpal bone and phalanges of middle finger.

saddle joints, the joint of the little finger most nearly approaching a true saddle joint. A careful inspection of these joints on the skeleton will probably lead the reader to agree with Fick. In regard to the carpometacarpal joint of the thumb, that is, the joint between the first metacarpal and greater multangular bones, there is no disagreement. It is clearly a saddle joint (Fig. 91). It is en-closed in an articular capsule which is stronger in back than in front. The capsule is thick but loose, and serves to restrict motion rather than to prevent it. There are no additional ligaments.

The carpometacarpal joints of the four fingers are not only en-cased in capsules, but are also protected by the dorsal, volar and interosseous carpometacarpal ligaments (Figs. 93 and 94). Closely associated with these joints are the intermetacarpal articulations, the joints between the bases of the metacarpal bones of the four fingers. These are irregular joints. They share the capsules of the carpometacarpal joints and are further reinforced by the dorsal, volar and interosseous basal ligaments, also by the transverse metacarpal ligament, a narrow fibrous band which connects the heads of the four outer metacarpal bones.

Movements of the Carpometacarpal and Intermetacarpal Joints
Carpometacarpal Joint of Thumb*

ABDUCTION. (Fig. 92, *A*).   A forward movement of the thumb at right angles to the palm.

ADDUCTION.   Return movement from abduction.

HYPERADDUCTION (Fig. 92, *B*).   A backward movement of the thumb at right angles to the hand.

EXTENSION (Fig. 92, *C*).   A lateral movement of the thumb away from the index finger.

FLEXION (Fig. 92, *D*).   Return movement from extension.

HYPERFLEXION (Fig. 92, *E*).   A medialward movement of the thumb from a position of slight abduction. The thumb slides across the front of the palm.

CIRCUMDUCTION.   A movement in which the thumb as a whole describes a cone and the tip of the thumb describes a circle. It consists of all the movements described above, performed in sequence in either direction.

OPPOSITION (Fig. 92, *F*).   This movement, which makes it possible to touch the tip of the thumb to the tip of any of the four fingers, is essentially a combination of abduction and hyperflexion and, according to some investigators, slight inward rotation. Others claim that what appears to be inward rotation of the metacarpal is actually a slight medial movement of the greater multangular bone with which the metacarpal articulates. The movements of the metacarpal are accompanied by flexion of the two phalanges, especially the distal. The apparent rotatory movement is explained in part by the oblique axis of motion about which abduction and adduction of the thumb take place, and in part by the movement of the greater multangular bone which accompanies flexion of the thumb. The total movement of the thumb in opposition might well be described as a movement of partial circumduction.

Carpometacarpal and Intermetacarpal Joints of Fingers.   The motion taking place in most of these joints is slight. It serves to supplement the movements of the wrist. The fifth carpometacarpal joint is slightly more mobile and permits a limited motion

---

* Anatomists differ as to the definitions of the movements of the thumb. In the first two editions of this book the author adopted the definitions which seemed to her to be consistent with the definitions of the movements of diarthrodial axial joints, as given in Chapter 2. In the present edition the nomenclature has been changed to agree with that of standard anatomy texts commonly used by physical and occupational therapists. The change seems expedient in view of the fact that the therapists are the persons most concerned with the movements of the thumb.

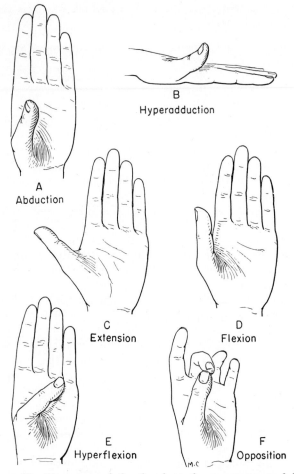

Figure 92. Movements of the thumb at the carpometacarpal joint.

of the fifth metacarpal bone, resembling somewhat the motion of the thumb.

Structure of the Metacarpophalangeal Joints (Figs. 91, 93 and 94).   The joint at the base of each of the four fingers, uniting the proximal phalanx with the corresponding metacarpal bone, is an ovoid (also called condyloid) joint. The oval, convex head of the metacarpal fits into the shallow oval fossa at the base of the phalanx. The fossa is deepened slightly by the fibrocartilaginous volar accessory ligament. The joint is incased in a capsule and is protected on each side by strong collateral ligaments.

The metacarpophalangeal joint of the thumb has flatter joint surfaces than do the joints of the four fingers and has more of the characteristics of a hinge joint. In addition to the articular capsule, it is protected by a collateral ligament on each side and by a dorsal ligament.

Movements of the Metacarpophalangeal Joints. *Of the Four Fingers.* FLEXION. The anterior surface of the finger approaches the palmar surface of the hand.

EXTENSION. Return movement from flexion. Most individuals are able to get slight hyperextension in these joints.

ABDUCTION. For the fourth, fifth and index fingers this is a lateral movement away from the middle finger. This movement is limited and cannot be performed when the fingers are fully flexed.

ADDUCTION. Return movement from abduction.

Note: In place of abduction and adduction, the lateral movements of the middle finger are radial and ulnar flexion. These are comparable to radial and ulnar flexion at the wrist.

CIRCUMDUCTION. The combination of flexion, abduction, extension and adduction performed in sequence in either direction.

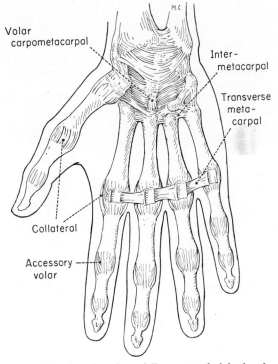

Figure 93. Anterior view of ligaments of right hand.

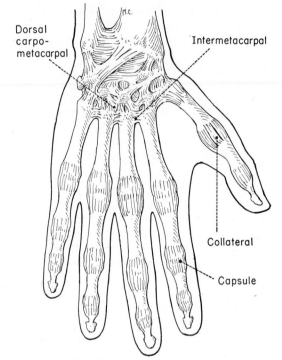

Figure 94. Posterior view of ligaments of right hand.

Of the Thumb.   FLEXION.   The volar surface of the thumb approaches that of the thenar eminence (base of thumb).

EXTENSION.   Return movement from flexion. Individuals vary greatly in their ability to hyperextend the thumb at this joint.

The Interphalangeal Joints (Figs. 91, 93 and 94).   As the name implies, these are the joints between the adjacent phalanges of the fingers or thumb. They are all hinge joints; hence their only movements are flexion and extension. These correspond to flexion and extension of the first phalanx at the metacarpophalangeal joints. Hyperextension is slight, if present at all. Each joint is enclosed within an articular capsule which is strengthened in front by an accessory volar ligament and on each side by a strong collateral ligament.

Muscles of the Wrist, Fingers and Thumb.   These muscles are treated in the same section because movement of the hand at the wrist joint is brought about almost as much by the forearm muscles of the fingers and thumb as by the wrist muscles proper. Certainly no analysis of wrist movements would be complete without mention of the finger and thumb muscles that assist the muscles of the wrist.

Muscles of the Wrist

Anterior	Posterior
Flexor carpi radialis	Extensor carpi radialis longus
Palmaris longus	Extensor carpi radialis brevis
Flexor carpi ulnaris	Extensor carpi ulnaris

Muscles of the Fingers and Thumb

Located on the Forearm	Located in the Hand
Fingers:	Fingers:
Flexor digitorum sublimis	Lumbricales
Flexor digitorum profundus	Palmar interossei
Extensor digitorum communis	Dorsal interossei
Extensor indicis proprius	Abductor digiti quinti
Extensor digiti quinti	Flexor digiti quinti brevis
	Opponens digiti quinti
Thumb:	Thumb:
Flexor pollicis longus	Flexor pollicis brevis
Extensor pollicis longus	Abductor pollicis brevis
Extensor pollicis brevis	Opponens pollicis
Abductor pollicis longus	Adductor pollicis

Flexor Carpi Radialis (Fig. 95)

PROXIMAL ATTACHMENT. (O)   Medial epicondyle of humerus.

DISTAL ATTACHMENT. (I)   Anterior surface of base of second metacarpal.

NERVE SUPPLY.   Median.

ACTION.   Flexion; assists in radial flexion of wrist.

WHERE TO PALPATE.   Anterior surface of wrist, just lateral to the tendon of palmaris longus.

Palmaris Longus (Figs. 95 and 99)

PROXIMAL ATTACHMENT. (O)   Medial epicondyle of humerus.

DISTAL ATTACHMENTS. (I)   Annular ligament and palmar aponeurosis.

NERVE SUPPLY.   Median.

ACTION.   Flexion of wrist.

WHERE TO PALPATE.   Anterior surface of wrist in exact center. It is the most prominent of the flexor tendons.

Flexor Carpi Ulnaris (Fig. 95)

PROXIMAL ATTACHMENTS. (O)   By two heads, from medial condyle of humerus and medial border of olecranon process of ulna.

DISTAL ATTACHMENTS. (I)   Palmar surface of pisiform and hamate carpal bones, and proximal end of fifth metacarpal.

NERVE SUPPLY.   Ulnar.

ACTION.   Flexion and ulnar flexion of wrist.

WHERE TO PALPATE.   Anterior surface of ulnar side of forearm.

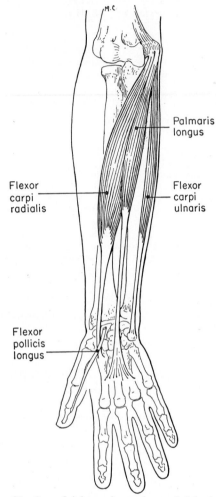

Figure 95. Superficial muscles on front of right forearm.

Tendon may be felt on medial side of anterior surface of wrist, just proximal to the pisiform bone.

Extensor Carpi Radialis Longus (Fig. 96, *A*)

PROXIMAL ATTACHMENTS. (O)   Lateral epicondyle and condyloid ridge of humerus.

DISTAL ATTACHMENT. (I)   Posterior surface of base of second metacarpal.

NERVE SUPPLY.   Radial.

ACTION.   Extension and radial flexion of wrist; assists in flexion of forearm against resistance when forearm is pronated.

WHERE TO PALPATE. Center of dorsal surface of forearm, about 2 inches below the elbow when forearm is in pronated position, as when palm rests on table. Also dorsal surface of wrist in line with index finger.

Extensor Carpi Radialis Brevis (Fig. 96, A)

PROXIMAL ATTACHMENT. (O) Lateral epicondyle of humerus.

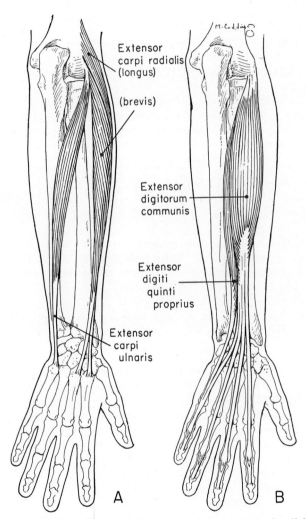

Extensor carpi radialis (longus)

(brevis)

Extensor digitorum communis

Extensor digiti quinti proprius

Extensor carpi ulnaris

A B

Figure 96. Muscles on back of right forearm. *A,* Extensor carpi radialis longus and brevis and extensor carpi ulnaris. *B,* Extensor digitorum communis and extensor digiti quinti proprius.

DISTAL ATTACHMENT. (I)   Posterior surface of base of third metacarpal.

NERVE SUPPLY.   Radial.

ACTION.   Extension and radial flexion of wrist; assists in flexion of forearm against resistance when forearm is pronated.

WHERE TO PALPATE.   Dorsal surface of forearm, slightly below the extensor carpi radialis longus. Difficult to distinguish from the latter.

Extensor Carpi Ulnaris (Fig. 96, A)

PROXIMAL ATTACHMENTS. (O)   By two heads, from lateral epicondyle of humerus and middle third of posterior ridge of ulna.

DISTAL ATTACHMENT. (I)   Posterior surface of base of fifth metacarpal.

NERVE SUPPLY.   Deep radial.

ACTION.   Extension and ulnar flexion of wrist; assists in flexion of forearm against resistance when forearm is pronated.

WHERE TO PALPATE.   Ulnar margin of posterior surface of forearm, halfway between elbow and wrist.

Flexor Digitorum Sublimis (Fig. 97, A)

PROXIMAL ATTACHMENTS. (O)   Humero-ulnar head: Medial epicondyle of humerus, ulnar collateral ligament, medial margin of coronoid process.

Radial head: Oblique line on anterior surface of shaft of radius.

DISTAL ATTACHMENTS. (I)   By four tendons to the four fingers, each tendon splitting to attach to the sides of the base of the middle phalanx.

NERVE SUPPLY.   Median.

ACTION.   Flexion of middle phalanges of fingers; assists in flexion of first phalanges and of wrist.

WHERE TO PALPATE.   Palm of hand.

Flexor Digitorum Profundus (Fig. 97, B)

PROXIMAL ATTACHMENT. (O)   Upper two thirds of anterior and medial surfaces of ulna.

DISTAL ATTACHMENTS. (I)   By four tendons to the four fingers, each tendon passing through the corresponding tendon of the flexor digitorum sublimis and attaching to the base of the distal phalanx.

NERVE SUPPLY.   Interosseous branch of median.

ACTION.   Flexion of distal phalanges of fingers; assists in flexion of proximal and middle phalanges and of wrist.

Cannot be palpated.

Flexor Pollicis Longus (Fig. 97, B)

PROXIMAL ATTACHMENT. (O)   Anterior surface of middle half of radius.

DISTAL ATTACHMENT. (I)   Anterior surface of base of distal phalanx of thumb.

NERVE SUPPLY.   Volar interosseous branch of median.

ACTION.   Flexion of both phalanges of thumb; flexion of wrist; assists in adduction of thumb metacarpal.

Cannot be palpated.

Extensor Digitorum Communis (Fig. 96, *B*)

PROXIMAL ATTACHMENT. (O)   Lateral epicondyle of humerus.

DISTAL ATTACHMENTS. (I)   By four tendons to the four fingers.

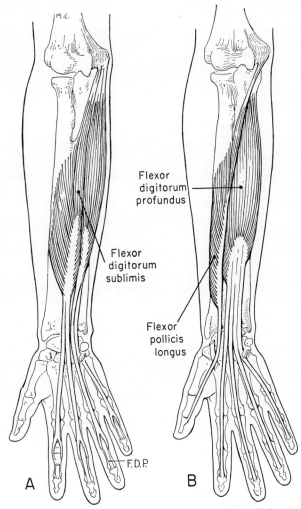

Figure 97. Deep muscles on front of right forearm. *A*, Flexor digitorum sublimis; *B*, flexor digitorum profundus and flexor pollicis longus.

Each tendon divides into three slips, the middle one attaching to the dorsal surface of the second phalanx and the other two uniting and attaching to the dorsal surface of the base of the distal phalanx.

NERVE SUPPLY.   Deep radial.

ACTION.   Extension of proximal phalanges of fingers; assists in extension of second and third phalanges and of wrist.

WHERE TO PALPATE.   Dorsal surface of hand and arm.

Extensor Indicis Proprius (Fig. 98)

PROXIMAL ATTACHMENT. (o)   Dorsal surface of lower half of ulna.

DISTAL ATTACHMENT. (I)   Unites with index finger tendon of extensor digitorum communis.

NERVE SUPPLY.   Deep radial.

ACTION.   Extension of proximal phalanx of index finger; assists in extension of wrist.

Cannot be palpated.

Extensor Digiti Quinti Proprius (Fig. 96, B)

PROXIMAL ATTACHMENT. (o)   Proximal tendon of extensor digitorum communis.

DISTAL ATTACHMENT. (I)   Unites with little finger tendon of extensor digitorum communis.

NERVE SUPPLY.   Deep radial.

ACTION.   Extension of proximal phalanx of fifth finger; assists in extension of wrist.

Cannot be palpated.

Extensor Pollicis Longus (Fig. 98)

PROXIMAL ATTACHMENT. (o)   Dorsal surface of middle third of ulna.

DISTAL ATTACHMENT. (I)   Dorsal surface of base of distal phalanx of thumb.

NERVE SUPPLY.   Deep radial.

ACTION.   Extension of both phalanges of thumb; assists in adduction and, under some circumstances, extension of thumb metacarpal; assists in extension, and probably radial flexion, of wrist.

WHERE TO PALPATE.   If the hand is placed palm down on a table and the thumb raised as high as possible, the tendon may be clearly seen and palpated on the dorsal surface of the thumb and radial side of hand.

Extensor Pollicis Brevis (Fig. 98)

PROXIMAL ATTACHMENT. (o)   Dorsal surface of radius below abductor pollicis longus.

DISTAL ATTACHMENT. (I)   Dorsal surface of base of first phalanx.
NERVE SUPPLY.   Deep radial.

ACTION.   Extension of first phalanx of thumb; assists in extension and abduction of thumb metacarpal and in radial flexion of
wrist.

WHERE TO PALPATE.   If the first phalanx is extended against
resistance, the tendon stands out between the wrist and first metacarpophalangeal joint.

COMMENTS.   If the thumb is slightly hyperadducted and force-

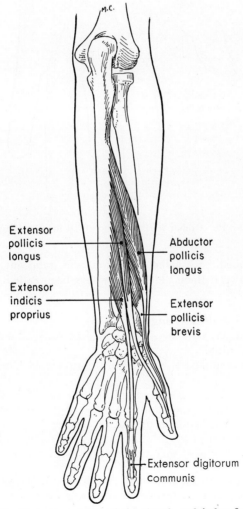

Extensor
pollicis
longus

Abductor
pollicis
longus

Extensor
indicis
proprius

Extensor
pollicis
brevis

Extensor digitorum
communis

Figure 98.   Posterior muscles of the thumb and index finger.

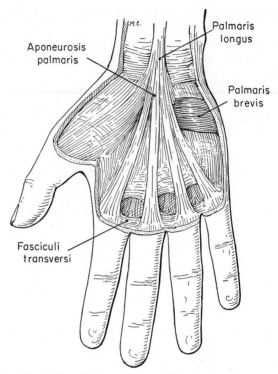

Figure 99. Palmar fascia and superficial muscles of right palm.

fully extended, both extensor tendons will stand out, leaving a deep hollow between them. This hollow has been called the anatomical snuff-box.

Abductor Pollicis Longus (Fig. 98)

PROXIMAL ATTACHMENT. (o)   Middle third of dorsal surfaces of radius and ulna.

DISTAL ATTACHMENT. (i)   Dorsal surface of base of first metacarpal.

NERVE SUPPLY.   Deep radial.

ACTION.   Extension and abduction of thumb metacarpal; radial flexion of wrist; assists in flexion of wrist.

WHERE TO PALPATE.   Just anterior to tendon of extensor pollicis brevis at base of metacarpal. The two tendons lie side by side.

Comments on Flexion and Extension of Wrist and Fingers. An interesting characteristic of the long finger muscles is the fact that they do not have sufficient length to permit the full range of motion in the joints of the fingers and wrist at the same time. For instance, it is impossible to achieve simultaneously complete flexion both of the fingers and of the hand because the antagonistic muscle, the extensor communis digitorum, will not stretch sufficiently to permit it. Likewise, it is impossible to achieve simultaneously complete extension of the fingers and hyperextension at the wrist because the two finger flexors, the digitorum sublimis and profundus, will not stretch sufficiently to permit it. Whether complete flexion is desired, or complete extension, in either case the antagonistic muscles act as a check rein. Thus, if complete flexion of the fingers is desired, the wrist can be flexed to only about half of its usual range, and if complete flexion at the wrist is desired, the fingers can be flexed only about half way.

Conversely, it is impossible to extend the fingers completely when the wrist is hyperextended to its limit of motion because of the pull on the finger flexors. This involuntary movement due to the tension of the opposing muscles is what is known as the tendon or pulley action of multijoint muscles (see p. 33). Because of this arrangement of the muscles the strongest finger flexion can be obtained when the wrist is held rigid in either a straight or slightly hyperextended position; the strongest finger extension, when the wrist is rigid in either a straight or slightly flexed position. The most powerful wrist action—either flexion or hyperextension— can take place only when the fingers are relaxed. In other words, strong finger action requires a rigid wrist; strong wrist action requires relaxed fingers. The whole subject of wrist and finger action has been discussed exceptionally well by Wright.

Muscles of the Fingers and Thumb Located in the Hand

Abductor Digiti Quinti (Fig. 100)

PROXIMAL ATTACHMENTS. (O)   Pisiform bone and tendon of flexor carpi ulnaris.

DISTAL ATTACHMENTS. (I)   Ulnar side of base of first phalanx of little finger and ulnar border of aponeurosis of extensor digitorum quinti proprius.

NERVE SUPPLY.   Ulnar.

ACTION.   Abduction of little finger; assists in flexion of first phalanx and extension of second and third phalanges.

WHERE TO PALPATE.   Ulnar border of hand.

Flexor Digiti Quinti Brevis (Fig. 100)

PROXIMAL ATTACHMENTS. (O)   Hook of hamate bone and adjacent parts of transverse carpal ligament.

DISTAL ATTACHMENT. (I)   Ulnar side of base of first phalanx of little finger.

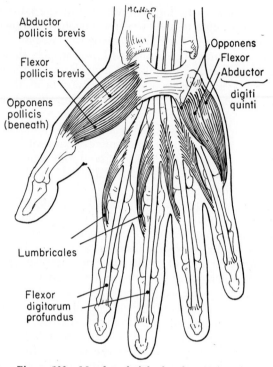

Figure 100. Muscles of right hand, anterior view

NERVE SUPPLY.   Palmar division of ulnar nerve.

ACTION.   Flexion of proximal phalanx of little finger.

WHERE TO PALPATE.   On palm of hand just beside abductor digiti quinti. It is difficult to distinguish it from the latter muscle.

Opponens Digiti Quinti (Figs. 100 and 101)

PROXIMAL ATTACHMENTS. (O)   Hook of hamate bone and adjacent parts of transverse carpal ligament.

DISTAL ATTACHMENT. (I)   Whole length of ulnar border of fifth metacarpal bone.

NERVE SUPPLY.   Deep palmar branch of ulnar nerve.

ACTION.   Combination of flexion and adduction of fifth metacarpal bone, as in "cupping" the palm.

Cannot be palpated.

COMMENT.   This muscle is situated directly beneath the flexor brevis and abductor muscles for the same finger.

Flexor Pollicis Brevis (Fig. 100)

PROXIMAL ATTACHMENTS. (O)   Superficial head: Greater multangular bone and adjacent part of transverse carpal ligament. Deep head: Ulnar side of first metacarpal bone.

DISTAL ATTACHMENTS. (I)   Superficial head: Radial side of base
of first phalanx of thumb. Deep head: Ulnar side of base of phalanx
of thumb with adductor pollicis.

NERVE SUPPLY.   Median.

ACTION.   Flexion of proximal phalanx of thumb; assists in abduction and hyperextension of thumb metacarpal.

WHERE TO PALPATE.   The superficial head may be palpated
along the ulnar margin of the anterior surface of the thenar eminence, but it is difficult to distinguish it from the abductor pollicis
brevis.

COMMENT.   The deep head is sometimes described as part of
the palmar interossei. A sesamoid bone lies in the tendon of insertion of the superficial head.

Abductor Pollicis Brevis (Fig. 100)

PROXIMAL ATTACHMENTS. (O)   Anterior surface of transverse
carpal ligament, greater multangular bone and navicular bone.

DISTAL ATTACHMENT. (I)   Radial side of base of first phalanx of
thumb.

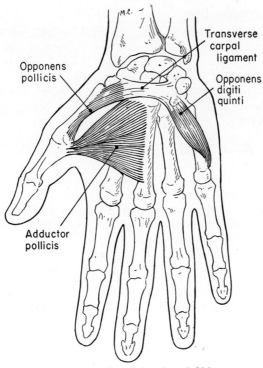

Figure 101. Deep muscles of thumb and fifth metacarpal.

NERVE SUPPLY.   Median.

ACTION.   Abduction of thumb metacarpal; assists in flexion of proximal phalanx of thumb.

WHERE TO PALPATE.   Anterior surface of thenar eminence.

COMMENTS.   This is the most superficial muscle on the radial side of the thenar eminence.

Opponens Pollicis (Figs. 100 and 101)

PROXIMAL ATTACHMENTS. (o)   Anterior surface of greater multangular bone and transverse carpal ligament.

DISTAL ATTACHMENT. (i)   Whole radial border of anterior surface of first metacarpal.

NERVE SUPPLY.   Median.

ACTION.   A combination of abduction, hyperflexion and possibly slight inward rotation of the thumb metacarpal, making it possible, when flexing the phalanges, to touch the tip of any of the four fingers.

WHERE TO PALPATE.   If the thumb is pressed hard against the middle finger, this muscle can be palpated along the lateral margin of the thenar eminence, close to the metacarpal bone.

Adductor Pollicis (Fig. 101)

PROXIMAL ATTACHMENTS. (o)   Carpal or oblique head: Deep carpal ligaments, capitate bone and bases of second and third metacarpal bones. Metacarpal or transverse head: Lower two thirds of anterior surface of third metacarpal bone.

DISTAL ATTACHMENT. (i)   Ulnar side of base of proximal phalanx of thumb.

NERVE SUPPLY.   Deep palmar branch of ulnar nerve.

ACTION.   Adduction, flexion and hyperflexion of thumb metacarpal; flexion of proximal phalanx of thumb.

WHERE TO PALPATE.   On the inner anterior surface of the metacarpophalangeal joint of the thumb. It can easily be palpated when the thumb is pressed against one of the fingers.

COMMENTS.   The two parts of this triangular shaped muscle are sometimes described as two separate muscles. A sesamoid bone is present in the tendon.

Lumbricales (four in number) (Fig. 100)

PROXIMAL ATTACHMENTS. (o)   Tendons of the flexor digitorum profundus in the middle of the palm.

DISTAL ATTACHMENTS. (i)   Radial side of the tendons of the extensor digitorum communis.

NERVE SUPPLY.   First and second lumbricales: Median. Third and fourth lumbricales: Ulnar.

ACTION.   Flexion of proximal phalanges of fingers and extension of middle and distal phalanges.
Cannot be palpated.
COMMENTS.   The lumbrical muscles, so named because of their
wormlike appearance, are situated deep in the palm of the hand.

Palmar Interossei (three in number) (Fig. 102)
PROXIMAL ATTACHMENTS (O):
   First: Ulnar side of second metacarpal bone.
   Second: Radial side of fourth metacarpal bone.
   Third: Radial side of fifth metacarpal bone.
DISTAL ATTACHMENTS (I):
   First: Ulnar side of base of first phalanx of index finger and
expansion of extensor digitorum communis tendon.
   Second: Radial side of base of first phalanx of fourth finger and
expansion of extensor digitorum communis tendon.
   Third: Radial side of base of first phalanx of fifth finger and
expansion of extensor digitorum communis tendon.
NERVE SUPPLY.   Ulnar.
ACTION.   Adduction and flexion of the second, fourth and fifth
fingers at the metacarpophalangeal joints; extension of second and
third phalanges of second, fourth and fifth fingers.
Cannot be palpated.

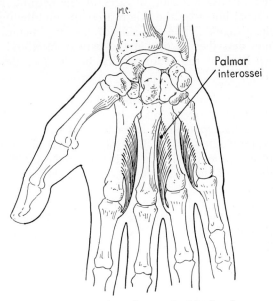

Figure 102. Palmar interossei, right hand

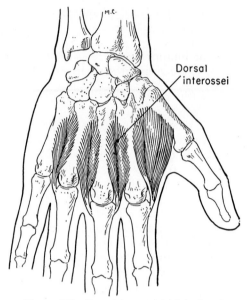

Figure 103. Dorsal interossei, right hand

COMMENTS. These three small "between-the-bones" muscles are situated on the anterior surfaces of the second, fourth and fifth metacarpal bones on the side nearest the middle finger. A similar muscle, situated along the side of the first metacarpal bone, is sometimes described as one of the palmar interossei, sometimes as the deep head of the flexor pollicis brevis. (See description of latter muscle.)

Dorsal Interossei (four in number) (Fig. 103)

PROXIMAL ATTACHMENTS. (O)   By two heads from the adjacent sides of the metacarpal bones in each interspace.

DISTAL ATTACHMENTS. (I)   Base of proximal phalanx and aponeurosis of extensor muscles on each side of the middle finger, on the thumb side of the index finger, and on the ulnar side of the fourth finger.

NERVE SUPPLY.   Palmar branch of ulnar nerve.

ACTION.   Abduction of index and fourth fingers; radial and ulnar flexion of middle finger; flexion of proximal row of phalanges of second, third and fourth fingers, and extension of middle and distal rows.

Cannot be palpated.

COMMENTS.   These are small bipenniform muscles. They occupy the intervals between the metacarpal bones.

Muscular Analysis of the Fundamental Movements of the Wrist, Fingers and Thumb

WRIST

Flexion

Movers ....

Principal .... { Flexor carpi ulnaris
Flexor carpi radialis
Palmaris longus

Assistant .... { Flexor digitorum profundus (when prevented from flexing fingers)
Flexor digitorum sublimis (when prevented from flexing fingers)
Flexor pollicis longus
Abductor pollicis longus

Neutralizers .... When strong wrist flexion requires the aid of the finger flexors, the finger extensors contract to counteract the effect of the finger flexors on the fingers, thus permitting them to affect only the wrist joint
Flexor carpi ulnaris is mutually neutralizing with flexor carpi radialis and abductor pollicis longus with respect to ulnar and radial flexion

Stabilizers .... When strong wrist flexion is desired, the triceps provides a firm support for the origins of the wrist flexors by preventing flexion at the elbow

Extension

Movers ....

Principal .... { Extensor carpi radialis longus
Extensor carpi radialis brevis
Extensor carpi ulnaris

Assistant .... { Extensor communis digitorum
Extensor pollicis longus

Neutralizers .... When strong wrist extension requires the aid of the finger extensors, the finger flexors contract to prevent extension of the fingers
Extensor carpi radialis longus and brevis and extensor carpi ulnaris are mutually neutralizing with respect to radial and ulnar flexion

Stabilizers .... When strong wrist extension is desired, the triceps provides a firm support for the origins of the wrist extensors by preventing flexion at the elbow

Ulnar Flexion

Movers .... { Extensor carpi ulnaris
Flexor carpi ulnaris

Neutralizers...................Extensor carpi ulnaris and flexor carpi ulnaris are mutually neutralizing with respect to extension and flexion

Stabilizers ....⎰Triceps provides a firm base of support for the ulnar flexors by preventing flexion at the elbow
Palmar interossei prevent abduction of little finger by ulnar flexors

Radial Flexion

Movers.........⎰

⎰Principal.........⎰Extensor carpi radialis longus
Extensor carpi radialis brevis

⎰Assistant.........⎰Abductor pollicis longus
Extensor pollicis longus
Extensor pollicis brevis
Flexor carpi radialis

Neutralizers....................Extensor carpi radialis longus and brevis and flexor carpi radialis are mutually neutralizing with respect to one another's extension and flexion tendencies

Stabilizers........................Biceps steadies the elbow joint. Abductor pollicis longus is prevented from abducting and extending the thumb by the stabilizing action of the thumb flexors and adductors

FINGERS

Flexion

Movers.........⎰

⎰Principal.........⎰Flexor digitorum sublimis (middle phalanges)
Flexor digitorum profundus (distal phalanges)
Lumbricales (proximal phalanges)
Flexor digiti quinti brevis (proximal phalanx of fifth finger)

⎰Assistant.........⎰Palmar interossei (proximal phalanges of second, fourth and fifth fingers)
Dorsal interossei (proximal phalanges of second, third and fourth fingers)
Opponens digiti quinti (fifth metacarpal)
Abductor digiti quinti (proximal phalanx of fifth finger)

Neutralizers and stabilizers............ {
(These are grouped together because the muscles overlap in the functions of neutralizing and stabilizing)

Extensor carpi radialis longus and brevis and extensor carpi ulnaris stabilize the wrist during flexion of the fingers, thus neutralizing the wrist-flexing tendency of the long finger flexors

If the middle and distal phalanges of the fingers are flexed, but not the proximal phalanges, the extensor digitorum communis stabilizes the proximal phalanx, and the flexor carpi ulnaris and radialis and palmaris longus stabilize the wrist against the pull of the extensor digitorum communis

If the proximal phalanges of the fingers are flexed, but not the middle or distal phalanges, the extensor digitorum communis stabilizes the latter two phalanges, and the flexor carpi ulnaris, flexor carpi radialis and palmaris longus stabilize the wrist against the pull of the extensor digitorum communis

Extension

Movers......... {

Principal......... {
Extensor digitorum communis (proximal phalanges)
Extensor indicis proprius (proximal phalanx of index finger)
Extensor digiti quinti proprius (proximal phalanx of fifth finger)

Assistant......... {
Lumbricales (middle and distal phalanges)
Palmar interossei (middle and distal phalanges of second, fourth and fifth fingers)
Dorsal interossei (middle and distal phalanges of second, fourth and fifth fingers)
Abductor digiti quinti (middle and distal phalanges of fifth finger)

Neutralizers and stabilizers............. Flexor carpi ulnaris, flexor carpi radialis and palmaris longus stabilize the wrist during extension of the fingers, thus neutralizing the wrist-extending tendency of the long finger extensors

Abduction

Movers......... {

Principal......... {
Dorsal interossei (second and fourth fingers)
Abductor digiti quinti (fifth finger)

Assistant......... Lumbricales (index finger)

Neutralizers and stabilizers . . . . Various muscles of the wrist and hand serve in these capacities, depending upon the position of the hand, upon which fingers are being abducted, and upon the force of the movement

Adduction

Movers . . . .
- Principal . . . .
  - Palmar interossei (second, fourth and fifth fingers)
  - Opponens digiti quinti (fifth metacarpal)
- Assistant . . . . Lumbricales (fourth and fifth fingers)

Neutralizers and stabilizers . . . . Various muscles of the wrist and hand serve in these capacities, depending upon the position of the hand, upon which fingers are being adducted, and upon the force of the movement

Radial and Ulnar Flexion of the Middle Finger

Movers . . . .
- Dorsal interossei (both radial and ulnar flexion of middle finger)
- Lumbricales (radial flexion of middle finger)

Neutralizers and stabilizers . . . . Various muscles of the other fingers and of the wrist serve in these capacities, depending upon the position of the hand and the force of the movement

Thumb

Flexion

Movers . . . .
- Principal . . . .
  - Flexor pollicis longus (both phalanges)
  - Flexor pollicis brevis (proximal phalanx)
- Assistant . . . .
  - Adductor pollicis (metacarpal and proximal phalanx)
  - Abductor pollicis brevis (proximal phalanx)

Neutralizers and stabilizers . . . . The extensors of the wrist and other muscles of the wrist and hand, depending upon the position of the hand and the force of the movement

Extension

Movers . . . .
- Principal . . . .
  - Extensor pollicis longus (both phalanges)
  - Extensor pollicis brevis (proximal phalanx)
- Assistant . . . . Abductor pollicis longus (metacarpal)

Neutralizers and stabilizers . . . . The flexors of the wrist and other muscles of the wrist and hand, depending upon the position of the hand and the force of the movement

Abduction

Movers
{
Principal......... { Abductor pollicis longus (metacarpal)
{ Abductor pollicis brevis (metacarpal)

Assistant......... { Extensor pollicis brevis (metacarpal)
{ Flexor pollicis brevis (metacarpal)

Neutralizers and stabilizers.............The ulnar flexors of the wrist and other muscles of the wrist and hand, depending upon the position of the hand and the force of the movement

Adduction

Movers
{
Principal..........Adductor pollicis (metacarpal)

Assistant......... { Flexor pollicis longus (metacarpal)
{ Extensor pollicis longus (metacarpal)

Neutralizers and stabilizers.............None unless the movement is forceful, in which case all the muscles of the wrist and fingers seem to be in static contraction

Opposition

Movers
{
Principal..........Opponens pollicis (metacarpal)

Assistants in different phases of opposition
{
Flexor pollicis longus (both phalanges)
Flexor pollicis brevis (metacarpal and proximal phalanx)
Abductor pollicis longus (metacarpal)
Abductor pollicis brevis (metacarpal and proximal phalanx)
Adductor pollicis (metacarpal and proximal phalanx)

Neutralizers.......................In the second part of the movement the tendency of the flexor pollicis longus to flex and radially flex the wrist is neutralized by the extensor carpi ulnaris, extensor carpi radialis longus and extensor carpi radialis brevis. The tendency of the flexor pollicis brevis to flex the metacarpal bone at the same time that it is flexing the first phalanx is neutralized by the extensor pollicis longus and brevis

Stabilizers..........................All the muscles of the wrist contract to stabilize it, particularly when the thumb is pressing forcefully against the fingers

Demonstrations and Laboratory Exercises

Joint Structure and Function

1. Using a form like the one on page 150, record the essential information regarding the radiocarpal, the carpometacarpal, the metacarpophalangeal and the interphalangeal articulations. Study the movements both on the skeleton and

on the living body. Pay particular attention to the carpometacarpal joint of the thumb.

2. With a Lufkin rule or protractor-goniometer measure the amount of hyperextension possible at the wrist, (a) with the fingers flexed; (b) with the fingers extended. Likewise measure the amount of flexion possible at the wrist, (a) with the fingers flexed; (b) with the fingers extended. Explain.

Muscular Action

(If possible, get someone who plays the piano to serve as subject.)

3. Flexion at wrist

Subject: Sit with forearm resting on table with palm up. Flex hand at wrist.

Assistant: Resist movement by holding palm.

Observer: Palpate, identify and explain the action of as many muscles as possible.

CHECK LIST FOR MUSCULAR ANALYSIS OF MOVEMENTS OF THE HAND AT THE WRIST

	Flexion	Extension	Ulnar Flexion	Radial Flexion
MUSCLES OF WRIST				
Flexor carpi radialis				
Flexor carpi ulnaris				
Palmaris longus				
Extensor carpi radialis longus				
Extensor carpi radialis brevis				
Extensor carpi ulnaris				
MUSCLES OF THUMB AND FINGERS				
Flexor digitorum sublimis				
Flexor digitorum profundus				
Extensor digit. communis				
Extensor indicis proprius				
Extensor digiti quinti				
Flexor pollicis longus				
Extensor pollicis longus				
Extensor pollicis brevis				
Abductor pollicis longus				

4. Extension and hyperextension at wrist

Subject: Sit with forearm resting on table, palm down, hand hanging over edge of table. Extend hand at wrist.

Assistant: Resist movement by pressing on back of hand.

Observer: Palpate, identify and explain the action of as many muscles as possible.

5. Radial flexion at wrist

Subject: Sit with forearm resting on table, ulnar side (little finger side of hand) down. Keeping thumb against hand, raise hand from table without moving forearm.

Assistant: May give slight resistance to hand.

Observer: Palpate and identify the muscles responsible for radial flexion.

6. Ulnar flexion at wrist

Subject: Lie face down or bend forward in such a way that radial side of hand (thumb side) is on supporting surface, with forearm supported and wrist neither flexed nor hyperextended. Keeping little finger against hand, raise hand without moving forearm.

Assistant: May give slight resistance to hand.

Observer: Palpate and identify the muscles responsible for ulnar flexion.

7. Finger flexion

Subject: Sit with forearm resting on table with palm up. Flex fingers without flexing at wrist.

CHECK LIST FOR MUSCULAR ANALYSIS OF MOVEMENTS OF THE FINGERS

	Metacarpophalangeal				Interphalangeal	
	Flex.	*Ext.*	*Abd.*	*Add.*	*Flex.*	*Ext.*
ON FOREARM						
Flexor digiti sublimis						
Flexor digiti profundus						
Extensor digiti communis						
Ext. indicis proprius						
Extensor digiti quinti						
IN HAND						
Lumbricales						
Palmar interossei						
Dorsal interossei						
Abductor digiti quinti						
Flexor dig. quint. brev.						
Opponens digiti quinti						

CHECK LIST FOR MUSCULAR ANALYSIS OF MOVEMENTS OF THE THUMB

	Carpometacarpal					Metacarpophalangeal		Interphalangeal	
	Flex.	Ext. & Hyp. Ex.	Abd.	Add. & Hyp. Add.	Opp.	Flex.	Ext.	Flex.	Ext.
On Forearm									
Fl. pol. long.									
Ext. pol. long.									
Ext. pol. brev.									
Abd. pol. long.									
In Hand									
Fl. pol. brev.									
Abd. pol. brev.									
Opponens pol.									
Adductor pol.									

Assistant: Resist movement by hooking own fingers over those of subject.

Observer: Palpate, identify and explain the action of as many muscles as possible.

8. Finger extension

Subject: Sit with forearm resting on table with palm down, fingers curled over edge of table. Extend fingers.

Assistant: Resist movement by holding hand over subject's fingers.

Observer: Palpate, identify and explain the action of as many muscles as possible.

9. Abduction of thumb

Subject: Place the hand on a table with the palm up and the thumb slightly separated from the index finger. Abduct the thumb at the carpometacarpal joint by raising it vertically upward.

Assistant: Give slight resistance to the thumb at the proximal phalanx.

Observer: Palpate the abductor pollicis brevis in the thenar eminence.

10. Hyperflexion of thumb in position of slight abduction

Subject: Place the hand on a table with the palm up and the thumb slightly raised from the table. Hyperflex the thumb at the carpometacarpal joint.

Assistant: Give slight resistance to the proximal phalanx of the thumb.

Observer: Palpate the flexor pollicis brevis in the thenar eminence.

11. Extension of thumb

Subject: Rest the fully extended hand on its ulnar border with the thumb uppermost. Extend the thumb as far as possible.

Observer: Identify the tendons of the abductor pollicis longus, the extensor pollicis longus and the extensor pollicis brevis.

12. Opposition of thumb

Subject: Press the thumb hard against the tip of the middle finger.

Observer: Palpate and identify the opponens pollicis and adductor pollicis.

Action of Muscles Other Than Movers

13. Perform a movement in which the extensor carpi ulnaris and extensor carpi radialis longus and brevis act as neutralizers to prevent flexion at the wrist.

14. Perform a movement in which the extensor carpi ulnaris and flexor carpi ulnaris act as mutual neutralizers.

Bibliography

1. Duvall, E. N.: Kinesiology; The Anatomy of Motion. Englewood Cliffs, N. J., Prentice-Hall, 1959.
2. Eyler, D. L., and Markee, J. E.: The Anatomy and Function of the Intrinsic Musculature of the Fingers. J. Bone & Joint Surg., *36A:* 1–9, 18, 1954.
3. Gray, H.: Anatomy of the Human Body. 26th ed. Philadelphia, Lea & Febiger, 1954.
4. Kendall, H. O., and Kendall, F. P.: Muscles; Testing and Function. Baltimore, Williams & Wilkins Company, 1949.
5. Markee, J. E., and Eyler, D. L.: The Functional Anatomy of the Hand. Brochure to go with film. Department of Anatomy, Duke University School of Medicine.
6. Morris' Human Anatomy. 11th ed. New York, McGraw-Hill Book Company, Inc., 1953.
7. Wright, W. G.: Muscle Function. New York, Hoeber, 1928.

Recommended Reading

Wright, W. G.: Muscle Function. (See 7 above.) Pages 29–53.

10 · The Lower Extremity: The Hip Joint and the Pelvic Girdle

THE RELATIONSHIP between the hip joint and the pelvic girdle is somewhat similar to that between the shoulder joint and shoulder girdle. Just as the scapula tilts or rotates to put the glenoid fossa in a favorable position for the movements of the humerus, so the pelvic girdle tilts and rotates to put the acetabulum in a favorable position for the movements of the femur. There are these differences, however. Whereas the left and right sides of the shoulder girdle can move independently of each other, the pelvic girdle can move only as a unit. Furthermore, whereas the movements of the shoulder girdle take place in its own joints (sternoclavicular and acromioclavicular), the pelvic girdle is dependent upon the lumbosacral joint and the hip joints for its movements. Hence an analysis of the movements of the pelvic girdle must always be in terms of spinal and hip action.

The Hip Joint

Structure (Figs. 104, 105, 106, 107, 108).   The hip joint is formed by the articulation of the spherical head of the femur with the deep cup-shaped acetabulum of the pelvis (Figs. 104 and 105). It is a typical ball-and-socket joint. The femoral head is completely covered with hyaline cartilage except for a small pit near the center, known as the fovea capitis, at which point the ligamentum teres

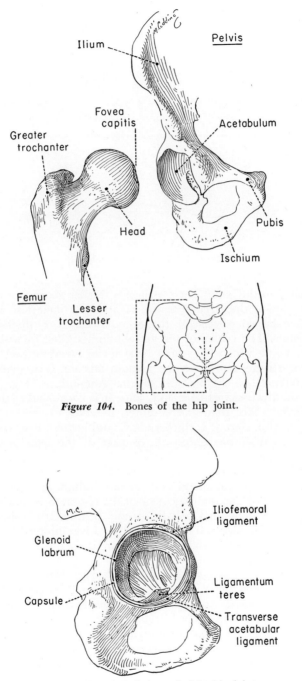

Figure 104. Bones of the hip joint.

Figure 105. Acetabulum of right hip joint.

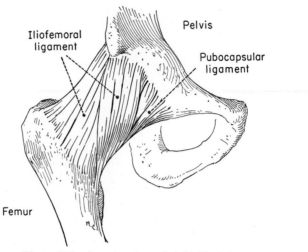

Figure 106. Anterior view of right hip joint.

is attached to the bone. The cartilage is thicker above and tapers to
a thin edge at the circumference. Hyaline cartilage also lines the
horseshoe-shaped surface of the acetabulum. It is thicker above
than below. The center of the acetabulum is filled in with a mass
of fatty tissue which is covered by synovial membrane. A flat rim
of fibrocartilage, known as the glenoid labrum, is attached by its
circumference to the margin of the acetabulum (Fig. 105). It
covers the hyaline cartilage, and, since it is considerably thicker at
the circumference than at the center, it serves to deepen the acetabulum. Also, since it is thicker above and behind, it serves to protect the acetabulum against the impact of the femoral head in
forceful movements.

The joint is enveloped in a loose, sleevelike capsule which is
attached above to the margin of the acetabulum, and below to the
distal margin of the anatomic neck of the femur. It is much thicker
above and in front than it is below and behind. It consists of two
sets of fibers, circular and longitudinal, and is reinforced by the iliofemoral, pubocapsular and ischiocapsular ligaments. It is lined with
an extensive synovial membrane.

Ligaments. *Iliofemoral Ligament* (Fig. 106).   This ligament, nicknamed the Y ligament because of its inverted Y shape,
is an extraordinarily strong band of fibers located at the front of
the capsule and intimately blended with it. Its shape is actually
more that of a triangle or an inverted V than that of a Y. It is attached above to the anterior inferior spine of the ilium, and below
by two divisions to the upper and the lower parts of the intertro-

chanteric line. It serves to check extension and both outward and inward rotation.

Pubocapsular Ligament (Fig. 106).   This is a narrow band of fibers, attached above to the obturator crest and upper ramus of the pubis. Below, it blends with the fibers of the capsule. It prevents excessive abduction and helps to check extension and outward rotation.

Ischiocapsular Ligament (Fig. 107).   This is a strong triangular ligament on the back of the capsule. It is attached by its base to the ischium behind and below the margin of the acetabulum, and by its apex to the trochanteric fossa, the fibers blending with those of the capsule. It limits inward rotation and adduction in the flexed position.

Transverse Acetabular Ligament (Fig. 108).   This is a strong flat band of fibers, continuous with the glenoid labrum. It bridges the acetabular notch, thus completing the acetabular ring.

Ligamentum Teres (Fig. 108).   This is a flat, narrow triangular band, sheathed in synovial membrane, lying within the hip joint. It is attached by its apex to the fovea capitis, the little pit near the center of the femoral head, and by its base to the margins of the acetabular notch and to the transverse acetabular ligament.

Position and Shape of Femur.   The movements of the femur are similar to those of the humerus, but are not quite so free as the latter because of the deeper socket. In studying the movements of the femur the student should first be aware of the position of the femur in the fundamental standing position. If viewed from the front in this position, it is seen that the shaft of the femur is not vertical, but that it slants somewhat medialward. This serves to place the center of the knee joint more nearly under the center of motion of the hip joint. Hence the mechanical axis of the femur

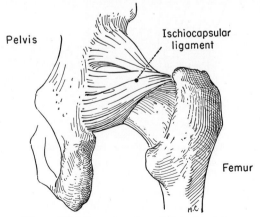

Pelvis

Ischiocapsular ligament

Femur

Figure 107. Posterior view of right hip joint.

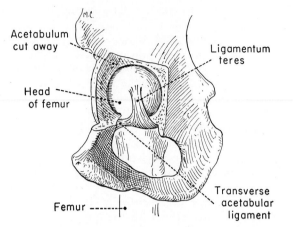

Figure 108. Right hip joint from within, looking toward head of femur.

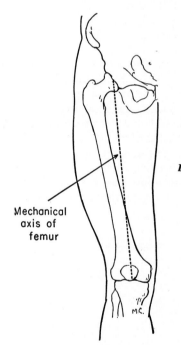

Figure 109. Mechanical axis of femur.

—a line connecting the center of the femoral head with the center of the knee joint—is almost vertical (Fig. 109). The degree of slant of the femoral shaft is related both to the size of the angle between the neck and shaft and to the width of the pelvis. A report on the variations found in the neck-shaft angle may be found at the end of this chapter (see p. 226 ff.).

As seen from the side, the shaft of the femur bows forward. These characteristics of the femur—the obtuse neck-shaft angle and the forward bowing of the shaft—are not signs of weakness, as the uninformed might suppose, but, as Steindler has explained, are provisions for resisting the strains and stresses sustained in walking, running and jumping, and for assuring the proper transmission of weight through the femur to the knee joint.

Movements of the Femur at the Hip Joint. *Flexion.* A forward movement of the femur in the sagittal plane. If the knee is straight, the movement is restricted by the tension of the hamstring muscles. In extreme flexion the pelvis tilts to supplement the movement at the hip joint.

Extension. Return movement from flexion.

Hyperextension. A backward movement of the femur in the sagittal plane. This movement is extremely limited. Except in dancers and acrobats, it is possible only when the femur is rotated outward and is probably completely absent in many individuals. The restricting factor is the iliofemoral ligament at the front of the joint. The advantage of this restriction of movement is that it provides a stable joint for weight-bearing without the need for strong muscular contraction.

Abduction. A sideward movement of the femur in the frontal plane so that the thigh moves away from the midline of the body. A greater range of movement is possible when the femur is rotated outward.

Adduction. Return movement from abduction. Hyperadduction is possible only when the other leg is moved out of the way. In extreme hyperadduction the ligamentum teres becomes taut.

Outward Rotation. A rotation of the femur around its longitudinal axis so that the knee is turned outward.

Inward Rotation. A rotation of the femur around its longitudinal axis so that the knee is turned inward.

Circumduction. A combination of flexion, abduction, extension and adduction, performed sequentially in either direction.

Muscles. Several of the muscles which act at the hip joint act with equal or greater effectiveness at the knee joint. These are known as the two-joint muscles of the lower extremity. Only their action at the hip joint is recorded in this section.

Anterior:
  Psoas
  Iliacus
  Sartorius
  Pectineus
  Tensor fasciae latae
  Rectus femoris

Posterior:
  Gluteus maximus
  Biceps femoris
  Semitendinosus
  Semimembranosus
  Six deep outward rotators

Lateral:
  Gluteus medius
  Gluteus minimus

Medial:
  Gracilis
  Adductor magnus
  Adductor longus
  Adductor brevis

Psoas (see also muscles of spine and pelvis) (Fig. 110)

PROXIMAL ATTACHMENTS. (O)   Sides of bodies and intervertebral cartilages of last thoracic and all lumbar vertebrae; front and lower borders of transverse processes of lumbar vertebrae.

DISTAL ATTACHMENT. (I)   Lesser trochanter of femur.

NERVE SUPPLY.   Femoral.

ACTION (AT HIP).   Flexion; assists in adduction, especially from position of extreme abduction.

WHERE TO PALPATE.   Because of the location of this muscle at the back of the abdomen, it can be palpated only on slender subjects and only when the abdominal muscles are relaxed. Two methods of attempting palpation are suggested.

1. The subject should lie on the side, rolled toward the face, and flex the thigh against resistance without contracting the abdominal muscles. The muscle may be palpated in the groin.

2. The subject should lie on the back with the lower back arched as much as possible. From this position he should flex one thigh without contracting the abdominal muscles. An assistant should support the pelvis underneath and attempt to prevent it from moving. The psoas may be palpated through the abdomen.

COMMENTS.   The psoas and the iliacus have a common tendon for their distal attachment. The two muscles are usually called the iliopsoas muscle. The brim of the pelvis, over which the psoas passes, serves to increase the muscle's angle of pull.

Iliacus (Fig. 110)

PROXIMAL ATTACHMENTS. (O)   Anterior surface of ilium and base of sacrum.

DISTAL ATTACHMENTS. (I)   Psoas tendon and shaft of femur below lesser trochanter.

NERVE SUPPLY.   Femoral.

ACTION.   Flexion.

WHERE TO PALPATE.   See psoas.

Sartorius (see also muscles of the knee) ((Fig. 111)

PROXIMAL ATTACHMENT. (O)   Anterior superior iliac spine and upper half of notch below it.

DISTAL ATTACHMENT. (I)   Anterior and medial surface of tibia just below condyle.

NERVE SUPPLY.   Femoral.

ACTION (AT HIP).   Flexion.

WHERE TO PALPATE.   At the anterior superior iliac spine. The entire muscle may be seen and palpated on the front of the thigh in a slender subject.

COMMENTS.   This is a long, slender ribbon-like muscle, directed obliquely downward and inward across the front of the thigh. It is the most superficial of the anterior muscles of the thigh. Its name is derived from the fact that it is supposed to produce the movements of the thigh and leg which enable one to sit "tailor-fashion."

Pectineus (Fig. 110)

PROXIMAL ATTACHMENT. (O)   Pectineal line between iliopectineal eminence and tubercle of pubis.

DISTAL ATTACHMENT. (I)   Pectineal line of femur, between lesser trochanter and linea aspera.

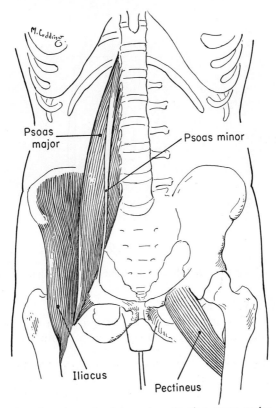

Figure 110.   Anterior view of pelvic region showing psoas major and minor, iliacus and pectineus.

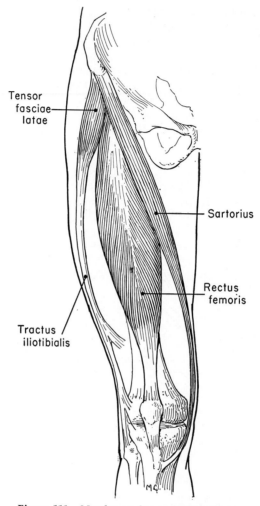

Figure 111. Muscles on front of right thigh.

NERVE SUPPLY.   Femoral.

ACTION.   Flexion; assists in adduction when hip is in flexed position. Whether or not it also contributes to outward rotation is debatable.

WHERE TO PALPATE.   At the front of the pubis, just lateral to the adductor longus. Difficult to distinguish from the latter muscle.

COMMENTS.   This is a short, thick, quadrilateral muscle situated lateral and superior to the adductor longus and more or less parallel to it. It has a good angle of pull which, together with its internal structure, accounts for its ability to overcome considerable resistance.

Tensor Fasciae Latae (Figs. 111 and 112)

PROXIMAL ATTACHMENTS. (O).   Anterior part of outer lip of iliac crest and outer surface of anterior superior iliac spine.

DISTAL ATTACHMENT. (I)   Iliotibial band of fascia lata on lateral-anterior aspect of thigh, about one third of the way down.

NERVE SUPPLY.   Superior gluteal.

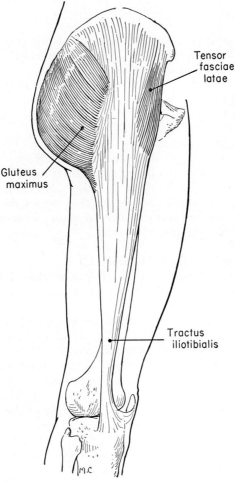

Tensor fasciae latae

Gluteus maximus

Tractus iliotibialis

M.C

Figure 112.   Lateral view of gluteus maximus, tensor fasciae latae and iliotibial band.

ACTION.   Flexion; abduction; tenses the fascia lata. Whether or not it also contributes to inward rotation is debatable.

WHERE TO PALPATE.   About 2 inches anterior to the greater trochanter.

COMMENTS.   This is a small muscle located close in front of, and slightly lateral to, the hip joint. Because its pull on the fascia lata is transmitted by means of the iliotibial band down to the lateral condyle of the tibia, it helps to extend the leg at the knee. Together with the gluteus maximus, which also unites with the fascia lata, it helps to stabilize the knee joint in weight-bearing positions. When the lower extremities are fixed, both these muscles help to steady the pelvis and trunk on the thighs.

Rectus Femoris (see also muscles of the knee) (Fig. 111)

PROXIMAL ATTACHMENTS. (o)   Anterior inferior iliac spine and groove above brim or acetabulum.

DISTAL ATTACHMENT. (i)   Base of patella. It may be said to attach indirectly, by means of the patellar ligament, to the tuberosity of the tibia.

NERVE SUPPLY.   Femoral.

ACTION (AT HIP).   Flexion.

WHERE TO PALPATE.   Anterior surface of thigh.

COMMENTS.   This is a large bipenniform muscle, located superficially on the front of the thigh. It is the only one of the four muscles in the quadriceps femoris group that crosses the hip joint. It is therefore a two-joint muscle. For the pulley or tendon action of such muscles, see page 33.

Gluteus Maximus (Figs. 112 and 113)

PROXIMAL ATTACHMENTS. (o)   Posterior gluteal line of ilium and adjacent portion of crest; posterior surface of lower part of sacrum and side of coccyx.

DISTAL ATTACHMENTS. (i)   Posterior surface of femur on ridge below greater trochanter; iliotibial band of fascia lata.

NERVE SUPPLY.   Inferior gluteal nerves.

ACTION.   Extension; outward rotation in extended position; lower fibers assist in adduction and upper fibers in abduction.

WHERE TO PALPATE.   Posterior surface of buttock.

COMMENTS.   This large superficial muscle of the buttocks is a powerful hip extensor. It contracts in all kinds of walking, but is particularly active in rapid and uphill walking and in stair climbing. It acts powerfully in running, jumping, stooping, bicycling, and in climbing a ladder or steep incline.

In order to understand all the movements which the gluteus maximus is capable of producing, it is helpful to study the position of the muscle with reference to the hip joint. A diagram such as that in Figure 114 makes clear the fact that about one third of the muscle lies above the center of motion, and two thirds of the muscle below it. Hence the gluteus maximus as a whole cannot be said either to abduct or to adduct the thigh. The uppermost fibers are in a position to abduct it; the lower portion of the muscle to adduct it. Few writers mention the adductory function of the gluteus maximus, yet anyone can determine it for himself by standing with one leg raised sideward, the foot resting on the seat of a chair. If adduction is attempted in this position with the inner

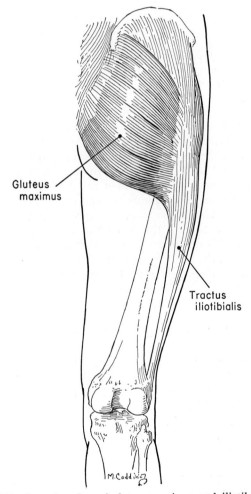

Figure 113. Posterior view of gluteus maximus and iliotibial band.

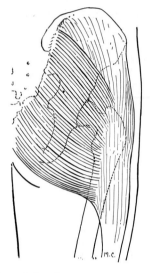

Figure 114. Diagram showing relation of gluteus maximus to hip joint.

border of the foot pressing down on the chair, the gluteus maximus can easily be palpated.

When the thighs are held motionless, the gluteus maximus pulls on the pelvis. If the trunk is flexed on the lower extremities, the muscle will extend it to the erect position. If the trunk remains in the erect position and the feet remain in place on the ground, contraction of the gluteus maximus produces two results interesting from the point of view of posture. The pull on the femur produces slight outward rotation at the hip joint. Since friction keeps the foot in contact with the ground, thus preventing free outward rotation of the femur, the result is a lifting of the arch, or supination of the foot. At the same time the pull at the muscle's origin decreases the inclination of the pelvis. This setting or tensing of the gluteus muscles is frequently advocated as a posture exercise.

Biceps Femoris, Long Head (see also muscles of the knee) (Fig. 115)

PROXIMAL ATTACHMENT. (O)   Lower and medial impression on tuberosity of ischium.

DISTAL ATTACHMENTS. (I)   Lateral side of head of fibula and lateral condyle of tibia.

NERVE SUPPLY.   Sciatic.

ACTION (AT HIP).   Extension.

WHERE TO PALPATE.   Lateral aspect of posterior surface of knee.

COMMENTS.   The biceps femoris forms the outer hamstring muscle. Only its long head crosses the hip joint. Its effectiveness as an extensor of the hip is in reverse proportion to the degree of flexion at the knee joint. If the knee is sharply flexed, the muscle has insufficient tension to act effectively at the hip joint. The tendon or pulley action of the two-joint muscles is discussed on page 33.

Semitendinosus (see also muscles of the knee) (Fig. 115)

PROXIMAL ATTACHMENT. (O)   Lower and medial impression on tuberosity of ischium with biceps femoris.

DISTAL ATTACHMENT. (I)   Upper part of medial surface of shaft of tibia.

NERVE SUPPLY.   Sciatic.

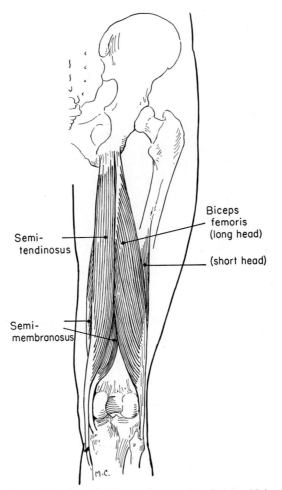

Figure 115. Superficial posterior muscles of right thigh.

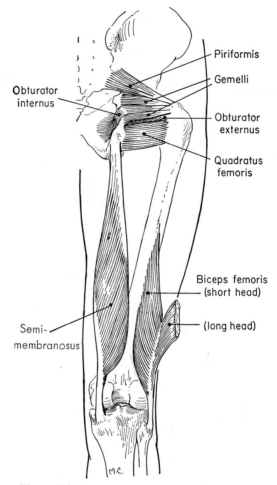

Figure 116. Deep posterior muscles of right thigh.

ACTION (AT HIP).   Extension.

WHERE TO PALPATE.   Medial aspect of posterior surface of knee. The more lateral of the two small tendons which can be felt in this region.

COMMENTS.   See semimembranosus.

Semimembranosus (see also muscles of the knee) (Fig. 116)

PROXIMAL ATTACHMENT. (O)   Upper and lateral impression on tuberosity of ischium.

DISTAL ATTACHMENT. (I)   Horizontal groove on posterior surface of medial condyle of tibia.

NERVE SUPPLY.   Sciatic.

ACTION (AT HIP).   Extension.

Cannot be palpated with certainty.

COMMENTS.   The semitendinosus and semimembranosus muscles form the inner component of the hamstring group. Their relation to the hip joint is similar to that of the long head of the biceps femoris.

The Six Deep Outward Rotators (Obturator Externus and Internus, Gemellus Superior and Inferior, Quadratus Femoris, and Piriformis) (Fig. 116)

PROXIMAL ATTACHMENTS. (o)   Outer and inner surfaces of sacrum and of pelvis in region of obturator foramen.

DISTAL ATTACHMENT. (i)   Posterior aspect of femur in region of greater trochanter.

NERVE SUPPLY.   Third, fourth and fifth lumbar, and first and second sacral.

ACTION.   Outward rotation.

Cannot be palpated.

COMMENTS.   These muscles are situated behind the hip joint, the piriformis, the most superior, being slightly above it, and the obturator externus, the most inferior, being slightly below it. Some of the muscles in this group have a secondary function such as abduction or adduction, but neither of these functions compares in importance with that of outward rotation.

Gluteus Medius (Fig. 117, A)

PROXIMAL ATTACHMENT. (o)   Posterior surface of ilium, between crest, posterior gluteal line and anterior gluteal line.

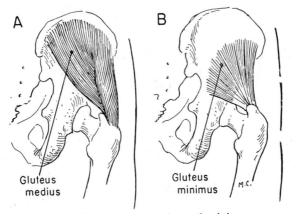

Figure 117. Gluteus medius and minimus.

DISTAL ATTACHMENT. (I)   Oblique ridge on lateral surface of greater trochanter.

NERVE SUPPLY.   Superior gluteal.

ACTION.   Abduction; anterior fibers rotate inward.

WHERE TO PALPATE.   About 2 or 3 inches above the greater trochanter.

COMMENTS.   The gluteus medius is situated at the side of the hip between the iliac crest and the greater trochanter. The posterior portion lies beneath the gluteus maximus. The anterior portion is covered only by the fascia lata. The muscle is an important one in walking and in standing in good posture. When the weight is shifted onto one foot, tension of the gluteus medius prevents the supporting hip from sagging. If the muscle is allowed to relax, the pelvis tilts laterally and the supporting hip protrudes in an awkward fashion. Paralysis of this muscle causes a typical limping gait known as the "gluteus medius gait." It is characterized by a sideward thrust of the hip and a lateral tilt of the trunk to the opposite side.

Gluteus Minimus (Fig. 117, B)

PROXIMAL ATTACHMENT. (O)   Posterior surface of ilium between anterior and inferior gluteal lines.

DISTAL ATTACHMENT. (I)   Anterior border of greater trochanter.

NERVE SUPPLY.   Superior gluteal.

ACTION.   Inward rotation; abduction.

Cannot be palpated.

COMMENTS.   This is a smaller muscle than the gluteus medius and is situated beneath it. Whereas the medius is primarily an abductor and secondarily an inward rotator, the minimus is primarily an inward rotator and secondarily an abductor. The muscles work together as partners, each muscle acting as an assistant in the other's strongest action.

Gracilis (see also muscles of the knee) (Figs. 118, 133 and 134)

PROXIMAL ATTACHMENT. (O)   Anterior aspect of lower half of symphysis pubis and upper half of pubic arch.

DISTAL ATTACHMENT. (I)   Medial surface of tibia just below condyle.

NERVE SUPPLY.   Obturator.

ACTION (AT HIP).   Adduction; assists in flexion.

WHERE TO PALPATE.   Medial aspect of posterior surface of knee, immediately anterior to the semitendinosus tendon.

COMMENTS.   As the name indicates, this is a slender muscle. Being an adductor, it is sometimes called the adductor gracilis.

Like the hamstrings, the sartorius and the rectus femoris, the gracilis is a muscle of the knee as well as of the hip joint.

Adductor Magnus (Fig. 118)

PROXIMAL ATTACHMENTS. (O)   Inferior rami of pubis and ischium and lateral border of inferior surface of ischial tuberosity.

DISTAL ATTACHMENTS. (I)   Linea aspera, medial supracondylar line, and adductor tubercle on medial condyle of femur.

NERVE SUPPLY.   Obturator and sciatic.

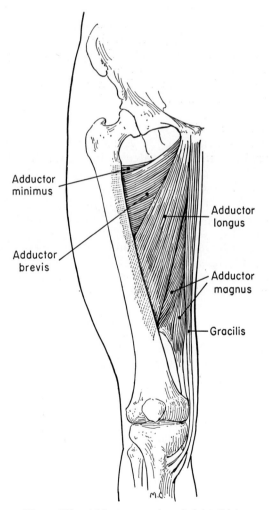

Figure 118. Adductor muscles of right thigh.

ACTION.   Adduction; extension; condyloid portion assists in inward rotation.

WHERE TO PALPATE.   Medial surface of middle half of thigh.

COMMENTS.   As its name implies, this is the largest of the hip adductors. It is likewise the most powerful. It fans out from its relatively small origin on the lower arms of the pubis and ischium to its extensive attachment to the linea aspera along the whole length of the shaft of the femur. The upper portion, i.e., the portion attached to the lower ramus of the pubis, is sometimes described separately as the adductor minimus. Kinesiologists are not in complete agreement regarding its functions, other than that of hip adduction. Bowen and Steindler both observed that the upper part of the muscle acts as a flexor of the thigh, and the lower portion as an extensor. Wright called the muscle a prime mover in the act of extension and claimed that it adducts only when the hip is in a position of extension. All agreed on its inward rotatory action, but Steindler and Wright considered this very slight.

Adductor Longus (Fig. 118)

PROXIMAL ATTACHMENT. (O)   Anterior surface of pubis.

DISTAL ATTACHMENT. (I)   Medial lip of middle half of linea aspera.

NERVE SUPPLY.   Obturator.

ACTION.   Adduction; assists in flexion.

WHERE TO PALPATE.   Just below its origin at the medial aspect of the groin.

COMMENTS.   Steindler has pointed out that, while the adductor longus ordinarily helps to flex the thigh, when the flexion exceeds about 70 degrees, this muscle becomes an extensor. This is due to the shift in the relationship between the muscle's line of pull and the joint's center of motion. This is another example of reversal of a muscle's customary function (see p. 27).

Adductor Brevis (Fig. 118)

PROXIMAL ATTACHMENTS. (O)   Outer surface of body and inferior ramus of pubis.

DISTAL ATTACHMENTS. (I)   Line from lesser trochanter to linea aspera and upper fourth of linea aspera.

NERVE SUPPLY.   Obturator and accessory obturator nerves.

ACTION.   Adduction; assists in flexion.

Cannot be palpated.

COMMENTS.   This lies just above the adductor longus. Like the latter, it acts as a flexor in the normal position, but later becomes an extensor after considerable hip flexion has been attained.

Muscular Analysis of the Fundamental Movements of the Thigh

Flexion

Movers —
  Principal —
  - Tensor fasciae latae, especially during first half of movement
  - Sartorius, continues throughout movement, especially if knee is in extended position
  - Pectineus, especially during first half of movement
  - Iliopsoas, especially during second half of movement

  Assistant —
  - Rectus femoris, especially if knee is in flexed position
  - Adductor longus
  - Adductor brevis
  - Gracilis

Neutralizers — The tensor fasciae latae and the pectineus are mutually neutralizing with respect to abduction and adduction

Stabilizers — Abdominal muscles and lumbar spine extensors stabilize the pelvis

Extension

Movers —
  - Gluteus maximus, especially against resistance and when thigh is flexed beyond a 45 degree angle
  - Hamstrings, especially if knee is in extended position
  - Adductor magnus, when thigh is flexed beyond a 45 degree angle

Neutralizers — Gluteus medius neutralizes the adductor tendency of adductor magnus

Stabilizers — Abdominal muscles and lumbar spine extensors stabilize the pelvis

Abduction

Movers —
  Principal —
  - Gluteus medius
  - Gluteus minimus, less effective than medius

  Assistant —
  - Tensor fasciae latae, when thigh is extended
  - Gluteus maximus, uppermost fibers, only during early part of movement

Neutralizers — Gluteus maximus and gluteus medius and minimus are mutually neutralizing with respect to outward and inward rotation

Stabilizers — These depend upon the position of the body and whether one or both thighs are being abducted. If one thigh is abducted against resistance, the abdominal muscles, spinal extensors and quadratus lumborum help to stabilize the pelvis

Adduction

Movers......... {

 Principal......... { Adductor magnus
Adductor longus
Adductor brevis
Gracilis

 Assistant......... { Pectineus, when thigh is flexed
Gluteus maximus, except uppermost fibers
Iliopsoas

Neutralizers......................The adductors magnus and longus are mutually neutralizing with respect to extension and flexion; likewise the pectineus and gluteus maximus

Stabilizers........................The abdominal muscles, spinal extensors and quadratus lumborum help to stabilize the pelvis when one thigh is adducted against resistance

Outward Rotation
Movers......................... { Six deep rotators
Gluteus maximus, when thigh is extended

Neutralizers......................The secondary actions of the six deep rotators neutralize one another

Stabilizers........................When the weight is not on the foot, the abdominal muscles, spinal extensors and quadratus lumborum stabilize the pelvis

Inward Rotation

Movers......... {

 Principal......... { Gluteus minimus
Gluteus medius, anterior fibers

 Assistant......... { Tensor fasciae latae
Adductor magnus, lower fibers, when thigh is extended

Neutralizers......................Adductor magnus neutralizes the abductory tendency of the other movers

Stabilizers........................When the weight is not on the foot, the abdominal muscles, spinal extensors and quadratus lumborum stabilize the pelvis

The Pelvic Girdle

Structure (Fig. 119). Each hip bone (os innominatum) is made up of three bones—the ilium, ischium, and pubis. These bones become fused into a single bone by about the time of puberty. The two hip bones together form the pelvic girdle. This bony girdle or basin, as it is sometimes called, is firmly attached to the sacrum at the sacroiliac articulation. The articulation is a difficult one to classify. It presents some of the characteristics of a diarthrodial joint, an articular cavity being present for part of the articulation. It is unlike other diarthrodial joints in one important respect, however. No movement can be voluntarily effected at the sacroiliac joint. Any movement which does occur is involuntary. Just how much motion can take place at the sacroiliac joint is a debatable matter. Some anatomists say that a slight "giving" may occur there as a shock absorption device; others claim that no motion occurs at the joint normally, except in women during pregnancy and parturition, when the ligaments relax in order to permit a slight spreading of the bones.

The sacrum is firmly bound to the two iliac bones by means of the anterior, posterior and interosseus sacroiliac ligaments (Figs. 120 and 121). It is further reinforced by the iliolumbar, sacrotuberous and sacrospinous ligaments and by the lower portion of the sacrospinalis muscle. Because of this firm attachment, the sacrum might well be considered a part of the pelvic girdle. From the point of view of function it is more truly a part of the pelvis than of the spine.

The joints at which the movements of the pelvic girdle occur are the two hip joints and the joints of the lumbar spine, particularly the lumbosacral articulation.

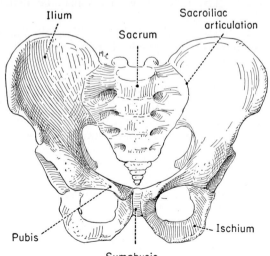

Figure 119. Anterior view of pelvis.

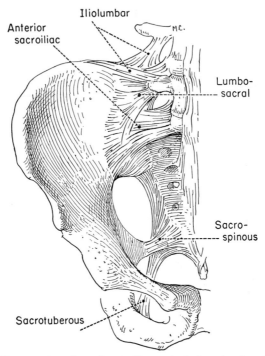

Figure 120. Anterior view of sacroiliac articulation showing ligaments.

Movements.   The pelvic movements may be defined as follows:

1. Increased inclination (forward tilt) (Fig. 122, *C*). A rotation of the pelvis in the sagittal plane about a frontal-horizontal axis in such a manner that the symphysis pubis turns downward and the posterior surface of the sacrum turns upward.

2. Decreased inclination (backward tilt) (Fig. 122, *B*). A rotation of the pelvis in the sagittal plane about a frontal-horizontal axis in such a manner that the symphysis pubis moves forward-upward and the posterior surface of the sacrum turns somewhat downward.

3. Lateral tilt. A rotation of the pelvis in the frontal plane about a sagittal-horizontal axis in such a manner that one iliac crest is lowered and the other is raised. The tilt is named in terms of the side which moves downward. Thus in a lateral tilt of the pelvis to the left, the left iliac crest is lowered and the right is raised.

4. Rotation (lateral twist). A rotation of the pelvis in the horizontal plane about a vertical axis. The movement is named in terms of the direction toward which the front of the pelvis turns.

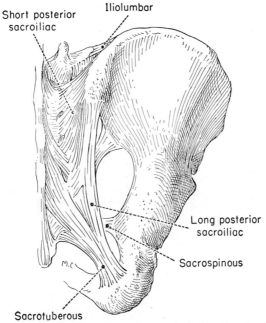

Figure 121. Posterior view of sacroiliac articulation showing ligaments.

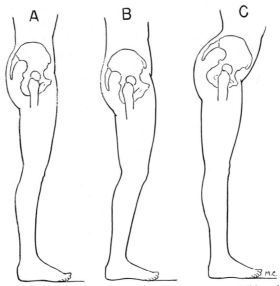

Figure 122. Anteroposterior inclinations of the pelvis. *A*, Mid-position; *B*, decreased inclination; *C*, increased inclination.

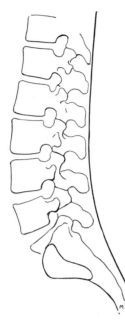

Figure 123. Lumbar and lumbosacral regions of the spine showing discrepancy in the lower lumbar curve as seen in the vertebral bodies and as seen in the contour of the back. (The sketch is based on an x-ray.)

The Relationship of the Pelvis to the Trunk and Lower Extremities. Architecturally, the pelvis is strategically located. Linking the trunk with the lower extremities, it must cooperate with the motion of each, yet at the same time, contribute to the stability of the total structure. When the body is in the erect standing position, the pelvis receives the weight of the head, trunk and upper extremities, divides it equally, and transmits it to the two lower extremities. When, for any reason, the individual decides to stand on one foot, the pelvis adapts itself to this position and transmits the entire weight of the upper part of the body to one of the lower extremities. It requires a fine adjustment to do this in such a way that the balance of the total structure is maintained.

The pelvis depends upon the joints of the lower spine and the hips for its movements. Hence it is not surprising that its motion sometimes seems to be associated with the motion of the trunk or spine, and sometimes with that of the thighs. In such cases the movement of the pelvis may be said to be secondary to that of the spine, or of the thighs, as the case may be. In fact, most of its motion belongs in one or the other category. Occasionally, however, the movement seems to be initiated in the pelvis itself, with the spine and thighs cooperating with it. In such an event, the movement of the pelvis might be considered primary, and that of the spine and hips, secondary. One sees this type of movement when the individual "tucks his hips under" or makes other postural adjustments (see Fig. 122, *B*).

It is not always easy to judge the habitual tilt of the pelvis from the contours of the body. Prominent buttocks, heavy layers of fat or an unusually convex sacrum (see Fig. 41, *B*) can easily mislead the observer. Figure 123 shows a sketch based on an x-ray which illustrates a type of build in which the contour of the lower back and pelvic region does not correspond to the bony structure. In this illustration the tilt, as judged by the position of the sacrum, is greater than it appears to be from the contour of the lower back. This observation is of importance to those who tend to place emphasis on the position of the pelvis in giving posture instruction.

The joint analysis of the primary movements of the pelvis, as performed when the person is in the fundamental standing position, is given below.

A movement of the pelvis which is secondary to the movement of the lower extremity is seen, for instance, in a high kick. In activities such as this the pelvis seems to move with the lower extremity for the purpose of increasing the latter's range of motion. Hence, when the thigh is flexed at the hip joint, the pelvic inclination is decreased; when the lower extremity is raised backward in apparent hyperextension, the pelvic inclination is increased; when one thigh is widely abducted, the pelvis tilts laterally; and when one leg is placed forward and the other backward as though taking a long stride, the pelvis rotates in the horizontal plane about a vertical axis.

Pelvic movements are secondary to movements of the spine when the latter are performed through the full range of motion. Thus complete flexion of the spine necessitates a decrease in the pelvic inclination; complete hyperextension necessitates an increased inclination; complete lateral flexion necessitates a lateral tilt; complete spinal rotation necessitates horizontal rotation of the pelvis.

It has already been stated that the movements of the pelvic girdle take place at the lumbar spine, the lumbosacral junction and the hip joints. The exact combination of movements of these joints depends upon whether the motion of the pelvis is primary, whether it is secondary to movements of the lower extremity, or whether it is secondary to spinal movements.

Joint Analysis of Primary Movements of the Pelvis

Pelvis	*Spinal Joints*	*Hip Joints*
Increased tilt	Hyperextension	Slight flexion
Decreased tilt	Slight flexion	Complete extension
Lateral tilt to left	Slight lateral flexion right	R: Slight adduction L: Slight abduction

Rotation to left (without
turning the head or mov-
ing the feet)..........Rotation right................$\begin{cases} \text{R: Sl. outward rot.} \\ \text{L: Sl. inward rot.} \end{cases}$

Joint Analysis of Movements of the Pelvis Secondary to Those of the Spine

Spine	Pelvis
Flexion.......................................	Decreased tilt
Hyperextension...............................	Increased tilt
Lateral flexion to left...........................	Lateral tilt to left
Rotation to left................................	Rotation to left

All the muscles which attach to the pelvic bones or to the sacrum serve either to initiate or to control pelvic movements. As one would expect, these are all muscles either of the hip joint or of the spine.

Supplementary Material

Individual Variations in Structure.   Three aspects of the femur have been investigated from the point of view of structural variations. These are obliquity of the shaft, the angle formed by the neck and the shaft, known as the collodiaphysial angle, and torsion of the shaft. Such variations as these are of particular interest to the physical therapist and the teacher of corrective physical education because of their influence on locomotion. A knowledge of likely variations in structure will help to provide the teacher of body mechanics with a background for analyzing peculiar gaits. The teacher or therapist who is familiar with the types of variations likely to be seen will be more intelligent in prescribing corrective exercises. He will be more capable of judging the cause of a particular peculiarity of motion, whether it be a matter of habit, of muscular function or of bony structure.

In his study of 100 pairs of femurs, Ingalls included among his measurements the collodiaphysial angle and the angle of obliquity of the shaft. The former is the angle formed between the long axis of the shaft and the long axis of the neck. The obliquity of the shaft is the slant of the shaft from the vertical when the femur is held upright with both condyles supported squarely on a horizontal surface. It is measured in terms of the angle between the long axis of the shaft and the vertical. Ingalls' findings are recorded in Tables 6 and 7. Figure 124 depicts two femurs, representing the lower and upper limits of obliquity of the shaft. Figure 125 does the same for the angulation between the neck and shaft.

Elftman investigated the torsion of both the femur and the tibia in 35 male cadavers. It was his opinion that extremes at either end of the scale might well

Table 6. Measurements of the Collodiaphysial Angle (Ingalls) (N = 100 Pairs)

	Range	Mean	S.D.
Right...............	152.5°–109.5°	129.64° ± .452	6.701 ± .319
Left..................	145.0°–106.0°	127.10° ± .495	7.346 ± .350

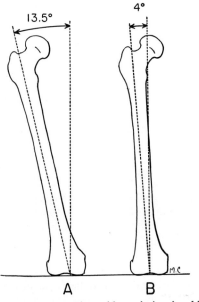

Figure 124. Two femurs illustrating wide variation in obliquity of shaft.

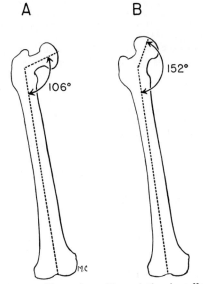

Figure 125. Two femurs illustrating wide variation in collodiaphysial angle.

*Table 7.   Measurements of the Obliquity of the Femoral Shaft
(Ingalls) (N = 100 Pairs)*

	Range	Mean	S.D.
Right....................	12.5°–4°	8.63° ± .118	1.758 ± .084
Left....................	13.5°–4°	8.70° ± .130	1.926 ± .092

*Table 8.   Measurements of Femoral and Tibial Torsion
(Elftman) (N = 35)*

	Range	Mean	S.D.
Femoral torsion.........	0°–26°	11.86°	6.21 ± 0.74
Tibial torsion..........	12°–44°	27.40°	7.40 ± 0.89

account for peculiarities of gait. The possibility of femoral or tibial torsion should be taken into consideration when judging exaggerated toeing-in or toeing-out gaits. The results of Elftman's findings are recorded in Table 8.

References to other investigations may be found in the bibliography at the end of this chapter.[5, 6, 8, 9]

Demonstrations and Laboratory Exercises

Joint Structure and Function

1. Take a pelvic bone and a femur and "construct" a hip joint, using felt for the fibrocartilage and adhesive tape for the ligaments. Be as accurate as possible in the attachments of these structures. It is suggested that two or three students work together on this project.

2. Using a form like the one on page 150, record the essential information regarding the hip joint. Study the movements both on the skeleton and on the living body.

3. Using a Lufkin rule or a protractor type of goniometer, measure the range of motion in the following joint movements on five different subjects:

   a. Hip flexion, with straight knee.

   b. Hip flexion, with flexed knee.

   c. Total abduction of both thighs.

Muscular Action

Identify as many muscles as possible in the following experiments.

4. Hip flexion

   a. *Subject:* Sit on table with legs hanging over edge. Raise thigh.

   Assistant: Resist movement slightly by pressing down on knee.

   Observer: Palpate pectineus, tensor fasciae latae, sartorius, rectus femoris and adductor longus. Does the gracilis contract?

   b. *Subject:* Lie on one side, rolled toward face. Flex thigh of top leg, allowing knee to flex passively.

   Assistant: Resist movement by pushing against knee.

   Observer: Palpate iliopsoas.

5. Hip extension

a. *Subject:* Stand facing table with trunk bent forward until it rests on table. Grasp sides of table. Raise one leg, keeping the knee straight.

Assistant: Resist movement by pushing down on thigh close to knee. Second time, give resistance at heel.

Observer: Palpate gluteus maximus, adductor magnus and hamstrings.

b. *Subject:* Lie face down on table and raise one leg with knee straight.

Assistant: Resist movement by pushing down on knee.

Observer: Palpate same muscles as in *a*.

6. Hip abduction

Subject: Lie on one side and raise top leg.

Assistant: Resist movement by pushing down on knee.

Observer: Palpate gluteus maximus, gluteus medius and tensor fasciae latae.

7. Hip adduction

Subject: Lie on one side with top leg raised; then lower it.

Assistant: Resist movement by pushing up on thigh from underneath.

Note: Unless resistance is applied, the action will be performed by means of the eccentric contraction of the abductors.

Observer: Palpate three adductors and name them.

CHECK LIST FOR MUSCULAR ANALYSIS OF MOVEMENTS OF THE PELVIC GIRDLE

	Increased Inclination	Decreased Inclination	Lateral Tilt	Rotation
Rectus abdominis				
External oblique				
Internal oblique				
Sacrospinalis				
Quadratus lumborum				
Psoas				
Gluteus maximus				
Gluteus medius and minimus				
Tensor fasciae latae				
Others:				

Note: Because of the numerous two-joint muscles found in the lower extremity, the check list for the muscular analysis of movements of the hip is combined with that for the knee. See page 248.

8. Outward rotation of thigh

Subject: Stand on one foot with the other knee bent at right angles so that the lower leg extends horizontally backward. Rotate the free thigh outward by swinging the lower leg medially.

Assistant: Steady subject's knee and resist movement of leg at ankle.

Observer: Palpate gluteus maximus.

9. Inward rotation of thigh

Subject: Stand on one foot with other knee bent at right angles so that the lower leg extends horizontally backward. Rotate the free thigh inward by swinging the lower leg laterally.

Assistant: Steady subject's knee and resist movement of leg at ankle.

Observer: Palpate gluteus medius, tensor fasciae latae and lower adductor magnus.

10. Decrease of pelvic inclination

Subject: Lie on back with knees drawn up and feet resting on floor. Tilt pelvis in such a manner that lumbar spine becomes flatter.

Assistant: Kneeling at subject's head and facing his feet, place thumbs on his anterior superior iliac spines, and fingers under his lower back. Resist movement by pushing iliac spines toward subject's feet.

Observer: Palpate rectus abdominis and gluteus maximus. Do the hamstrings contract?

11. Increase of pelvic inclination

Subject: In erect standing position, stiffen knees, and push buttocks as far to the rear as possible.

Observer: Palpate tensor fasciae latae, sartorius, pectineus and iliocostalis. Does the adductor longus or gracilis contract?

12. Lateral tilt of pelvis

Subject: Stand on stool on one foot, with other leg hanging free. Pull free hip up as far as possible.

Assistant: Give slight resistance by holding ankle down.

Observer: Palpate oblique abdominals, iliocostalis, adductor magnus, adductor longus and gracilis on side of free leg.

Bibliography

Kinesiology

1. Bowen, W. P., and Stone, H. A.: Applied Anatomy and Kinesiology, 7th ed. Philadelphia, Lea & Febiger, 1953.
2. Duvall, E. N.: Kinesiology; The Anatomy of Motion. Englewood Cliffs. N. J., Prentice-Hall, 1959.
3. Steindler, A.: Kinesiology of the Human Body. Springfield, Ill., Charles C Thomas, 1955.
4. Wright, W. G.: Muscle Function. New York, Hoeber, 1928.

Structural Variations

5. Boynton, B.: Individual Differences in the Structure of Pelvis and Lumbar Spine as a Factor in Body Mechanics. Thesis, State University of Iowa, 1934.
6. Brown, L. T.: The Mechanics of the Lumbosacral and Sacroiliac Joints. J. Bone & Joint Surg., *19:* 770–775, 1937.
7. Elftman, H.: Torsion of the Lower Extremity. Am. J. Phys. Anthropology, *3* (new series): 255–265, 1945.
8. Frost, R. B.: Individual Differences in the Structure of Pelves as Shown by Lateral X-Rays. Thesis, State University of Iowa, 1938.

9. Howland, I. S.: A Study of the Position of the Sacrum in the Adult Female Pelvis and Its Relationship to Body Mechanics. Thesis, State University of Iowa, 1933.
10. Ingalls, N. W.: Studies on the Femur. Am. J. Phys. Anthropology, 7: 207–255, 1924.

Range of Motion

11. Boscoe, A. R.: The Range of Active Abduction and Lateral Rotation at the Hip Joint of Men. J. Bone & Joint Surg., 14: 325–331, 1932.

11 · The Lower Extremity: The Knee Joint

THE KNEE JOINT is a masterpiece of anatomic engineering. Placed midway in each supporting column of the body, it is subject to severe stresses and strains in its combined functions of weight-bearing and locomotion. As Steindler has pointed out, it meets the requirements made of it with remarkable efficiency. To take care of the weight-bearing stresses it has massive condyles; to facilitate locomotion it has a wide range of motion; to resist the lateral stresses due to the tremendous lever effect of the long femur and tibia, it is reinforced at the sides by strong ligaments; to combat the downward pull of gravity and to meet the demands of such violent locomotor activities as running and jumping, it is provided with powerful musculature. It would be difficult, indeed, to find a mechanism better adapted for meeting the combined requirements of stability and mobility than the knee joint.

In this connection, however, mention should be made of two forms of malalignment at the knee joint, one of which is common. These are the conditions popularly known as "knock-knees" and "bowlegs." In "knock-knees" (genu valgum) the knees are nearer the midline of the body than is normal. In the standing position the knees will be closer together than the feet. When the feet are brought side by side, either the knees will be tightly pressed together or one will have to be placed behind the other. Mechanically, the condition means that the weight-bearing line of the lower extremity passes lateral to the center of the knee joint. This puts the medial ligament (tibial collateral) under increased tension and subjects the lateral meniscus to increased pressure and friction. Such a joint is an unstable one. Not only is it more prone to injury than is the well-aligned joint, but in all weight-bearing positions it means that postural strains are constantly present. The condition of "bowlegs" (genu varum) is just the reverse of "knock-knees," with the additional complication of involvement of the long bones themselves.

Structure.   Although the knee is classified as a hinge joint, its bony structure resembles that of two ovoid or condyloid joints lying side by side. The lateral flexion which is permitted in a single ovoid joint is not possible in the knee joint because of the presence of the second condyle. The two rocker-like condyles of the femur rest on the two slightly concave areas on the top of the tibia's broad head (Fig. 126). These articular surfaces of the tibia are separated by a roughened area, called the intercondyloid eminence, which terminates both anteriorly and posteriorly in a slight hollow, but rises at the center to form two small tubercles not unlike miniature twin mountain peaks (Fig. 127). The medial articular surface is oval; the lateral is smaller and more nearly round. Each is overlaid by a somewhat crescent-shaped fibrocartilage, known as a semilunar cartilage or meniscus.

The lower end of the femur terminates in the two rocker-like condyles already mentioned. The lateral condyle is broader and more prominent than the medial. The medial condyle projects downward further than the lateral. This, however, is only evident

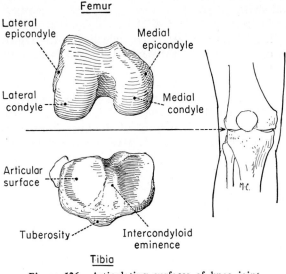

Figure 126. Articulating surfaces of knee joint.

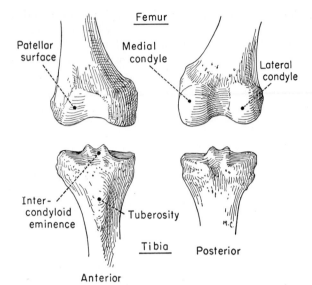

Figure 127. Anterior and posterior views of bones of knee joint.

when a disarticulated femur is held vertically. In its normal position in the body the femur slants inward from above downward. This slant is known as the obliquity of the femoral shaft (see p. 203). Observation of the mounted skeleton will show that the downward projection of the medial condyle compensates for the obliquity of the femoral shaft.

Another interesting feature of the condyles is that they are not quite parallel. While the lateral condyle lies in the sagittal plane, the medial condyle slants slightly medially from front to back. This is an important factor in the movements of the knee.

Anteriorly, the two condyles are continuous with the smooth, slightly concave surface of the patellar facet for the articulation of the patella. The patella, or knee cap, is a large sesamoid bone located slightly above and in front of the knee joint. It is held in place by the quadriceps tendon above, by the patellar ligament below, and by the intervening fibers which form a pocket for the patella (Fig. 128).

The articular cavity is inclosed within a loose membranous capsule which lies under the patella and folds around each condyle, but which excludes the intercondyloid tubercles and the cruciate ligaments. It is supplemented by expansions from the fascia lata, iliotibial band and various tendons. The oblique popliteal ligament covers the posterior surface of the joint completely, shielding the cruciate ligaments and other structures not inclosed within the capsule (Fig. 129).

The synovial membrane of the knee joint is the most extensive of any in the body. It folds in and around the joint in a manner far too complicated to attempt to describe here. There are numerous bursae in the vicinity of the knee joint, among the largest and most important being the prepatellar, infrapatellar and suprapatellar bursae.

The Semilunar Cartilages (Fig. 130).   These cartilages, or menisci as they are called, are somewhat circular rims of fibrocartilage, situated on the articular surfaces of the head of the tibia. They are relatively thick at their peripheral borders, tapering

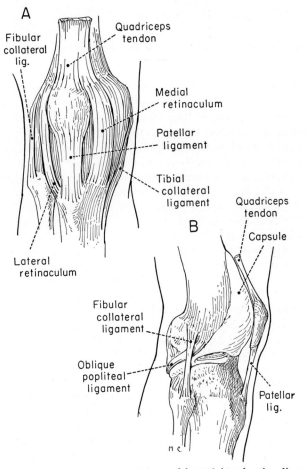

Figure 128.   Anterior and lateral views of knee joint showing ligaments.

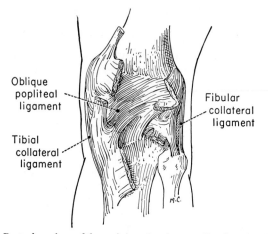

Figure 129. Posterior view of knee joint showing popliteal and collateral ligaments.

toward their inner circumferences to a thin edge. Thus they deepen the articular facets of the tibia and, at the same time, serve in a shock absorption capacity. The inner edges are free, but the peripheral borders are attached loosely to the head of the tibia.

The lateral semilunar cartilage forms an incomplete circle, conforming closely to the nearly round articular facet. Its anterior and posterior horns, which almost meet at the center of the joint, are attached to the intercondyloid eminence.

The medial cartilage is shaped like a large letter C, broader toward the rear than in front. Its anterior horn tapers off to a thin strand which is attached to the anterior intercondyloid fossa. It is not so freely movable as the lateral cartilage, one reason for this being its secure anchorage to the tibial collateral ligament at the medial side of the knee. Largely because of this point of attachment, the medial cartilage is more frequently injured than the lateral. One of the most common injuries is caused either by a sudden twist or a lateral blow when the knee is bearing weight in a flexed position. In either case the tibial collateral ligament is wrenched, and instead of pulling loose from the medial cartilage, it pulls the medial cartilage loose from the head of the tibia. Once the cartilage is loose, it tends to slip around and get jammed in the joint, making it impossible to extend the knee completely. The usual remedy for this type of injury is removal of the meniscus. Surprisingly enough, the joint loses little of its usefulness when this is done.

Ligaments. *Patellar Ligament* (Fig. 128). This is a strong flat ligament connecting the lower margin of the patella with the tuberosity of the tibia. The superficial fibers, passing over the front of the patella, are continuations of the central fibers of the quadriceps femoris tendon.

Tibial Collateral Ligament (Figs. 128, *A*, 129 and 131). This is a broad, flat, membranous band on the medial side of the joint. It is attached above to the medial epicondyle of the femur below the adductor tubercle, and below, to the medial condyle of the tibia. It is firmly attached to the medial meniscus. This fact should be noted because of its significance in knee injuries. It serves to check extension and to prevent motion laterally.

Fibular Collateral Ligament (Figs. 128, 129 and 131). This is a strong, rounded cord, attached above to the back of the lateral epicondyle of the femur, and below, to the lateral surface of the head of the fibula. It serves to check extension and to prevent motion medially.

Oblique Popliteal Ligament (Figs. 128, *B,* and 129). This is a broad, flat ligament, covering the back of the knee joint. It is attached above to the upper margin of the intercondyloid fossa and posterior surface of the femur, and below, to the posterior margin of the head of the tibia. Medially, it blends with the tendon of the semimembranosus muscle, and laterally with the lateral head of the gastrocnemius.

The Cruciate Ligaments (Fig. 131). These are two strong, cordlike ligaments situated within the knee joint, although not inclosed within the joint capsule. They are called cruciate from the fact that they cross each other, and are further designated anterior and posterior, according to their attachments to the tibia. They serve to check certain movements at the knee joint. They limit ex-

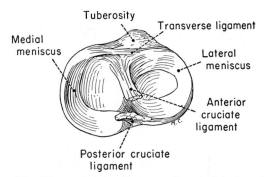

Figure 130. The menisci (semilunar cartilages) of the knee joint.

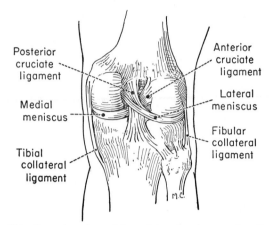

Posterior cruciate ligament

Medial meniscus

Tibial collateral ligament

Anterior cruciate ligament

Lateral meniscus

Fibular collateral ligament

Figure 131. Posterior view of knee joint showing cruciate ligaments.

tension and prevent rotation in the extended position. They also check the forward and backward sliding of the femur on the tibia, thus safeguarding the anteroposterior stability of the knee.

Anterior Cruciate Ligament (Fig. 131).   This passes upward and backward from the anterior intercondyloid fossa of the tibia to the back part of the medial surface of the lateral condyle of the femur.

Posterior Cruciate Ligament (Fig. 131).   This is a shorter and stronger ligament than the anterior. It passes upward and forward from the posterior intercondyloid fossa of the tibia to the lateral and front part of the medial condyle of the femur.

Coronary Ligaments.   These are fibers from the inner surface of the capsule, connecting the outer circumference of each meniscus to the corresponding margin of the tibial head.

Transverse Ligament (Fig. 130).   This is a short, slender cordlike ligament, connecting the anterior convex margin of the lateral meniscus to the anterior end of the medial meniscus.

Movements.   The movements which occur at the knee joint are primarily flexion and extension. A slight amount of rotation can take place when the knee is in the flexed position.

Flexion and Extension.   The movements of flexion and extension at the knee are not so simple as are those of a true hinge joint. This can be demonstrated in the classroom by holding a disarticulated femur and tibia together in a position of extension, then, holding the tibia stationary, flexing the femur on the tibia as though the individual were assuming a squat or sitting position. If no other adjustment is made, the femoral condyles will roll back completely off the top of the tibia. What prevents this in real life is the fact that as the condyles roll backward they simultaneously glide forward, and thus remain in contact with the menisci throughout each phase of the movement. Conversely, when the femur extends on the tibia, the forward roll of the femoral condyles is accompanied by a backward glide.

Because the femoral condyles are not quite parallel, and differ in size, a slight degree of rotation occurs during the initial phase of flexion and the final phase of extension. This can be readily seen on the living subject if he stands with the knees slightly flexed and then extends them completely. The patellae are seen to turn slightly medialward, indicating slight inward rotation of the thighs. Because of the inequality of the two condyles, the medial condyle continues to roll forward after the lateral condyle has ceased its movement. The inward rotation of the femur which accompanies the completion of extension is commonly known as "locking" the knees. In persons who tend to hyperextend their knees habitually the rotation is more pronounced.

When the leg is flexed or extended in a non-weight-bearing position, the tibia rotates on the femur, instead of vice versa. The final phase of extension is accompanied by slight outward rotation of the tibia. At the beginning of flexion the tibia rotates inward until the mid-position is attained.[4]

The rotation which occurs in the final phase of extension and the initial phase of flexion is an inherent part of these movements and should not be confused with the voluntary rotation that can be performed when the leg is not bearing weight and the knee is in a flexed position.

Inward and Outward Rotation in the Flexed Position. When the leg has been flexed at the knee to a right angle and beyond, it is possible to rotate the leg on the thigh through a total range of about 50 degrees. This can occur, however, only when the leg is not bearing the body weight. It would be impossible, for instance, to rotate the leg (or the thigh, either, for that matter) when in a stooping position. A good way to demonstrate rotation of the tibia is to sit on a chair with the heel resting lightly on the floor. In this position, with the knee and thigh held motionless, the foot should be turned first in and then out. The action will be that of inward and outward rotation of the tibia. The movement taking place within the foot itself should be discounted.

Muscles. The muscles acting on the knee joint are listed below according to whether their distal tendons lie anterior or posterior to the transverse axis of the joint.

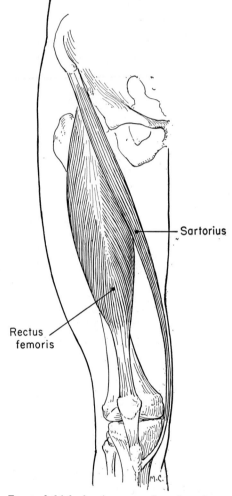

Figure 132. Front of thigh showing rectus femoris and sartorius muscles.

Anterior:
  Rectus femoris
  Vastus intermedius
  Vastus lateralis
  Vastus medialis

Posterior:
  Biceps femoris
  Semimembranosus
  Semitendinosus
  Sartorius
  Gracilis
  Popliteus
  Gastrocnemius

Rectus Femoris (see also muscles of the hip) (Fig. 132)

PROXIMAL ATTACHMENTS. (O)   Anterior inferior iliac spine and groove above brim of acetabulum.

DISTAL ATTACHMENT. (I)   Base of patella, as part of the quadriceps femoris tendon. It may be said to attach indirectly to the tuberosity of the tibia by means of the patellar ligament.

NERVE SUPPLY.   Femoral.

ACTION (AT KNEE).   Extension.

WHERE TO PALPATE.   Anterior surface of thigh.

The Three Vasti (Vastus Lateralis, Vastus Intermedius, Vastus Medialis) (Fig. 133)

PROXIMAL ATTACHMENT (O):

Vastus Lateralis: Upper part of intertrochanteric line; ante-

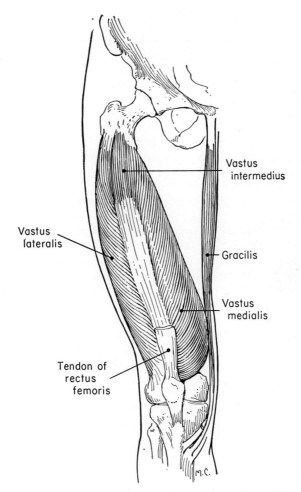

Figure 133. Front of thigh showing the three vasti muscles and the gracilis.

rior and lower borders of greater trochanter; lateral lip of gluteal tuberosity and upper half of linea aspera.

Vastus Intermedius: Anterior and lateral surfaces of upper two thirds of shaft of femur.

Vastus Medialis: Lower half of intertrochanteric line; medial lip of linea aspera; and upper part of medial supracondylar line.

DISTAL ATTACHMENT. (I) The tendons of the three vasti muscles unite with that of rectus femoris to form the quadriceps femoris tendon. This attaches to the base of the patella, and indirectly, by means of the patellar ligament, to the tuberosity of the tibia.

NERVE SUPPLY. Femoral.

ACTION. Extension.

WHERE TO PALPATE. Vastus lateralis may be palpated on the anterolateral aspect of the thigh, lateral to the rectus femoris, and vastus medialis on the anteromedial aspect of the lower third of the thigh, medial to the rectus femoris. Vastus intermedius cannot be palpated.

COMMENTS ON THE QUADRICEPS FEMORIS. The rectus femoris, situated on the front of the thigh, is the most superficial of the quadriceps group and is the only one of the four which also acts at the hip joint. The special characteristics of two-joint muscles are discussed on page 33. According to Wright, the rectus femoris also serves as an anterior ligament of the hip.

The vastus lateralis and vastus medialis are superficially located except for the anterior portions, which are covered by the rectus femoris. The vastus intermedius lies beneath the rectus and is completely covered by it. The three vasti muscles, with their fibers converging toward the patella, serve to steady the knee joint in all weight-bearing positions and to maintain a balanced tension on the patella. Being one-joint muscles, the vasti are powerful knee extensors, regardless of the position of the hip joint.

Static contraction of the quadriceps femoris muscles, when the knee is fully extended, serves to pull up or "set" the patella.

Biceps Femoris (see also muscles of the hip) (Fig. 134)

PROXIMAL ATTACHMENTS. (o) Long head: Lower and medial impression on tuberosity of ischium.

Short head: Lateral lip of linea aspera.

DISTAL ATTACHMENTS. (I) Lateral side of head of fibula and lateral condyle of tibia.

NERVE SUPPLY. Sciatic.

ACTION (AT KNEE). Flexion of leg at knee; outward rotation of tibia when knee is in flexed position.

WHERE TO PALPATE. Lateral aspect of posterior surface of knee.

COMMENTS. This is the outer hamstring muscle.

Semimembranosus (see also muscles of the hip) (Fig. 134)

PROXIMAL ATTACHMENT. (O) Upper and lateral impression on tuberosity of ischium.

DISTAL ATTACHMENT. (I) Horizontal groove on posterior surface of medial condyle of tibia.

NERVE SUPPLY. Sciatic.

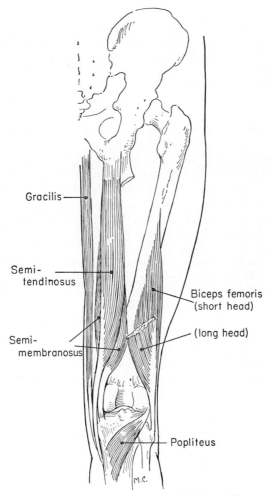

Figure 134. Posterior muscles of thigh and knee.

ACTION (AT KNEE).   Flexion of leg at knee; inward rotation of tibia when knee is in flexed position.

WHERE TO PALPATE.   The tendon lies beneath the tendons of gracilis and semitendinosus at the knee, and is difficult to identify.

COMMENTS.   This is one of the two inner hamstring muscles.

Semitendinosus (see also muscles of the hip) (Fig. 134)

PROXIMAL ATTACHMENT. (O)   Lower and medial impression on tuberosity of ischium, together with biceps femoris.

DISTAL ATTACHMENT. (I)   Upper part of medial surface of shaft of tibia.

NERVE SUPPLY.   Sciatic.

ACTION (AT KNEE).   Flexion of leg at knee; inward rotation of tibia when knee is in flexed position.

WHERE TO PALPATE.   Medial aspect of posterior surface of knee. It is the most posterior of the two small tendons which can be felt in this region.

COMMENTS.   This is one of the two inner hamstring muscles.

COMMENTS ON THE HAMSTRINGS.   The hamstrings, so named from their large, cordlike tendons behind the knee joint, consist of the biceps femoris, semimembranosus and semitendinosus muscles. Although the biceps femoris constitutes the lateral hamstring, its long head lies approximately along the midline of the posterior aspect of the thigh, as far down as the popliteal space. About this level the two heads unite to form their common tendon of attachment. The long head is fusiform in construction; the short head, penniform.

The semimembranosus and semitendinosus constitute the medial hamstrings. The former lies deeper than the latter and attaches higher on the tibia. The semitendinosus is attached to the medial surface of the tibia below the head, just below the attachment of the gracilis and behind that of the sartorius. Few writers mention any difference in the actions of these two muscles, but Bowen stated that the semimembranosus has more powerful action at the hip than does the semitendinosus.

Although the hamstrings act at both the knees and the hips, their primary function is knee flexion. Wright called attention to the usefulness of the hamstrings in preventing hyperextension at the knee, and in unlocking the knee (i.e., reducing hyperextension) when one is returning from a position in which the line of gravity falls in front of the knee joints (e.g., inclining the trunk forward without bending the knees). Nearly everyone is familiar with the limiting effect of the hamstrings. The difficulty experienced by most people in touching the toes with the fingers without bending the knees, and in sitting erect on the floor with the legs extended straight forward, is due to the fact that the hamstrings are frequently not long enough to permit such extreme stretching at the hips and knees simultaneously.

Sartorius (see also muscles of the hip) (Fig. 132)

PROXIMAL ATTACHMENT. (o)   Anterior superior iliac spine and upper half of notch below it.

DISTAL ATTACHMENT. (i)   Anterior and medial surface of tibia just below condyle.

NERVE SUPPLY.   Femoral.

ACTION (AT KNEE).   Flexion of leg at knee; assists in inward rotation of tibia when knee is flexed.

WHERE TO PALPATE.   At the anterior superior iliac spine. The entire muscle may be seen and palpated on the front of the thigh in a slender subject.

COMMENTS.   This superficial, ribbon-like muscle runs obliquely downward and medialward across the front of the thigh. On its way to its distal attachment, however, it curves around behind the bulge of the medial condyles in such a way that its line of pull is posterior to the axis of the knee joint. Thus, in spite of the fact that at least two thirds of the muscle—including its proximal and distal attachments—lie on the anterior aspect of the lower extremity, its action at the knee joint is not extension, but flexion.

Gracilis (see also muscles of the hip) (Figs. 133 and 134)

PROXIMAL ATTACHMENT. (o)   Anterior aspect of lower half of symphysis pubis and upper half of pubic arch.

DISTAL ATTACHMENT. (i)   Medial surface of tibia just below condyle.

NERVE SUPPLY.   Obturator.

ACTION (AT KNEE).   Flexion of leg at knee; assists in inward rotation of tibia when knee is in flexed position.

WHERE TO PALPATE.   Medial aspect of posterior surface of knee, anterior to the semitendinosus tendon, but close to it.

COMMENTS.   This is a long slender muscle situated on the medial side of the thigh.

Popliteus (Fig. 134)

PROXIMAL ATTACHMENT. (o)   Lateral surface of lateral condyle of femur.

DISTAL ATTACHMENT. (i)   Posterior surface of tibia, above popliteal line.

NERVE SUPPLY.   Tibial.

ACTION.   Inward rotation of tibia; assists in flexion of leg at knee.

Cannot be palpated.

COMMENTS.   This muscle is the "pronator teres" of the leg. It is similar to the latter muscle in structure, in its relation to the joint, and in function.

Gastrocnemius (see also muscles of the ankle) (Fig. 145)

PROXIMAL ATTACHMENTS.   (O)   Posterior surface of each femoral condyle and adjacent parts, by two separate heads.

DISTAL ATTACHMENT.   (I)   Posterior surface of calcaneus by means of calcaneal tendon (tendon of Achilles).

NERVE SUPPLY.   Tibial.

ACTION (AT KNEE).   Assists in flexion of leg at knee.

WHERE TO PALPATE.   Calf of leg and back of ankle.

COMMENTS.   Although this is primarily a muscle of the ankle joint, it is mentioned here because of its relation to the knee joint. As Wright pointed out, more important than its ability to help flex the leg at the knee joint is its function as a posterior ligament to protect the joint in movements of violent extension, such as running and jumping.

Muscular Analysis of the Fundamental Movements of the Leg at the Knee

Flexion

Movers
- Principal . . . .
  - Hamstrings (biceps femoris, semitendinosus, semimembranosus)
  - Sartorius
  - Gracilis
- Assistant . . . .
  - Popliteus
  - Gastrocnemius

Neutralizers . . . . The biceps femoris on the one hand, and the semimembranous, semitendinosus and popliteus on the other, neutralize one another's rotatory tendencies

Stabilizers . . . . The hip flexors help to stabilize the thigh against the pull of the hamstrings

Extension

Movers . . . . Quadriceps femoris

Neutralizers and Stabilizers . . . . The vastus lateralis and vastus medialis neutralize one another's lateral and medial components of force, thus steadying the knee. The hip extensors help to stabilize the thigh against the pull of the rectus femoris

Outward Rotation of Flexed Leg at Knee

Mover...........................Biceps femoris

Neutralizers......................The quadriceps femoris checks further
flexion if it is not desired

Stabilizers........................Hip adductors

Inward Rotation of Flexed Leg at Knee

Movers.........
- Principal.........
  - Semitendinosus
  - Semimembranosus
  - Popliteus
- Assistant.........
  - Gracilis
  - Sartorius

Neutralizers......................The quadriceps femoris checks further
flexion if it is not desired

Stabilizers........................Hip abductors

Demonstrations and Laboratory Exercises

Joint Structure and Function

1. Take a femur and a tibia and "construct" a knee joint, using felt for the fibrocartilage and adhesive tape for the ligaments. Be accurate in attaching these structures. It is suggested that two or three students work together on this project.

2. Using a form like that on page 150, record the essential information regarding the knee joint. Study the movements both on the skeleton and on the living body.

Muscular Action

3. Flexion at knee
Subject: Lie face down and flex leg at knee by raising foot.
Assistant: Steady subject's thigh and resist movement by pushing down on ankle.
Observer: Palpate biceps femoris, semitendinosus, gracilis, sartorius and gastrocnemius.

4. Extension at knee
a. *Subject:* Rise from a squat position.
Observer: Palpate quadriceps femoris.
b. *Subject:* Sit on table with legs hanging over edge. Extend leg.
Assistant: Steady subject's thigh and resist movement by holding ankle down.
Observer: Palpate quadriceps femoris.

5. Outward rotation of leg with knee in flexed position
Subject: Sit on edge of table with legs hanging over. Turn foot laterally as far as possible without moving thigh.
Assistant: Steady subject's thigh and give slight resistance by holding foot.
Observer: Palpate biceps femoris.

6. Inward rotation of leg with knee in flexed position
Subject: Sit on edge of table with legs hanging over. Turn foot medially as far as possible without moving thigh.
Assistant: Steady subject's thigh and give slight resistance by holding foot.
Observer: Palpate semitendinosus, gracilis and sartorius.

CHECK LIST FOR MUSCULAR ANALYSIS OF MOVEMENTS
OF THE THIGH AND LEG

| | Hip | | | | | | Knee | | | |
	Flex.	Ext.	Abd.	Add.	Out. Rot.	Inwd. Rot.	Flex.	Ext.	Out. Rot.	Inwd. Rot.
Iliopsoas										
Sartorius										
Pectineus										
Tensor fasciae latae										
Gluteus maximus										
Gluteus medius										
Gluteus minimus										
Six deep rotators										
Adductor magnus										
Adductor longus										
Adductor brevis										
Gracilis										
Biceps femoris										
Semitendinosus										
Semimembranosus										
Rectus femoris										
Vastus intermedius										
Vastus lateralis										
Vastus medialis										
Popliteus										
Gastrocnemius										

Bibliography

1. Bowen, W. P., and Stone, H. A.: Applied Anatomy and Kinesiology, 7th ed. Philadelphia, Lea & Febiger, 1953.
2. Duvall, E. N.: Kinesiology; The Anatomy of Motion. Englewood Cliffs, N. J., Prentice-Hall, 1959.

3. Markee, J. E., et al.: Two-Joint Muscles of the Thigh. J. Bone & Joint Surg., *37A:* 125–142, 1955.
4. Morris' Human Anatomy. 11th ed. New York, McGraw-Hill Book Company, Inc., 1953.
5. Steindler, A.: Kinesiology of the Human Body. Springfield, Ill., Charles C Thomas, 1955.
6. Wright, W. G.: Muscle Function. New York, Hoeber, 1928.

12 · The Lower Extremity: The Ankle and Foot

The foot has two functions of tremendous importance—support and propulsion. In studying the structure of the foot, these functions should be kept constantly in mind, for only by seeing the foot in terms of the combined static and dynamic demands made upon it can one fully appreciate its intricate mechanism.

The foot is united with the leg at the ankle joint. Within the foot itself are the seven tarsal bones. Two of the joints in this region are of sufficient importance to the kinesiologist to merit special description. These are the subtalar and the midtarsal joints, the latter including the talonavicular and calcaneocuboid articulations. The movements within the foot occur mainly at these two joints.

The structure of the ankle, the tarsal joints and the toes will be described separately, but the muscles of these three regions will be discussed together, since many of them act on more than one joint.

Structure of the Ankle (Figs. 135, 136 and 137).   The ankle is a hinge joint. It is formed by the articulation of the talus (astragalus) with the malleoli of the tibia and the fibula. The latter bones, bound together by the transverse tibiofibular ligament, the anterior and posterior ligaments of the lateral malleolus, and the interossei, constitute a mortise into which the upper, rounded portion of the talus fits. The joint is surrounded by a thin, membranous capsule which is thicker on the medial side of the joint. In the back it is a thin mesh of membranous tissue. It is not continuous like most capsules. It is reinforced by several strong ligaments.

Ligaments.   *Medial: Deltoid* (Fig. 136).   This is a triangular ligament which is attached by its apex to the medial malleolus and which radiates downward to a broad attachment. It consists of four bands. The posterior band, or posterior talotibial ligament, slants backward to its attachment on the talus. The posterior-middle band, or calcaneotibial ligament, passes downward to the sustentaculum tali, the little shelflike projection on the medial side of the calcaneus. The anterior-middle band, or tibionavicular ligament, passes downward and slightly forward to the navicular bone and the calcaneonavicular ligament. The short anterior band, or anterior talotibial ligament, comes from the anterior margin of the malleolus and is attached below to the front of the talus close to the joint. The deltoid ligament is a strong mass of fibers for protecting the medial side of the ankle joint.

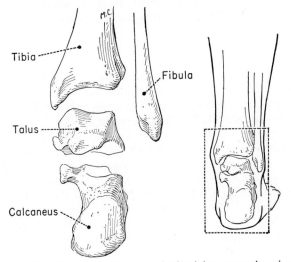

Figure 135. Bones of ankle and subtalar joints, posterior view.

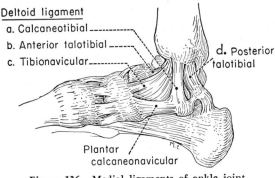

Figure 136. Medial ligaments of ankle joint.

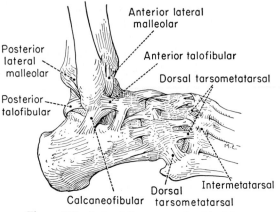

Figure 137.   Lateral ligaments of ankle joint.

Lateral (Fig. 137).   There are three ligaments on the lateral side of the joint, the calcaneofibular and the anterior and posterior talofibular. All are attached above to the lateral malleolus. The anterior talofibular ligament is a short flat band which crosses in front of the talofibular articulation to attach to the front of the talus. The calcaneofibular is a strong, cordlike ligament, coming from the tip of the lateral malleolus and passing downward and slightly backward to its attachment on the lateral surface of the calcaneus. The posterior talofibular ligament is a strong thick band which runs almost horizontally from the posterior margin of the lateral malleolus to a tubercle on the back of the talus.

Movements.   The movements of the ankle joint occur about an axis which is usually described as frontal-horizontal, but which is actually slightly oblique, as evidenced by the fact that the lateral malleolus is slightly posterior to the medial. This is of minor significance, but it explains the tendency of the foot to turn out when it is fully elevated, and to turn in when fully depressed.

Dorsal Flexion (Flexion).   A forward-upward movement of the foot in the sagittal plane, so that the dorsal surface of the foot approaches the anterior surface of the leg.

Plantar Flexion (Extension).   A forward-downward movement of the foot in the sagittal plane, so that the dorsal surface of the foot moves away from the anterior surface of the leg.

Structure of the Foot (Figs. 138 and 139).   The foot is made up of seven tarsal bones, five metatarsals and fourteen phalanges. The most posterior of the tarsals is the calcaneus, or heel bone. The knobby, irregular-shaped talus sits above and partly medial to it. It is supported medially by the shelflike projection of the calcaneus, called the sustentaculum tali. The navicular (scaphoid) is anterior to the talus, and the cuboid projects further forward than does the navicular. On the medial side of its anterior portion and in front of the navicular, the three cuneiform bones lie side by side. The first metatarsal articulates with the first cuneiform, the second metatarsal with the second cuneiform, the third metatarsal with the third cuneiform, and the fourth and fifth metatarsals with the cuboid. The phalanges are somewhat similar to those of the thumb and fingers, there being two in the great toe and three in each of the four lesser toes.

The foot as a whole is usually described as an elastic arched structure, the keystone of the arch being the talus. This bone has several marks of distinction. Aside from being the connecting link between the foot and the leg, it is distinguished by having no muscles attached to it and by receiving and transmitting the weight of the entire body (with the exception of the foot itself), a function which requires great strength and firm support.

The foot has two arches, a longitudinal and a transverse. The longitudinal arch passes from the heel to the heads of the five metatarsals. It is sometimes described as being made up of an inner and

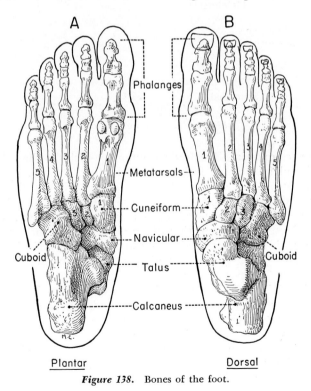

Figure 138. Bones of the foot.

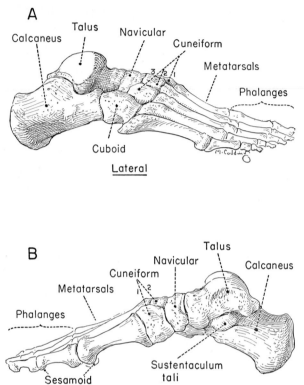

Figure 139. Bones of the foot.

an outer component. The outer component includes the calcaneus, cuboid and fourth and fifth metatarsals (Fig. 139, *A*). The inner component consists of the calcaneus, talus, navicular, three cuneiforms and the three medial metatarsals (Fig. 139, *B*). The outer component has a nearly flat contour and lacks mobility, hence is better adapted to the function of support, whereas the inner component, with its greater flexibility and its curving arch, is adapted to the function of shock absorption, so important in all forms of locomotion. Contrary to popular opinion, the height of the longitudinal arch is not indicative of the strength of the arch. Thus a low arch is not necessarily a weak one, *provided it is not associated with a pronated (i.e., abducted and everted) foot.*

The transverse arch is the side-to-side concavity on the under side of the foot formed by the anterior tarsal bones and the metatarsals. The anterior boundary of this arch, under the metatarsal heads, is known as the metatarsal arch. There is considerable controversy as to whether or not this should be called an arch, since, under the pressure of the body weight in standing and in walking, it flattens completely. The metatarsal arch exists, therefore, only in non-weight-bearing positions.

The toes, especially the large and powerful "big toe," constitute the mechanism for the function of propulsion. They provide the "push off" at the end of the step. Their use in locomotion is directly proportional to the vigor and speed of the walk or run.

The strength and elasticity of the foot are due in large measure to the ligaments which bind the bones together, and to the muscles which work to preserve the balance of the foot. Thus the ligaments and the muscles share the responsibility for maintaining the integrity of the arches.

The two tarsal joints to be considered here are the subtalar and the midtarsal.

Subtalar Joint. The subtalar joint consists of the articulation between the inferior surface of the talus bone with the superior and anterior surfaces of the calcaneus and the superior surface of the calcaneonavicular ligament. Ordinarily the point of contact between a bone and a ligament is not considered part of the articulation, but in this case it is, because of the presence of a cartilaginous articular facet which is lined with synovial membrane. The articulations are reinforced by the anterior, posterior, lateral and medial talocalcaneal ligaments and the talocalcaneal interosseus ligament (Fig. 140). They permit slight forward, backward and lateral gliding, also very slight inversion and eversion.

PLANTAR CALCANEONAVICULAR LIGAMENT (THE SPRING LIGAMENT) (Fig. 140). This ligament forms an inherent part of the subtalar joint. By connecting the sustentaculum tali of the calcaneus with the under side of the navicular, it forms a sling to give support to the talus. For the latter purpose it is covered with a fibrocartilaginous articular facet which has a smooth surface and is lined with synovial membrane. It is called the spring ligament because it contains yellow elastic fibers and has considerable elasticity. The importance of this can be readily seen when one remembers that the talus receives the weight of the entire body and is in turn supported largely by the spring ligament. The shock-absorption function of this arrangement is obvious. It is also fairly obvious that excessive prolonged pressure on this ligament (through improper use of the feet) will cause it to stretch permanently and will result in a lowered arch.

Midtarsal Joint (Transverse Tarsal; Chopart's). This consists of two articulations, the lateral one being the calcaneocuboid joint, and the medial one, the talonavicular. On looking down at these joints from above, the lateral one is seen to be convex to the rear

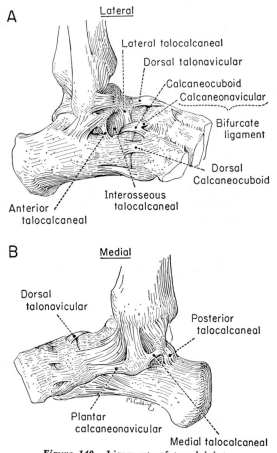

Figure 140. Ligaments of tarsal joints.

and the medial convex to the fore. The combined line of junction forms a horizontal letter S (Fig. 142). The talonavicular joint may be described as a shallow ball-and-socket joint, since it permits movements about three axes. The calcaneocuboid joint is non-axial, permitting only slight gliding motions. These would seem to be supplementary or secondary to the freer motions of the talonavicular joint. The movements of the midtarsal articulation, particularly of the talonavicular joint, are as follows:

Very slight dorsal and plantar flexion. These movements supplement dorsal and plantar flexion at the ankle joint.
Slight abduction and adduction of the front part of the foot on the rear part.
Very slight inversion and eversion of the front part of the foot on the rear.

LIGAMENTS OF THE MIDTARSAL JOINT (Figs. 140 and 141). The midtarsal joint is reinforced above by three dorsal ligaments—the dorsal talonavicular, the calcaneocuboidal part of the bifurcate ligament and the dorsal calcaneocuboid—and below by the long and short plantar ligaments. The short plantar ligament, also called the plantar calcaneocuboid, is a short, wide, thick ligament of great strength. It extends from the tubercle at the anterior end of the plantar surface of the calcaneus to the plantar surface of the cuboid behind the oblique ridge. The long plantar ligament is a longer, more superficial, but equally strong and dense band. It extends from the plantar surface of the calcaneus in front of the tuberosity to the oblique ridge on the plantar surface of the cuboid, with prolongations to the bases of the second, third, fourth and medial half of the fifth metatarsal bones.

The Tarsometatarsal Joints (Figs. 140 and 141). These are all non-axial joints, with the possible exception of the first, which presents a slightly saddle-shaped appearance. They are reinforced by the dorsal and plantar tarsometatarsal and the interosseous ligaments. The movements are of a gliding nature, resembling a restricted form of flexion, extension, abduction and adduction.

The Intermetatarsal Articulations (Figs. 137 and 141). These

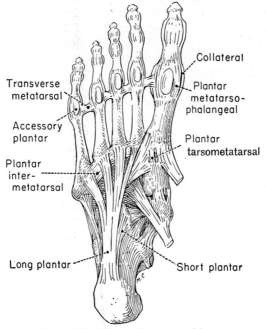

Figure 141. Plantar ligaments of foot.

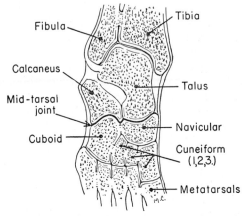

Figure 142. Oblique section of tarsal bones showing midtarsal joint.

include two sets of side-by-side articulations, those between the bases and those between the heads of the metatarsal bones. They are all non-axial joints, permitting only slight gliding movements. The bases of the metatarsals are united by the dorsal and plantar intermetatarsal and the interosseous ligaments. The heads of the metatarsals are connected by the transverse metatarsal ligament. The articulations between the heads of the metatarsal bones are an important part of the metatarsal arch. The total result of the movements occurring there is a spreading or flattening of the arch when the weight is on it, and a return to its plantar concavity when the weight is taken off it.

The Metatarsophalangeal Joints (Fig. 141).   These may best be described as a modified form of ovoid joints. They are reinforced by the dorsal and plantar metatarsophalangeal, and the collateral ligaments. The movements are flexion, extension, and limited abduction and adduction. The joint of the great toe differs somewhat from the corresponding joint in each of the four lesser toes. It is considerably larger than the others and it has two sesamoid bones under it in place of the plantar ligament.

The Interphalangeal Joints.   These are all hinge joints, permitting only flexion and extension. The ligaments reinforcing them are the dorsal and plantar interphalangeal and the collateral.

Summary of Movements of the Foot

Ankle Joint

Dorsal and plantar flexion (dorsal surface of foot moves toward and away from anterior surface of leg)

Tarsal Joints (especially subtalar and midtarsal)

Dorsal and plantar flexion (correspond to ankle joint movements)
Inversion and eversion (medial, lateral border of foot is raised)
Abduction and adduction (front part of foot bends laterally and medially)
Note: The terms "pronation" and "supination" of the feet represent composite movements, pronation being the combination of abduction and eversion; supination, the combination of adduction and inversion. Because of the structure of the joints, these movements always occur together in this manner.

Toes

Flexion and extension (toes curl under; toes straighten out)

Muscles.   The muscles of the ankle and foot, classified according to their location, are as follows:

Muscles on anterior aspect of leg:
  Tibialis anterior
  Extensor digitorum longus
  Extensor hallucis longus
  Peroneus tertius
Muscles on posterior aspect of leg:
  Gastrocnemius
  Soleus
  Tibialis posterior
  Flexor digitorum longus
  Flexor hallucis longus
Muscles on lateral aspect of leg:
  Peroneus longus
  Peroneus brevis

Intrinsic muscles of the foot:
  Extensor digitorum brevis
  Flexor digitorum brevis
  Quadratus plantae
  Lumbricales
  Abductor hallucis
  Flexor hallucis brevis
  Adductor hallucis
  Abductor digiti quinti
  Flexor digiti quinti brevis
  Opponens digiti quinti
  Dorsal interossei
  Plantar interossei

Tibialis Anterior (Fig. 143, *A*)

PROXIMAL ATTACHMENTS. (O)   Lateral condyle and upper two thirds of lateral surface of tibia.

DISTAL ATTACHMENTS. (I)   Plantar surface of base of first metatarsal and medial surface of first cuneiform.

NERVE SUPPLY.   Deep peroneal.

ACTION:

Ankle: Dorsal flexion.

Foot: Dorsal flexion; supination (adduction and inversion)

WHERE TO PALPATE.   Anterior surface of leg, just lateral to tibia.

COMMENTS.   About two thirds of the way down the leg the tibialis anterior becomes tendinous. The tendon crosses over to the medial side of the leg and passes in front of the malleolus on its way to the first cuneiform.

In his electromyographic study of the action of the leg muscles in movements of the free foot (the subject standing on the other foot), O'Connell found that dorsiflexion was initiated by the tibialis anterior.

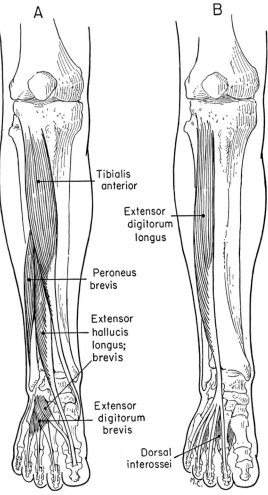

Figure 143. Anterior muscles of the leg.

Extensor Digitorum Longus (Fig. 143, *B*)

PROXIMAL ATTACHMENTS. (O)   Lateral condyle of tibia and upper three fourths of anterior surface of fibula.

DISTAL ATTACHMENTS. (I)   Dorsal surface of second and third phalanges of four lesser toes.

NERVE SUPPLY.   Deep peroneal.

ACTION:

Ankle: Dorsal flexion.

Foot: Dorsal flexion; assists in eversion and abduction.

Toes: Extension of four lesser toes.

WHERE TO PALPATE. Anterior surface of ankle and dorsal surface of foot, lateral to tendon of extensor hallucis longus.

COMMENTS. This is a penniform muscle and is situated lateral to the tibialis anterior in the upper part of the leg, and lateral to the extensor hallucis longus in the lower part. Just in front of the ankle joint the tendon divides into four tendons, one for each of the four lesser toes.

Extensor Hallucis Longus (Fig. 143, A)
PROXIMAL ATTACHMENT. (O) Middle half of anterior surface of fibula.

DISTAL ATTACHMENT. (I) Dorsal surface of base of distal phalanx of hallux (great toe).

NERVE SUPPLY. Deep peroneal.

ACTION:

Ankle: Helps in dorsal flexion.

Foot: Dorsal flexion.

Toes: Extension and hyperextension of great toe.

WHERE TO PALPATE. Dorsal surface of foot and great toe.

COMMENTS. Like the preceding muscle, this is penniform in structure. Its upper portion lies beneath the tibialis anterior and extensor digitorum longus, but about halfway down the leg the tendon emerges between these two muscles, thus becoming superficial. After it has reached the ankle the tendon slants medially across the dorsal surface of the foot to the top of the great toe.

Peroneus Tertius (Fig. 144)
PROXIMAL ATTACHMENT. (O) Anterior surface of lower third of fibula.

DISTAL ATTACHMENT. (I) Dorsal surface of base of fifth metatarsal.

NERVE SUPPLY. Deep peroneal.

ACTION:

Ankle: Dorsal flexion.

Foot: Dorsal flexion; pronation (eversion and abduction).

WHERE TO PALPATE. Dorsal surface of foot close to base of fifth metatarsal.

COMMENTS. This little muscle lies lateral to the extensor digitorum longus and is sometimes described as the fifth tendon of the latter muscle.

Peroneus Longus (Fig. 144)
PROXIMAL ATTACHMENTS. (O) Lateral condyle of tibia; head and upper two thirds of lateral surface of fibula.

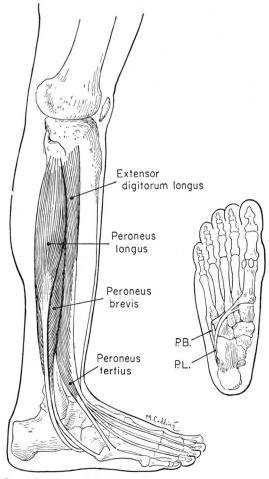

Figure 144. Lateral muscles of the leg. (*P.B.* = Peroneus brevis; *P.L.* = peroneus longus.)

DISTAL ATTACHMENTS. (1)   Lateral margin of plantar surface of first cuneiform and base of first metatarsal.

NERVE SUPPLY.   Superficial peroneal.

ACTION:

Ankle: Plantar flexion.

Foot: Plantar flexion; pronation (eversion and abduction).

WHERE TO PALPATE:

Muscle belly: Lateral surface of upper half of leg.

Tendon: Lateral surface of lower half of leg and just above and behind lateral malleolus.

COMMENTS.   This muscle is situated superficially on the lateral aspect of the leg. Its distal tendon passes behind the lateral malleolus and proceeds forward and downward to the margin of the foot where it passes behind the tuberosity of the fifth metatarsal. At this point it turns under the foot, passes through the peroneal groove of the cuboid, and slants forward across the plantar surface of the foot to its attachment at the base of the first metatarsal and first cuneiform, not far from the attachment of the tibialis anterior.

Peroneus Brevis (Figs. 143, *A* and 144)
PROXIMAL ATTACHMENT. (O)   Lower two thirds of lateral surface of fibula.
DISTAL ATTACHMENT. (I)   Tuberosity on lateral side of base of fifth metatarsal.
NERVE SUPPLY.   Superficial peroneal.
ACTION:
Ankle: Assists in plantar flexion.
Foot: Plantar flexion; pronation (eversion and abduction).
WHERE TO PALPATE.   Lateral margin of foot just posterior to base of fifth metatarsal.
COMMENTS.   This is a penniform muscle, lying beneath the peroneus longus on the lower half of the lateral aspect of the leg. Its tendon passes behind the lateral malleolus immediately anterior to the tendon of longus and continues forward just above the longus tendon to its attachment on the tuberosity of the fifth metatarsal, below the attachment of peroneus tertius.

Gastrocnemius (see also muscles of the knee) (Fig. 145)
PROXIMAL ATTACHMENTS. (O)   Posterior surface of each femoral condyle and adjacent parts, by two separate heads.
DISTAL ATTACHMENT. (I)   Posterior surface of calcaneus by means of calcaneal tendon (tendon of Achilles).
NERVE SUPPLY.   Tibial.
ACTION.   Plantar flexion of foot at ankle.
WHERE TO PALPATE.   Calf of leg and back of ankle.
COMMENTS.   The gastrocnemius is the large superficial muscle on the back of the leg and can be seen as two bulges in the upper part of the calf when it is well developed. Its two heads, together with the soleus, constitute the triceps surae. The lateral and medial portions of the muscle remain distinct from each other as far down as the middle of the back of the leg. Then they fuse to form the broad tendon of Achilles.
This muscle is a powerful plantar flexor of the ankle joint whose most familiar function is to enable one to rise on the toes. Many anatomists have thought that it acted only when the movement

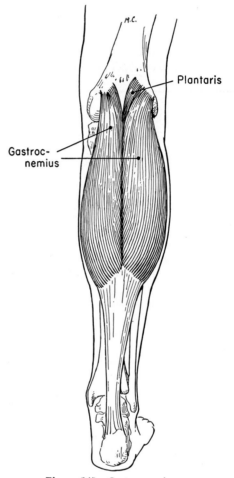

Figure 145. Gastrocnemius.

was resisted, but Sheffield, Gersten and Mastellone found that it was active in unresisted movements of plantar flexion with the subjects in a supine position. It has a large angle of pull, approximately 90 degrees when the foot is in its fundamental position. Its internal structure and its leverage combine to make it an exceedingly powerful muscle.

Soleus (Fig. 146)

PROXIMAL ATTACHMENTS. (O)   Posterior surface of head of fibula and upper two thirds of shaft; popliteal line and medial border of middle third of tibia.

DISTAL ATTACHMENT. (1)   Posterior surface of calcaneus by means of calcaneal tendon (tendon of Achilles).

NERVE SUPPLY.   Tibial.

ACTION.   Plantar flexion of foot at ankle.

WHERE TO PALPATE.   Slightly lateral to and below the lateral bulge of the gastrocnemius.

COMMENTS.   The soleus lies beneath the gastrocnemius, except along the lateral aspect of the lower half of the calf, where a portion of it lies lateral to the upper part of the calcaneal tendon. Its fibers are inserted into the calcaneal tendon in a bipenniform manner. In an electromyographic study of the leg muscles when

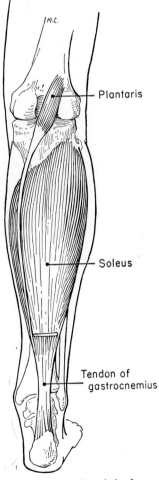

- Plantaris

- Soleus

Tendon of gastrocnemius

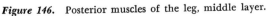

Figure 146. Posterior muscles of the leg, middle layer.

the subjects balanced on one foot, Sheffield, Gersten and Mastellone found that the soleus was consistently more active than the gastrocnemius.

Tibialis Posterior (Fig. 147)

PROXIMAL ATTACHMENTS. (O)   Posterior surface of upper two thirds of tibia beginning at popliteal line; medial surface of upper two thirds of fibula.

DISTAL ATTACHMENTS. (I)   Tuberosity of navicular bone with branches to sustentaculum tali of calcaneus, to the three cuneiforms, to cuboid, and to the bases of the three middle metatarsal bones.

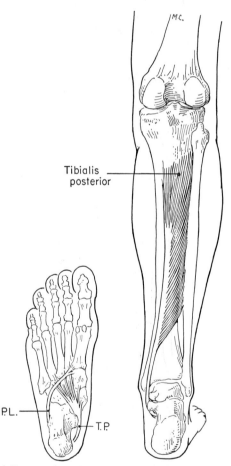

Figure 147. Tibialis posterior. (*P.L.* = Peroneus longus; *T.P.* = tibialis posterior.)

NERVE SUPPLY. Tibial.

ACTION:

Ankle: Assists in plantar flexion.

Foot: Supination (inversion and adduction); plantar flexion. Cannot be palpated.

COMMENTS. This is the deepest of the muscles on the back of the leg. The main part of the muscle covers the intermuscular septum between the tibia and fibula. In the lower fourth of the leg its tendon slants across to the medial side of the ankle, passes behind the medial malleolus and above the sustentaculum tali, then turns under the foot around the medial margin of the navicular bone to insert into its under side. The muscle is penniform in structure. Because of its direction of pull and its numerous attachments on the plantar surface of the tarsal bones, an important function of this muscle is maintenance of the longitudinal arch.

Flexor Digitorum Longus (Fig. 148)

PROXIMAL ATTACHMENT. (O)   Posterior surface of middle three fifths of tibia.

DISTAL ATTACHMENTS. (I)   Plantar surface of base of distal phalanx of each of the four lesser toes.

NERVE SUPPLY. Tibial.

ACTION:

Ankle: Assists in plantar flexion.

Foot: Plantar flexion; assists in supination (inversion and adduction).

Toes: Flexion of four lesser toes.

Cannot be palpated.

COMMENTS. This muscle is situated on the medial side of the back of the leg, behind the tibia. It is penniform in structure. Its distal tendon passes behind the medial malleolus between the tendons of tibialis posterior and flexor hallucis longus. Beneath the tarsal bones it divides into four tendons which go to the distal phalanx of each of the four lesser toes. Sheffield, Gersten and Mastellone found it to be a strong supinator in the non-weight-bearing position. Its supinatory action in weight-bearing is yet to be investigated electromyographically.

Flexor Hallucis Longus (Fig. 148)

PROXIMAL ATTACHMENT. (O)   Posterior surface of lower two thirds of fibula.

DISTAL ATTACHMENT. (I)   Plantar surface of base of distal phalanx of hallux (great toe).

NERVE SUPPLY. Tibial.

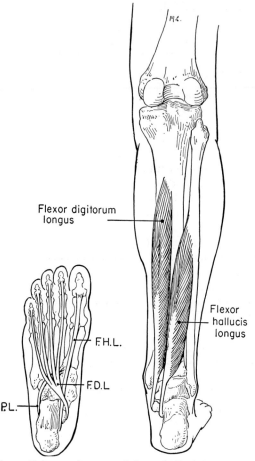

Figure 148.   Flexor digitorum longus and flexor hallucis longus. (*F.H.L.* = Flex. hal. long.; *F.D.L.* = flex. dig. long.; *P.L.* = per. long.)

ACTION:

Ankle: Assists in plantar flexion.

Foot: Plantar flexion; assists in supination (inversion and adduction).

Toes: Flexion of great toe.

WHERE TO PALPATE.   Medial border of calcaneal tendon close to calcaneus.

COMMENTS.   The flexor hallucis longus is situated on the lateral side of the back of the leg behind the fibula and the lateral portion of the tibia. The fibers unite with the distal tendon in a penniform manner. The tendon crosses behind the ankle to the medial side, passes around the medial malleolus and runs forward under the medial margin of the foot to the distal phalanx of the great toe. Even more important than flexion of the great toe is this muscle's task of giving the "push off" in walking, running and jumping.

Plantar Fascia (Fig. 149).   On the plantar surface of the foot the muscles are covered by fascia. This is divided into medial, central and lateral portions. The central portion, known as the plantar aponeurosis, is particularly strong and fibrous. It extends under the whole length of the foot, connecting the tuberosity of the calcaneus with the bases of the proximal phalanges of the five toes. This is an exceedingly strong band which serves as an effective binding rod for the longitudinal arch.

Intrinsic Muscles of the Foot (Figs. 150, 151 and 152).   These muscles will be treated as a group, rather than individually. All their attachments are within the foot itself. They are innervated by the deep peroneal, medial plantar and lateral plantar nerves. The muscles of the sole of the foot help in all weight-bearing activities and contribute to the maintenance of the arches. As is to be expected, these muscles are much more highly developed in primitive people than in people who wear shoes habitually.

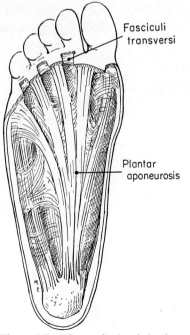

Figure 149.   Plantar fascia of the foot.

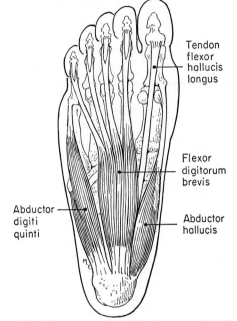

Figure 150. Plantar muscles of the foot, superficial layer.

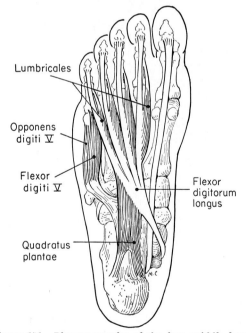

Figure 151. Plantar muscles of the foot, middle layer.

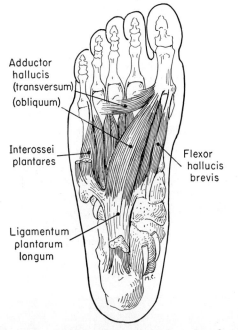

Figure 152. Plantar muscles of the foot, deep layer.

Muscular Analysis of the Fundamental Movements of the Ankle, Foot and Toes

ANKLE

Dorsal Flexion

Movers.........{
  Principal.........{ Tibialis anterior / Peroneus tertius / Extensor digitorum longus

  Assistant..........Extensor hallucis longus

Neutralizers.......................Tibialis anterior and peroneus tertius mutually neutralize one another's tendency to invert and evert the foot

Stabilizers..........................None

Plantar Flexion

Movers.........{
  Principal.........{ Gastrocnemius / Soleus / Peroneus longus

  Assistant.........{ Tibialis posterior / Peroneus brevis / Flexor digitorum longus / Flexor hallucis longus

*Neutralizers.. ....*Peroneus longus and brevis on the one
hand, and tibialis posterior on the
other, mutually neutralize one another's tendency to evert and invert
the foot

*Stabilizers... ....*None

FOOT

Dorsal Flexion

The muscular action is the same as for dorsal flexion at the ankle

Plantar Flexion

With the exception of the gastrocnemius and soleus, which do not
cross the tarsal joints, the muscular action is the same as for plantar
flexion at the ankle

Supination (inversion and adduction) (Fig. 153, *B*)

Movers......... { Principal......... { Tibialis posterior / Flexor digitorum longus

Assistant......... { Tibialis anterior / Flexor hallucis longus

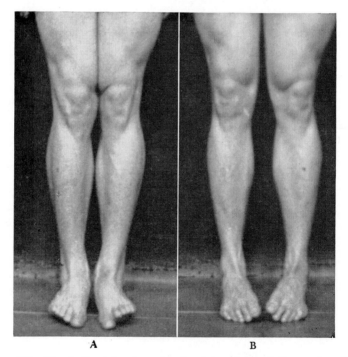

A   B

Figure 153. The feet and legs in weight-bearing position. *A,* In eversion; *B,* in
inversion.

Note: The axis of the ankle joint is such that the foot appears to be slightly inverted when it is plantar-flexed. For this reason the gastrocnemius and soleus are sometimes included as inverters of the foot. When one considers the attachment of the tendocalcaneus, however, it is obvious that these muscles can have no direct action on the tarsal joints

Neutralizers . . . . Tibialis anterior and posterior mutually neutralize one another's tendency to dorsiflex and plantar-flex the foot and ankle

Stabilizers . . . . None

Pronation (eversion and abduction) (Fig. 153, *A*)

Movers . . . . ⎰ Principal . . . . ⎰ Peroneus longus
⎱ ⎱ Peroneus brevis

⎰ Assistant . . . . ⎰ Peroneus tertius
⎱ ⎱ Extensor digitorum longus

Neutralizers . . . . The two principal muscles are mutually neutralizing with the two assistant muscles with respect to plantar and dorsal flexion

Stabilizers . . . . None

Toes

Note: Only the movers are listed

Flexion

Flexor digitorum longus
Flexor hallucis longus
Short flexors located on the foot

Extension

Extensor digitorum longus
Extensor hallucis longus
Short extensors located on the foot

Abduction

Short muscles located on the foot

Adduction

Short muscles located on the foot

Demonstrations and Laboratory Exercises

Joint Structure and Function

1. Using forms like the one of page 150, record the essential information regarding the ankle joint, the subtalar joint and the midtarsal joints. Study the movements of these joints both on the skeleton and on the living body.

2. Using a Lufkin rule or a protractor-goniometer, measure the range of motion at the ankle joint with the knee straight and with the knee flexed. Measure ten subjects.

Muscular Action

3. Plantar flexion
Subject: (a) Stand and rise on the toes. (b) Hold one foot off the floor and extend it vigorously.
Observer: Compare the muscular action of the leg in (a) and (b).

4. Dorsiflexion
Subject: Sit on a table with the legs straight and with the feet over the edge. Dorsiflex one foot as far as possible.
Assistant: Resist the movement by holding the foot down.
Observer: Identify the tibialis anterior, peroneus tertius, extensor digitorum and extensor hallucis longus.

5. Pronation (eversion and abduction)
Subject: In same position as in 4, turn one foot laterally without extending it.
Assistant: Steady the leg at the ankle and resist the movement by holding the foot.
Observer: Identify the muscles that contract.

6. Supination (inversion and adduction)
Subject: In same position as in 4 and 5, turn one foot medially as far as possible.
Assistant: Steady the leg at the ankle and resist the movement by holding the foot.
Observer: Identify the muscles that contract.

CHECK LIST FOR MUSCULAR ANALYSIS OF MOVEMENTS OF ANKLE, FOOT AND TOES

	Ankle		Foot				Toes	
	Dorsi-flex.	*Plant. Flex.*	*Dorsi-flex.*	*Plant. Flex.*	*Inv. & Adduc.*	*Evers. & Abd.*	*Flex.*	*Ext.*
Tibialis anterior								
Ext. halluc. long.								
Ext. digit. longus								
Peroneus tertius								
Peroneus longus								
Peroneus brevis								
Tibialis posterior								
Gastrocnemius								
Soleus								
Flexor hal. long.								
Flex. digit. long.								

Bibliography

1. Bettmann, E. H.: The Human Foot. Arch. Phys. Ther., 25: 13–26, 1944.
2. Duvall, E. N.: Kinesiology; The Anatomy of Motion. Englewood Cliffs, N. J., Prentice-Hall, 1959.
3. Jones, R. L.: The Human Foot; An Experimental Study of Its Mechanics and the Role of Its Muscles and Ligaments in the Support of the Arch. Am. J. Anat., 68: 1–39, 1941.
4. Jones, R., and Lovett, R. W.: Orthopedic Surgery. New York, Wm. Wood and Company, 1929, Chap. 30.
5. Kelly, E. D.: A Comparative Study of Structure and Function of Normal, Pronated and Painful Feet among Children. Research Quarterly of Am. Assn. for Health, Phys. Educ. and Recreation, 18: 291–312, 1947.
6. Lapidus, P. W.: Misconception about the "Springiness" of the Longitudinal Arch of the Foot. Arch. Surg., 46: 410–421, 1943.
7. O'Connell, A. L.: Electromyographic Study of Certain Leg Muscles during Movements of the Free Foot during Standing. Am. J. Phys. Med., 37: 289–301, 1958.
8. Sheffield, F. J., Gersten, J. W., and Mastellone, A. F.: Electromyographic Study of the Muscles of the Foot in Normal Walking. Am. J. Phys. Med., 35: 223–236, 1956.

Recommended Readings

Bettmann, E. H.: The Human Foot. (See 1 above.)
Jones, R. L.: The Human Foot. (See 3 above.)
Jones, R., and Lovett, R. W.: Orthopedic Surgery. (See 4 above.)
Kelly, E. D.: A Comparative Study of Structure and Function of Normal, Pronated and Painful Feet among Children. (See 5 above.)

II · The Mechanics of
Human Motion

13 · The Machinery of the Musculoskeletal System

THE WORD "machine" brings to mind a man-made device for transmitting or modifying force and motion in such a way as to accomplish certain desired work. But not all machines are man-made. Nature has provided the musculoskeletal system with at least three of the six basic machines, namely, the lever, the wheel and axle, and the pulley. These serve in essentially the same way as man-made machines in utilizing force to produce effective motion in a complex segmented structure. Let us take a look at these three simple machines and their counterparts in the musculoskeletal system.

The Lever. We use levers every day of our lives. In the kitchen the old-fashioned can opener, the nut pick, the beer can opener, the knife used to pry up a lid, are all examples of simple levers. In the workshop, or about the house and grounds, the tack lifter, the crowbar and the wheelbarrow are likewise levers. What do these have in common? They are rigid bars, even though their shapes vary. When a force is applied to them, they turn about a given fixed point, or fulcrum, and overcome a resistance or weight. All the levers mentioned are for the purpose of using a relatively small force to overcome a relatively large resistance. In levers such as these the range of movement of the object which is being acted upon by the lever is relatively slight. The tack lifter, for instance, lifts the tack only a fraction of an inch. In other words, the power to overcome a considerable resistance is gained at the expense of range of motion.

In the sports field particularly, we see levers that do the opposite of this. The golf club, for instance, is a lever used for gaining range of motion at the expense of force. The length of the shaft enables the club head to travel through a large arc of motion, but it is used to overcome the relatively slight resistance first of the weight of the club itself, and later of the golf ball. Tennis and squash rackets, baseball bats, hockey sticks and fencing foils are other examples of levers used for the purpose of gaining distance at the expense of force. These levers do not save the strength of the user, as do the household levers mentioned, but they increase his range and speed of movement. By striking a ball with a racket, for instance, he can impart more speed to it and send it a greater distance than he could by striking it with his hand. This is because the head of the racket travels a greater distance than the hand alone is able to do.

Still a different kind of lever is seen in the seesaw on the playground, the scales in the laboratory and the pole used by the Chinese coolie for carrying balanced loads across his shoulder. These levers gain neither force nor distance, but provide for a balancing of weights. If the loads are equal, they will balance each other when placed the same distance on opposite sides of the fulcrum. If they are unequal, they will balance only if the heavier load is placed closer to the fulcrum. There is an exact relationship between the magnitude of the weights and their respective distances from the fulcrum.

This kind of lever may also be used to balance a force and a load. The vagabond carrying a stick on his shoulder, with his bundle tied on one end and his hand holding the other end, is using this kind of lever. His use of the stick is similar to that of the coolie except that the vagabond has substituted his hand for one of the loads. The amount of force exerted by his hand depends upon what part of the stick is in contact with his shoulder. If it is the midpoint, then the force exerted by his hand must exactly equal the weight of the bundle. The closer the point of contact to the bundle, the less force his hand will need to exert.

The Body Segments as Levers.   Where in the human body do we have anything even faintly resembling a beer can opener, a hockey stick or a seesaw? The resemblance may not be apparent at first, but when we recognize each of these levers as a rigid bar which turns about a fulcrum when force is applied to it, it is then apparent that nearly every bone in the skeleton can be looked upon as a lever. The bone itself serves as the lever or rigid bar, the joint as the fulcrum, and the contracting muscle as the force. A large segment of the body, such as the trunk, the upper extremity or the lower extremity, can likewise act as a single lever if it is used as a

whether it be a first or a third class lever, is said to favor speed and distance. It lacks force, however. More force is required to move it than would be the case if the relative lengths of the force and resistance arms were reversed. Furthermore, an object of negligible weight can be moved a greater distance and more rapidly by this kind of lever than it could be without the aid of the lever. Regardless of the position of its fulcrum, or of the relative lengths of its two arms, a first class lever is always an arrangement for balance. Examples of these various levers are listed below:

1. First class lever with equal force and resistance arms: seesaw; balance scales.

2. First class lever with relatively long force arm: pump handle; crowbar when one end is placed under a rock, a log is placed under the crowbar, and the opposite end of the crowbar is pushed down.

3. First class lever with relatively long resistance arm: old-fashioned well-sweep; kitchen tongs.

4. Second class lever: wheelbarrow; crowbar when one end is placed under rock and other end is lifted.

5. Third class lever: screen door with spring supplying the force; fire tongs (hinged at end).

The Principle of Levers.   A lever of any class will balance when the product of the force and the force arm equals the product of the resistance and the resistance arm. This is known as the principle of levers. It enables us to calculate the amount of force needed to balance a known resistance by means of a known lever, or to calculate the point at which to place the fulcrum in order to balance a known resistance with a given force. In fact, if any three of the four values are known, the remaining one can be calculated by using the following equation:

$$F \times FA = R \times RA \text{ (force times force arm equals resistance times resistance arm)}$$

Examples of Anatomic Levers.   The head, tipping forward and backward, is a good example of a first class lever in the body (Fig. 155). To be sure, it is a sphere rather than a bar, and the axis of motion would seem to be an imaginary one located in the frontal plane approximately between the ears. The force is supplied by the extensors of the head, notably the splenius and upper portions of the semispinalis, and is applied to the head at the base of the skull. The resistance to the movement is furnished by the weight of the head itself, together with the tension of the antagonistic muscles and fasciae, as the limit of motion is approached. The center of concentration of the resistance is difficult to determine. If the head is acting like a seesaw, the resistance would seem to be centered in the front half of the head for extension, and in the rear half

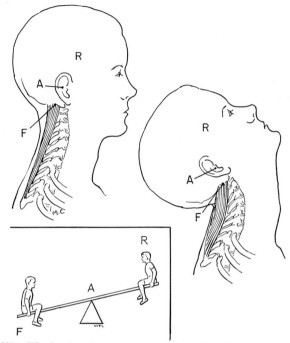

Figure 155. The head acting as a first class lever like the seesaw. $A =$ The approximate position of the axis or fulcrum; $F =$ the point where the force is applied; $R =$ the approximate point where the resistance is concentrated.

for flexion, rather than where it is shown in the illustration (Fig. 155).

Another first class lever is seen in the foot when it is not being used for weight-bearing, as when the knees are crossed in the sitting position. As the soleus pulls upward on the heel, the foot plantar-flexes at the ankle joint where the fulcrum is situated. The resistance seems to be provided by the tonus of the dorsiflexor muscles. The weight of the foot apparently is not a factor here, since the foot has already relaxed into a position of partial plantar flexion. The picture would be changed, however, if the person were lying face down with the leg bent at the knee and the lower leg extended vertically upward. If the foot were then plantar-flexed, the weight of the foot would be a factor in the resistance.

The forearm is another example of a first class lever when it is being extended by the triceps muscle (Fig. 156). The fulcrum is situated at the elbow joint; the force is applied at the olecranon process; and the resistance point is either at the center of gravity of the forearm or at the hand, if the latter is pushing against an external resistance. Internal resistance does not appear to be a factor in this movement. This is a good example of a first class lever in which the force arm is extremely short, relative to the resistance arm. It is therefore similar to a third class lever in that it favors speed and range of movement at the expense of force.

Whether or not there are any second class levers in the body seems to be a controversial matter among anatomists and kinesiologists. Some claim that when the foot is being plantar-flexed in a weight-bearing position, as when rising on the toes, it is a second class lever. The fulcrum is said to be at the point of contact with the ground, the force point at the heel where the tendon of Achilles attaches, and the resistance at the ankle joint where the weight of the body is transferred to the foot. Another second class lever might be the forearm if it were being flexed by the brachioradialis alone. Since ordinarily all the flexors contract together to flex the forearm, the latter serves as both a second class and a third class lever at the same time.

The forearm is a good example of a third class lever when it is being flexed by the biceps and the brachialis (Fig. 157). Another

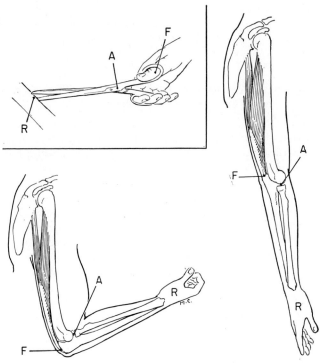

Figure 156.   The forearm acting as a first class lever with a short force arm and long resistance arm, like a pair of paper shears.

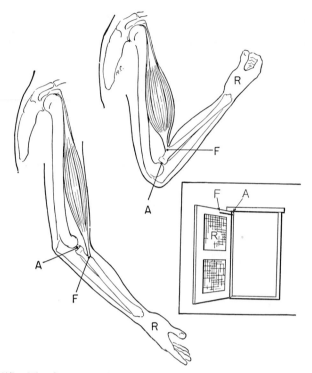

Figure 157. The forearm acting as a third class lever with a relatively short force arm, like a screen door.

third class lever is seen in the example cited earlier, namely the arm as it is raised sideward-upward by the deltoid muscle (Fig. 158).

Relation of Speed to Range in Movements of Levers. The observant reader will have noticed that in the foregoing discussion of levers the terms "speed and range" were usually linked together. There is a reason for this. In angular movements speed and range are interdependent. For instance, if two third class levers of different lengths each move through a 40-degree angle at the same *angular velocity*, the tip of the longer lever will be traveling a greater distance or range than the tip of the shorter lever. Since it covers this distance in the same time that it takes the tip of the shorter lever to travel the shorter distance, the former must be moving faster than the latter. This is easily seen if the shorter lever is superimposed on the longer, as in Figure 159. Here the shorter lever, *AB,* has been superimposed on the longer lever, *AC.* The levers are moving from the horizontal position to the diagonal one. Since the point *C* travels to its new position, *C′,* in the same time that it takes

B to travel to B', point C must obviously be moving faster than point B.

Characteristics of Anatomic Levers. In the levers of the body the force arm, with few exceptions, is shorter than the resistance arm. Thus anatomic levers tend to favor speed and range of movement at the expense of force. Examples of this are seen in the throwing of a baseball or the kicking of a soccer ball. The hand in the one case, and the foot in the other, travel through a relatively

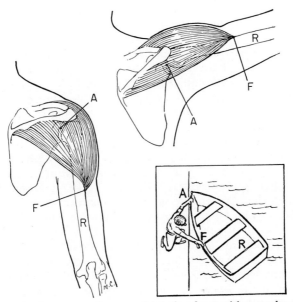

Figure 158. The humerus acting as a third class lever with a moderately long force arm, like a boat being pulled alongside the dock.

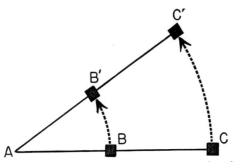

Figure 159. Comparison of a long and a short lever turning the same number of degrees. It takes B the same amount of time to reach B' that it takes C to reach C'.

long distance at considerable speed. Both these movements require strong muscular action, in spite of the fact that the balls are
relatively light in weight. This type of leverage is the reverse of
the kind usually seen in mechanical implements such as the crowbar
and the automobile jack, both of which are used to move heavy
weights a relatively short distance.

Sport Implements as Levers.   Sport implements may serve
either as levers in themselves or as artificial extensions of the human arm. Frequently the sport implement, the arm and a large part
of the rest of the body act together as a system of levers. In batting
a baseball, for instance, the trunk forms one lever, the upper arms
another, the forearms another, and the hands and bat still another.
This use of multiple leverage is for the purpose of building up
speed at the tip of the bat, for the greater this speed, the greater
the force that can be imparted to the ball.

Identification and Analysis of Levers.   Figures 155 to 158
depict certain anatomic levers and their mechanical counterparts.
These should enable the student to understand the principle of
leverage as it applies in the human body and to see how the anatomic levers compare with the levers of everyday life. For each of
these levers, and for every lever that the student observes, he should
answer these questions: (1) Where are the fulcrum, the force
point and the resistance point? (2) What class of lever is this?
(3) What are the relative lengths of the force and resistance arms?
(4) What kind of movement does this lever favor? After he has
studied components of force (p. 309) he should add the questions:
(5) At what angle is the force applied to the lever? (6) At what
angle is the resistance applied to the lever? (7) What is the true
force arm of the lever? and (8) What is the true resistance arm of
the lever?

The Wheel and Axle.   The wheel and axle device consists of
a wheel attached to a central axel about which it revolves. Force
may be applied to the wheel either at the rim, as in the case of the
steering wheel of the automobile, or to the axle, as in the case of
the automobile's rear wheels. The steering wheel is an example of
a wheel and axle which magnifies force at the expense of speed and
distance. The larger the diameter of the wheel, the greater the
magnification of force. Quantitatively, the turning effect of the
wheel is the product of the force and the radius. The radius thus
corresponds to the force arm of a lever. The doorknob, the water
wheel and the helm of the ship are common examples of this kind
of wheel and axle. In the helm of the ship the rim of the wheel is
absent, but the spokes constitute a wheel nevertheless. In many respects the wheel and axle device is similar to the lever, particularly
when the "wheel" consists of a single spoke, as in the case of the

meat grinder, the pencil sharpener, and the hand-operated clothes wringer. These correspond to a second class lever, in which the fulcrum (actually the center of the axle) is at one end, the force is applied to the other end, and the resistance is applied close to the fulcrum.

The type of wheel and axle which is used to gain speed and distance at the expense of force is seen less commonly, perhaps, yet it is present in many of our instruments of transportation. In the automobile the rear wheels are turned by means of force applied to their axles. The same is true of the bicycle, the velocipede and the old-fashioned bicycle, in which the pedals are attached directly to the axle. The Ferris wheel and the merry-go-round are further examples of this kind of wheel and axle. In each of these the force is applied to the axle and the resistance is applied to the outer circumference of the wheel. More careful inspection of these examples reveals the fact that they are actually combinations of both kinds of wheels and axles. In the velocipede, for instance, the pedal represents the first type of wheel and axle. The force is applied to the outer end of the pedal. This serves to revolve the common axle of the pedal and the front wheel of the velocipede. The front wheel represents the second type of wheel and axle. Force is applied to it at the axle (as the result of the action of the pedal) and resistance is applied at the rim at its point of contact with the ground.

Further consideration of wheels and axles, as seen in common household and industrial devices, shows that they frequently are combined in such a way that a wheel and axle of the first type connects with one of the second type. There may be several such combinations within one relatively simple mechanism. The common rotary egg beater, for instance, is found to combine four wheel and axle devices, the two types alternating with each other.

Most of the examples of the wheel and axle in the body, like anatomic levers, are arranged for gaining distance and speed at the expense of force. Both kinds are represented, however. A cross section of the upper trunk is a "wheel and axle" which represents both types (Fig. 160). Some of the force for rotating is applied directly to the "axle," i.e., the spinal column. This is the force provided by the deep posterior spinal muscles and the semispinalis. Some is applied to the "wheel," i.e., to the ribs. This force is provided by the oblique abdominal muscles (Fig. 161) and the iliocostalis.

A cross section of the arm or the thigh likewise presents the characteristics of a wheel and axle. Here the shaft of the long bone serves as the axle, and the peripheral tissues as the wheel. Rotation of the limb about its mechanical long axis constitutes the movement of the wheel and axle, with the force being furnished by the muscles producing the rotation and the resistance

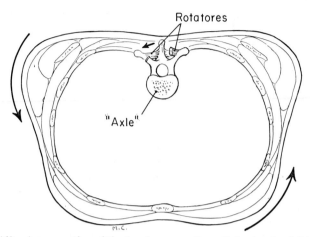

Figure 160. A cross section of the trunk representing a "wheel and axle" in which the force of the rotatores muscles is applied to the "axle."

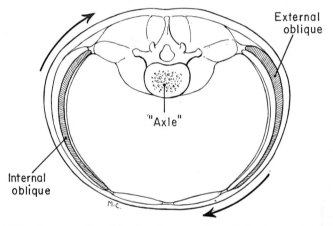

Figure 161. A cross section of the trunk representing a "wheel and axle" in which the force of the oblique abdominal muscles is applied to the "wheel."

by the antagonistic muscles, or by an external resistance, as the case may be. Unlike the usual mechanical wheel and axle, the resistance in an anatomic wheel and axle is frequently applied at the same distance from the center of motion as the force. This is the case when antagonistic muscles provide the only resistance to the movement.

The Pulley. A pulley is usually a spool or wheel with a rope running over it. Whereas we do not have wheels and ropes in the body, we do have pulleys. In the field of mechanics there are simple pulleys and there are complicated arrangements of block and

tackle. Only the fixed single pulley is represented in the musculo-skeletal system. It serves the same purpose as the mechanical fixed single pulley, namely, that of changing the direction of a force. This may take the form of giving a muscle a greater angle of pull than it would otherwise have, or of enabling it to produce a totally different movement than it could otherwise produce. For instance, the angle of pull of the gracilis muscle is increased by means of the bulging medial condyles of the knee over which the tendon passes just before it attaches to the tibia (Fig. 170). A pulley changing the nature of a movement is illustrated by the peroneus longus muscle, which, by passing behind the lateral malleolus before it turns under the foot to attach to the first cuneiform and base of the first metatarsal bone, plantar-flexes the foot at the ankle. If it passed in front of the malleolus, its pull would be shifted in front of the ankle joint and hence it would dorsiflex the foot. In the first example the medial condyles of the femur and tibia are the "fixed single pulley," and in the second example, the lateral malleolus serves in this capacity.

The function of these machines in the musculoskeletal system, and their significance in the total movements of the body, will be discussed at greater length in the chapters that follow.

The Efficiency of Machines.   Machines are judged good if they are efficient, poor if they are inefficient. How is the efficiency of a machine measured? Since the machines used in industry and in the workshop are usually for the purpose of magnifying force, it has become customary to measure their efficiency in terms of their *mechanical advantage,* in other words, their ability to magnify force. Another way of expressing this ability is to state the "output" of the machine relative to its "input." In the case of a lever this is the ratio between the force applied to the lever and the resistance overcome by the lever. It can be expressed in terms of the equation:

Mechanical Advantage $=$ the ratio of the resistance overcome to the force applied,

$$\text{or simply, M.A.} = \frac{R}{F}.$$

Since the balanced lever equation (p. 283) can also be expressed

$$\frac{R}{F} = \frac{FA}{RA},$$

it is seen that the mechanical advantage can be expressed in terms of the ratio of the force arm to the resistance arm. Hence, if

$$\text{M.A.} = \frac{R}{F},$$

it also holds that

$$\text{M.A.} = \frac{FA}{RA}.$$

The mechanical advantage of a wheel and axle is measured in a somewhat similar manner, namely, in terms of the ratio of the radius of the wheel (R) to the radius of the axle (r), or

$$\text{M.A.} = \frac{R}{r}.$$

Since the fixed single pulley is a device for changing the direction of a force, not for affecting its magnitude, and since this is the only kind of pulley represented in the body, we need not concern ourselves with the mechanical advantage of pulleys.

It is hoped that this elementary presentation of three of the basic machines and their counterparts in the musculoskeletal system of the human body will facilitate an understanding of the mechanical principles which are discussed in the following chapter.

Demonstrations, Laboratory Exercises and Problems

1. Place a window pole across the back of a chair, hang a pail or basket containing a 5-pound weight on the hook, and hold the other end of the pole. Now adjust the pole so that it becomes increasingly difficult for you to balance the weight of the pail with one hand. Stop at the point where you are just barely able to lift the pail by pushing down on the opposite end of the pole. Have an assistant measure the force arm and the weight arm of the lever. Without shifting the position of your hand, draw the pole toward you until you can easily lift the pail by pushing down on the opposite end of the pole with one finger. Again, have an assistant measure the force and weight arms of the lever. What do you conclude concerning the relative length of the two arms? In which case does the pail move through the greater distance? What do you conclude about the relationship between the force required to move an object by leverage and the distance that the object is moved? This experiment, as you did it, involved a first class lever. Could you perform a similar experiment using a third class lever?

2. Balance a pole across the back of a chair, hanging a 5-pound weight at each end. Let one of these represent the force and the other the weight or resistance. The force arm and the weight arm should be exactly equal if the pole is symmetrical. Now add 5 more pounds to the weight end and adjust the pole until it balances. Measure the force and weight arms. What do you conclude about:

a. The relationship between the weight and the weight arm; between the force and the force arm?

b. The relationship between the weight and the weight arm, given a changing weight and a constant force?

Explain the following equation: $F \times FA = W \times WA$.

$$F = \text{force}$$
$$W = \text{weight}$$
$$FA = \text{force arm}$$
$$WA = \text{weight arm}$$

3. Compute the amount of force necessary to lift a weight or resistance of 20 pounds with a 6-foot, first class lever whose fulcrum is located 2 feet from the point at which the weight is attached, and 4 feet from the point at which the force is applied. Assume that both the force and the resistance are applied at right angles to the lever.

4. Where would the fulcrum have to be located in the above-mentioned 6-foot first class lever if there were only 5 pounds of force available to balance the

20-pound weight? Determine this by experiment. Check your answer by the algebraic method.

5. For each of the anatomic levers listed below identify the class of lever represented; identify the fulcrum, the force point and the resistance point; and name the kind of movement favored by this type of lever.

a. Leg being flexed at knee by hamstrings.

b. Leg being extended at knee by quadriceps femoris.

c. Pelvis being tilted to right by left quadratus lumborum.

d. Clavicle being elevated by trapezius I.

e. Lower extremity being abducted by gluteus medius.

f. From supine lying position, lower extremities being raised by hip flexors.

g. From supine lying position, trunk being raised by hip flexors.

6. For each of the following levers in your own body find the force arm and the resistance arm by actual measurement, and calculate the force needed to balance the lever. Work with a partner to get the measurements of lever length and distances of force and resistance points from fulcrum. Although the results will not be mathematically accurate (since the factor of angle of pull is being disregarded), they illustrate the relation between the relative length of the force and resistance arms and the amount of force needed.

a. With the arm extended horizontally sideward, hold a 10-pound weight on the hand. Consider the middle deltoid as the only source of force.

b. With the upper arm extended horizontally sideward, suspend a 10-pound weight from the crotch of the elbow. Consider the middle deltoid as the only source of force.

7. Have a subject raise the arm sideward to the horizontal and, from this position, move it horizontally forward, taking two seconds to perform the horizontal movement. The arm has now moved through 90 degrees. Approximately how many inches did the subject's elbow move? Approximately how many inches did his hand move? Which was moving faster, his elbow or his hand?

8. Identify the "wheel," the "axle" and the place where the force is applied in the example of outward rotation of the humerus by the infraspinatus and teres minor muscles.

9. Using a string to represent the peroneus longus muscle, fasten one end to the proper spot on the leg of a skeleton for its proximal attachment. Making the string pass behind the external malleolus and under the foot, fasten the distal end to the proper point of attachment. Now take another string and fasten it at the same points, but have it pass in front of the malleolus. Be sure both strings are taut. Study the relationship between each string and the center of motion at the ankle joint. With a protractor measure the angle between the two strings at their distal attachment. Repeat this experiment with the foot in a position of complete dorsiflexion. What effect does the peroneus longus have at the ankle joint that it would not have if it passed in front of the malleolus? What is the mechanical function of the malleolus? (If no skeleton is available, it may be possible to fasten the strings on the skin of a subject's leg.)

10. Find an example of a pulley in the upper extremity.

11. Find the mechanical advantage of the levers in question 6, a and b.

Recommended Readings

(For those who have had no instruction in physics)

1. Luhr, O.: Physics Tells Why. 2nd ed. New York, Ronald Press, 1946, pp. 42–46.
2. Parker, B. M.: Machines. (The Basic Science Education Series.) Evanston, Ill., Row, Peterson and Co., 1948.

14 · Fundamental Principles of Motion

If WE ARE to understand the movements of the human musculo-skeletal system, we need first to turn our thoughts to the concept of motion itself. What causes motion? What kinds of motion are there? What determines the kind of motion that will result when an object—or a part of the human body—is made to move? Under what laws does motion operate and what are the principles that govern its behavior? And finally, how do these generalities about motion apply to the movements of the musculoskeletal system?

Cause of Motion. One cannot easily think of motion without visualizing a specific object in the act of moving. If we did not actually see how it changed from a stationary object to a moving object, we might wonder what caused it to be set in motion. Did someone pull on it, or push against it, or perhaps blow on it, or even attract it with a magnet? What are these assumed causes of motion? Without exception, they are a form of force. Force, then, is the instigator of movement. If we see an object in motion, we know that it is moving because a force has acted upon it. We know, too, that the force must have been sufficiently great to overcome the object's inertia, for unless a force is greater than the resistance offered by the object, it cannot produce motion. We can push against a stone wall all day without moving it so much as 1 millimeter, but a bulldozer can knock the wall down at the first impact. The magnitude of the force *relative to the magnitude of the resistance* is the determining factor in causing an object to move.

Kinds of Motion. What makes the object move in the way that

294

it moves? Why does the puck sometimes slide across the ice without turning, and why does it sometimes revolve as it slides? Why do arrows, balls and bullets move through the air in a pathway known as a parabola? Why does the hand move in an arc when the forearm turns at the elbow joint and the neighboring joints are held motionless? The student should try to answer these questions for himself before he reads further.

As we note the different ways in which objects move, we are impressed with the almost limitless variety in the patterns of movement. Objects move in straight paths and in curved paths; they roll, slide and fall; they bounce; they swing back and forth like a pendulum; they rotate about a center, either partially or completely; and they frequently rotate at the same time that they move as a whole from one place to another. Although the variety of ways in which objects move appears to be almost limitless, careful consideration of these ways reveals the fact that there are, in actuality, only two major classifications of movement patterns. Either an object turns about a center of motion, or it moves in its entirety from one place to another. Sometimes it does both simultaneously. The former kind of movement is termed *rotatory* or *angular*. This is the kind which is typical of levers and of wheels and axles. A phonograph record is undergoing rotatory motion when it is being played. The partial turning of a sticklike object, or lever, is also undergoing rotatory motion. Angular motion is perhaps a more descriptive term to use in the latter case. Rotatory or angular motion is characterized by movement about an axis with all parts of the object moving in an arc, like the movement of a spoke of a wheel or of a paper trimmer (Fig. 162). It may be a small arc of motion, or it may be a complete circle.

The second kind of motion is termed *translatory* because the object is translated as a whole from one location to another. Translatory movement may be further classified as *rectilinear* and *curvilinear motion*. Rectilinear motion, commonly called simply linear motion, is defined as the linear progression of an object as a

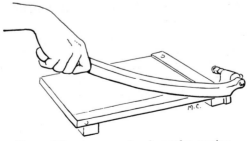

Figure 162. An example of angular motion.

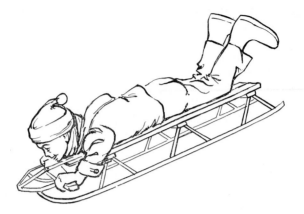

Figure 163. An example of rectilinear motion.

whole, with all its parts moving the same distance, in the same direction, and at a uniform rate of speed (Fig. 163). Curvilinear motion refers to all translatory, non-rectilinear movement. The object moves in a curved, but not necessarily circular, pathway.

Not infrequently an object displays a combination of rotatory and translatory movement, the latter often being caused by the former when aided by friction. The bicycle, the automobile and the train move linearly as the result of the rotatory movements of their wheels, provided there is enough friction between the wheels and the supporting surface to keep the former from spinning in place. Likewise man, as he walks or runs down the street, experiences translatory motion because of the angular movement of his lower extremities, aided by friction between his feet and the ground (Fig. 164). The angular motions of several segments of the body are frequently coordinated in such a way that a related segment will move linearly. This is true in throwing darts, in putting the shot, and in a lunge in fencing. Because of the angular motion of the forearm and upper arm, the hand is enabled to travel linearly, and thus to impart linear force to the dart and the shot prior to their release, and to the foil (Fig. 165).

Motion in a curved path other than a circle or arc is illustrated by the flight of a ball or an arrow—in fact, of any projectile. Although the initial movement of the object through space is rectilinear, the movement path becomes curvilinear as the effect of gravity becomes apparent. Hence the motion of the projectile is caused by two forces, the impetus imparted to it by the hand, the racket or the bow, and the force of gravity.

Reciprocating motion denotes repetitive movement. The use of the term is ordinarily limited to repetitive translatory movements, as illustrated by a bouncing ball or the repeated blows of a hammer, but technically includes all kinds. The term *oscillation* refers specifically to repetitive angular movements, that is, movements in an arc. A common type of object which moves in this manner is the pendulum. Other examples of oscillation are seen in the metronome and in the vibration of a tuning fork.

Kinds of Motion Experienced by the Body. The human body experiences all these kinds of motion. It has already been shown that most of the joints are axial and that the body segments, therefore, experience angular motion. A slight amount of translatory motion is seen in the gliding movements of the plane or irregular joints. These movements are negligible in themselves. They occur chiefly in the carpal and tarsal joints and in the joints of the vertebral arches in conjunction with angular movements in neighboring

Figure 164. An example of linear motion of the body as a whole resulting from the angular motion of some of its parts.

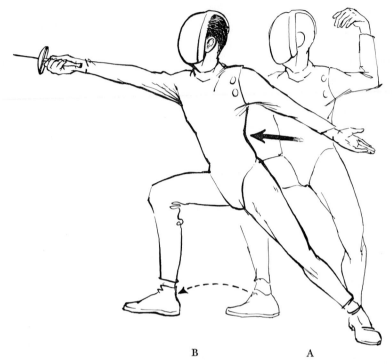

B   A

Figure 165.   Linear motion of one part of the body (the hand) resulting from angular motion of several segments of the body. *A,* Just before lunge (thrust). *B,* At completion of lunge.

axial joints. The body as a whole experiences rectilinear translatory movement when it is acted upon by the force of gravity, as in coasting (Fig. 163) and in the latter part of diving (Fig. 168); likewise when acted upon by an external force, as in water skiing (Fig. 167). It experiences rotatory motion in forward and backward rolls on the ground, in somersaults in the air, and in twirling on ice skates. It experiences curvilinear translatory motion in diving, broad jumping, high jumping, and hurdling, and it experiences reciprocating motion, specifically oscillation, when swinging back and forth on the rings, trapeze or horizontal bar.

Factors Which Determine the Kind of Motion.   Thus far we have considered the cause of motion and the various kinds of motion based on movement patterns or paths. Now we must turn to the question: What determines the kind of motion that will result when an object is made to move? The best way for the student to discover the answer is to produce each kind of motion

Figure 166. An example of movement of the body caused by the body's own muscular action.

Figure 167. An example of movement of the body caused by an external force.

Figure 168.   An example of movement of the body caused by the force of gravity.

and then to analyze what he did to obtain the kind of motion he wanted.

In order to make an object move linearly, we discover that either we must apply force uniformly against one entire side of the object, or we must apply it directly in line with the object's center of gravity. The object will move in a straight line provided it does not meet an obstacle or resistance of some sort. If its edge hits against another object, or if it encounters a rough spot on one side of its pathway, it will immediately turn about its point of contact with the interfering factor. If we attempt to push a tall cabinet across a supporting surface which provides excessive friction such as a cement floor, for instance, the cabinet will tip, even though we place our hands exactly in line with the cabinet's center of gravity and push in a horizontal direction. In order to move it linearly it will be necessary to apply the push lower than the cabinet's center of gravity to compensate for the friction.

If rotatory motion of a freely movable object is desired, it is necessary to apply force to it "off center" or to provide an "off-center" resistance which will interfere with the motion of part of the object. A lever undergoes rotatory motion because, by definition, one portion of it remains in place. If it is desired to move an object in the manner of a lever, it is only necessary to provide a fulcrum and to apply force to it at some point other than its point of contact with the fulcrum.

To make an object move in a circular path it is necessary to apply a secondary force or to provide a limited pathway, such as a circular track. When a key is tied to a string and whirled in a circle, the pull of the string is the secondary force. This is true of anything which serves to hold the object a uniform distance from the center of motion. An intentional combination of forces, such as consistently longer strides with one leg, or longer strokes with one oar, will also result in circular motion.

Reciprocating motion is caused by a uniform repetition of force applications, and the oscillation of a pendulum is produced by repeated applications of gravitational force to a suspended object which is free to move back and forth and which is in any position other than its resting position.

In summary, it may be said that the kind of motion that will be displayed by a moving object depends first of all upon the kind of motion permitted that particular kind of object. If it is a lever, it is permitted only angular motion; if it is a pendulum, oscillatory motion; and so on. If it is a freely movable object, it is permitted either translatory or rotatory motion, depending upon the circumstances. These circumstances include the point at which force is applied with reference to the object's center of gravity, the environmental pathways of movement available to the object, and the presence or absence of additional external factors which modify the motion.

Factors Modifying Motion. Motion is usually modified by a number of external factors, such as friction, air resistance, water resistance, and the like. Whether these factors are a help or a hindrance depends upon the circumstances and the nature of the motion. The same factor may facilitate one form of motion, yet hinder another. For instance, friction is a great help to the runner because it enables him to exert maximum effort without danger of slipping, yet on the other hand, friction hinders the rolling of a ball, as in hockey, golf and croquet. Again, wind or air resistance is indispensable to the sail boat's motion, but unless it is a "tail wind" it impedes the runner. Likewise, water resistance is essential for propulsion of the body by means of swimming strokes, and of boats through the use of oars and paddles, yet at the same time it hinders the progress of both the swimmer and the boat, especially if these present a broad surface to the water. It is for this reason that swimmers keep the body level and that boats are streamlined. One of the major problems in sports is to learn how to take advantage of these factors when they contribute to the movement in question, and on the other hand, how to minimize them when they are detrimental to the movement.

There are also anatomic factors which modify the motion of the segments of the body. These include friction in the joints (minimized by synovial fluid), tension of antagonistic muscles, tension of ligaments and fasciae, anomalies of bone and joint structure, atmospheric pressure within the joint capsule, and the presence of interfering soft tissues. Except for the limitations due to fleshiness, these modifying factors come under the heading of "internal resistance."

Laws of Motion.   Are there any general truths about motion that we can count on under all circumstances? Sir Isaac Newton found that there were such truths. As the result of his observations he defined three basic laws of motion. When the effect of modifying factors is discounted, it is seen that these laws hold true for the motion of all objects. The beginner will understand them more easily if he is able to imagine a situation in which extraneous factors such as friction, air resistance and water resistance are eliminated.

Law of Inertia.   An object which is at rest will remain so unless acted upon by an external force. An object which is moving will move in a straight line at a uniform speed and will continue to do so unless acted upon by an external force. (It is assumed that the external force is not counteracted by some other external force acting simultaneously.) Thus a ball which is rolling along the ground would continue to roll forever were it not for friction; and a ball sailing horizontally through the air would continue to sail forever, were it not for air resistance and the downward pull of gravity.

Law of Acceleration.   As was stated in the law of inertia, the velocity of a moving object (i.e., the distance traversed per unit of time) will remain constant unless a force acts on the moving object. When such a force does operate, the resulting change in velocity (either increase or decrease) will be directly proportional to the amount of force causing the change, and inversely proportional to the mass of the object. For instance, the amount of force which a horse must use to increase its speed in a race is in direct proportion to its velocity increase. Similarly, it takes more "braking force" to slow a train from 60 to 30 miles per hour than it does to slow the same train from 60 to 50 miles per hour. In both cases the amount of force is directly proportional to the amount of change in velocity.

As an illustration of the effect of variations in mass, the reader might imagine that two balls of equal size are rolling in parallel pathways toward him, an iron ball on the right and a wooden ball on the left. Just as they pass on either side of him he swings both hands, giving each ball a push to help speed it on its way. The speed of the wooden ball will be increased more than that of the iron ball, demonstrating the fact that the change in velocity is inversely proportional to the mass of the object.

   Law of Reaction.   To every action there is an equal and opposite reaction. Another way of stating this law is to say that when a body moves, that is, when it develops momentum, the supporting surface or other object against which it applies its force develops an equal and opposite momentum. To understand this, it is necessary to know that momentum is the product of mass times velocity. When one steps out of a canoe onto the dock, the reaction of the canoe is apparent. This is because the mass of the canoe is so small that the canoe's velocity is great by comparison. When one steps off an ocean liner, on the other hand, the reaction of the boat is imperceptible because its mass is so great that its velocity is infinitesimal by comparison. Nevertheless, in both instances, the mass of the person times his velocity is equal to the mass of the boat (canoe or ocean liner) times its velocity.

   When the human body is unsupported in the air, as when diving, it cannot voluntarily alter the pathway of its total movement. In other words, it cannot displace its center of gravity. Hence there is no question of action and reaction of the body as a whole. If one part moves, however, such as an arm or a leg, the equal and opposite reaction of the rest of the body is clearly seen. This principle underlies much of the movement in fancy diving.

   Circular Motion: Centripetal and Centrifugal Force.   An object undergoing circular motion is subject to the same laws as an object which is moving in a straight path. That this is not obvious is due to the fact that the object is being restrained in its movement by the centripetal force which is pulling it toward the center of motion. The fact that it is still subject to the Law of Inertia is demonstrated by its tendency to fly off in a straight line, or tangent to the arc of motion, the instant the centripetal force is removed.

   The experiment of twirling a string with a key tied to the other end demonstrates this nicely. It is important for the experimenter to understand that the only forces acting on the key are (1) the force causing it to move, provided by the circling finger, and (2) the inward pull of the string on the key causing its motion to be circular instead of linear. *Centrifugal force does not operate on the key.* According to Newton's third Law of Motion, every force has an equal and opposite force. Centrifugal force is the equal and opposite reaction to centripetal force, and as such is acting on the finger holding the string, not on the key. When the string is released, there is no longer any centripetal force acting on the key, and therefore no centrifugal counterpull on the finger. The key is now free to travel forward through space in a straight path, which it proceeds to do. Since it is characteristic of centripetal force to act at right angles to an object's normal direction of motion, once this force ceases, the key moves at right angles to the radius of the circle in which it had previously been moving.

Whether an object is moving in a complete circle, as the key on the end of the string, or is moving in a small arc, these same characteristics hold true. Even in the flexing of the forearm centripetal force is present, pulling inward from the finger-tips to the elbow joint, and centrifugal force pulling outward from the elbow joint. When a ball is grasped by the fingers, the centripetal force makes it move in the same arc as the hand. When the fingers release it, the ball leaves the hand and starts moving through the air in a straight line at right angles to the forearm.

Demonstrations and Laboratory Exercises

1. Take a ruler or a book and make it move in each of the ways listed below. Analyze the cause of each kind of motion produced.
   a. Rectilinear motion.
   b. Curvilinear motion.
   c. Angular motion.
   d. Oscillation.
2. For each of the following activities identify the upper extremity joints at which angular motion occurs, thus making it possible for the hand to move linearly.
   a. Drawing a 2-foot straight line on the blackboard at shoulder level.
   b. Putting the shot or throwing a dart.
   c. Drawing the string of an archery bow.
   d. Lunge in fencing.
3. Draw a diagram to represent the path taken by the hand in the sagittal plane in each of the following movements.
   a. Underwater portion of crawl stroke.
   b. Underhand softball pitch (not including the wind-up).
   c. Overhand baseball pitch (not including the wind-up).
   d. Bowling.
4. Place a book on a table and stand a small bottle on top of it. Pull the book toward you with a quick jerk. Which way does the bottle fall? Stand the bottle on the book again and pull the book across the table with a steady pull. Pull it against an obstacle, such as your other hand, so that the movement is stopped abruptly. Which way does the bottle fall now? Explain. Which of the three laws of motion does this experiment illustrate?
5. For this experiment it is necessary to have a smooth surface and a rough surface side by side. A rug partially covering a smooth floor will do nicely. Take two tennis balls and place one on the rug and the other in line with the first one, on the floor. Take a yardstick, stand behind the balls and tap them simultaneously with the stick. What causes the difference in the distance traveled by the two balls? Was there any difference in the force applied to them, or in the resistance offered by them?

6. Roll a ball on a table. Without stopping it, make it turn to the right. How did you change its direction? Is there another way in which you could change the direction of the rolling ball?

7. Attempt to hit a 10-inch target with a tennis ball from a distance of 10 feet in each of the two ways described below. Compare the pathway of the hand's movement in the two methods. Which way is more difficult? Why?

a. Face the target squarely. Keep the upper arm raised in a side-horizontal position and keep the forearm at right angles to it. Throw the ball by moving the forearm in a forward-downward arc. Use as much wrist snap as desired.

b. Throw the ball in the manner that you would normally use if you were playing catch with a friend, or were throwing from one base to another in baseball.

Recommended Readings

1. Luhr, O.: Physics Tells Why. 2nd ed. New York, Ronald Press, 1946, Chaps. 2 and 3. (Especially for those whose knowledge of physics is slight.)

2. Smout, C. F. V., and McDowall, R. J. S.: Anatomy and Physiology for Students of Physiotherapy, Occupational Therapy and Gymnastics. 3rd ed. Baltimore, Williams & Wilkins Company, 1956. (Section on levers.)

3. Wright, W. G.: Muscle Function. New York, Paul B. Hoeber, Inc., 1928, pp. 3–6.

15 · Fundamental Principles of Force and Work

Force

WE SAW in the preceding chapter that an object is put in motion when force is applied to it, a force great enough to overcome the object's resistance. The force exerted by muscles on bones obeys the same principles and has the same characteristics as does any force, the only limitation being that muscles always pull; they cannot push.

What is meant by force? It can be felt, and its effect can be both seen and measured, but force itself, like the wind, is invisible. It can nevertheless be described. Force is a push or a pull exerted against something. If we know the strength of the force, the direction in which it is acting, and the exact portion of the object on which it is exerting its pull or push, we have the essential information about the force. Hence force can be described in terms of its magnitude, its direction and the point of its application. Since we are primarily interested in muscular force, these three aspects of force will be discussed only as they relate to the muscles.

Magnitude. The magnitude of muscular force is in direct proportion to the number and size of the fibers in the muscle which is contracting. In the living human body it is impossible to gauge the magnitude of a single muscle's force because of the fact that muscles contract in groups, not individually. Hence the strength of muscle groups is tested by means of instruments such as dynamometers, instruments which measure force in terms of the number of pounds or kilograms of pull or push exerted. The force of a single muscle can be estimated only by first dissecting the muscle, then measuring its physiologic cross section and multiplying this figure by the number of pounds (or kilograms) the average muscle has been found by experiment to exert per square inch (or centimeter). By "physiologic cross section" is meant the perpendicular section of all the muscle's fibers. It should be noted that the fibers are not arranged in the same manner in all muscles. In some muscles they are arranged longitudinally; in some, in spindle-like fashion; in some, fanlike; and in some, feather-like (see p. 22). Obviously a simple cross section of a penniform or a bipenniform muscle will miss a large number of the fibers; hence a true cross section of the muscle's fibers is one which cuts across every fiber in the muscle. Figure 169 illustrates the method of measuring the physiologic cross section of several types of muscles. The cross section does not tell us the actual number of fibers, to be sure, but it corresponds closely enough for us to use this measurement in estimating the muscle's total potential force.

In order to determine the amount of force a particular muscle can exert, it is first necessary to know the amount of force which can be exerted by the average human muscle per unit of its cross section. For this information the student must depend upon the results of experimentation done in the physiology laboratory. Fick, one of the early investigators, found that human muscles exerted a force of 6 to 10 kg. per square centimeter of their cross section. This is approximately 85 to 141 pounds per square inch. Recklinghausen, according to Steindler, concluded from his experimentation that human muscles exerted only 3.6 kg. per square centimeter (approximately 51 pounds per square inch) of cross section. It is as-

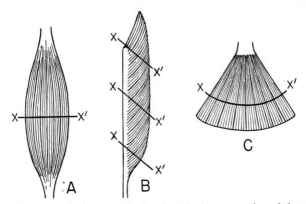

Figure 169. Method of measuring the physiologic cross section of three types of muscles. *A,* A fusiform or spindle muscle; *B,* a penniform muscle; *C,* a triangular or fan-shaped muscle.

sumed that these two investigators used male subjects. A more recent investigator, Morris, found that the muscles of male subjects exerted 9.2 kg. per square centimeter (130 lbs. per square inch), and of female subjects, 7.1 kg. per square centimeter (101 lbs. per square inch). Because of the wide range of figures presented to date, further investigation of this matter would seem desirable. A study of the effect of training on muscular force, per unit of cross section, would also be of interest.

Direction.   The direction of muscular force is determined by the relation of the tendon to the mechanical axis of the segment which it is moving. The axis of the segment does not necessarily pass through the center of the bony lever; in fact, if the bone curves considerably, the greater part of the axis may lie outside the shaft. *The mechanical axis of a bone is a straight line connecting the midpoint of the joint at one end of the bone with the midpoint of the joint at the other end.* The angle between the muscle's line of pull and the mechanical axis of the bone is known as the angle of pull. It is frequently referred to as the angle of insertion, but this is not strictly correct, since the latter term refers to the angle between the tendon and the surface of the bone, rather than to the bone's mechanical axis. In the femur there is a noticeable difference between the two.

The angle of pull is not a fixed angle for every muscle. It changes

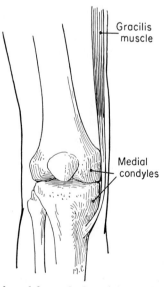

Figure 170.   The medial condyles at the knee joint serving as a pulley to increase the angle of pull of the gracilis tendon.

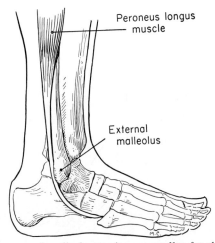

Figure 171. The external malleolus serving as a pulley for the peroneus longus tendon.

its size with every degree of motion. Owing to the anatomic arrangement of muscles, it is likely to be small. The usefulness of the anatomic pulleys (p. 290) is seen here. Were it not for these projecting knobs of bone, some muscles would have very small angles of pull indeed (Fig. 170). It would be extremely difficult for them to move the bony levers. In fact, if ever there were a situation in which a muscle's pull was parallel with the bone's mechanical axis, no motion would result. Hence, in order to produce motion, a force must not only be of sufficient magnitude to overcome the part's inertia, but, in the case of levers, and hence of body segments, it must be applied at an angle.

Point of Application. Although the muscle's attachment is commonly given as the point at which the force is applied to the segment, it is more accurate to give as this point the intersection of the muscle's line of pull with the mechanical axis of the segment. The relation of this point to the fulcrum of the lever, that is, the center of motion in the joint, and the point at which the resistance is applied, determines the class of the lever. Figure 172 shows both the point of application and the angle of pull of a muscle (the biceps) as it acts on a third class lever (the radius).

Components of Muscular Force. As was pointed out above in the discussion of direction, unless a muscle pulls at an angle to the bone's mechanical axis, no motion will result. To the best of the author's knowledge, such a situation does not exist in the body. There are muscles, however, which pull at such a small angle that their importance in contributing to motion would seem to be neg-

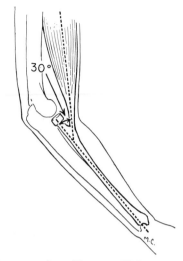

Figure 172. The biceps muscle pulling at a 30-degree angle to the mechanical axis of the radius.

ligible. The coracobrachialis is such a muscle. The subclavius is another. Has nature, then, been grossly inefficient in designing these muscles? Or could it be that these muscles have another function, besides making a direct contribution to the motion of the arm or shoulder girdle? The upper extremity is frequently called upon to perform violent, powerful movements and to support the body weight in suspension. The joints which bear the brunt of this violence and strain are the shoulder and sternoclavicular joints. The violent movements of the arm might easily cause dislocation at these two points, were it not for the coracobrachialis and the subclavius, which pull the bones lengthwise toward their proximal joints and thus serve to stabilize them. Hence muscles are seen to have two functions, movement and *stabilization*. In this way they supplement the ligaments. It is a remarkable example of efficiency, since they contract to perform this stabilizing function only during the period when the part is moving, hence when the integrity of the joints is threatened.

This brings us to the realization that, except when a muscle is pulling at exactly right angles to a bone, muscular force has two components. These are the working or rotatory component (the one that causes the lever to turn) and the nonworking or nonrotatory component. Since the latter is usually in the direction of the proximal joint, it is frequently called the stabilizing component. The fact must not be overlooked, however, that occasionally the position of a body segment is such that a muscle's angle of pull is greater than a right angle. In such instances the nonrotatory component is pulling away from the proximal joint and is therefore a dislocating component. This happens with few muscles, however, and only when the muscle has contracted to its shortest position, which means that it has little force left (Fig. 173). Hence the pull is too weak to produce a dislocation. Furthermore, other muscles assisting in the movement have adequate stabilizing components.

Since a muscle has a completely rotatory effect at the moment it is pulling at right angles to the bone, the rotatory component of force is, by definition, perpendicular to the lever. On the other hand, a muscle pulling lengthwise through the bone (if there were such a case) would be exerting its force parallel with the lever. Hence, by definition, the rotatory and nonrotatory components of force are perpendicular to each other. When the angle of pull is 90 degrees, the force is completely rotatory, there being no components. When the angle of pull is 45 degrees, the rotatory and nonrotatory components are equal. Since more often than not the majority of muscles pull at an angle less than a right angle, a stabilizing component is usually present.

Components of External Force.   External force, like muscular force, may consist of more than one component. If a horizontal push is applied to a piece of furniture, and the push is applied in line with the object's center of gravity, the object will move straight

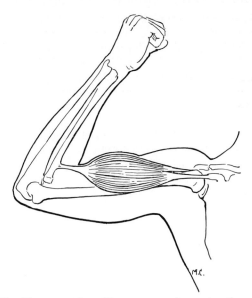

Figure 173. The biceps muscle pulling at an angle greater than a right angle. The nonrotatory component is pulling away from the joint.

forward in a horizontal direction, provided there is no additional conflicting force or resistance to interfere with the object's motion. This is an example of a force which consists of only one component. On the other hand, if one pushes a low piece of furniture by standing close to it with the arms held at a forward-downward slant, there will be two components, a forward one and a downward one. Only the forward component, in this case, is effective for producing the desired motion. The downward component merely increases friction.

If a child's cart is drawn by too short a rope, there will be a relatively large lifting component and a small forward-pulling component. Since the purpose is to pull the cart horizontally, it is more efficient to use a long rope, because this gives a relatively greater horizontal, or pulling, component.

In the case of any object projected through the air there are always two forces operating on it, the propulsive force and the downward force of gravity. The propulsive force frequently consists of two components, a forward and an upward component. If a ball is thrown at an angle of 45 degrees from the horizontal, the upward and forward components of propulsion are equal. The force of gravity, which becomes operative as soon as the ball is released, may not show its effect immediately. The distance traveled by the ball, before the effect of the gravitational force becomes apparent, depends largely upon the magnitude of the propulsive force.

Graphic Representation of Force.   It is sometimes desirable to use diagrams to represent muscular force. For this the same method is used as is used in physics. A force may be represented graphically by an arrow. A short linear unit, such as ⅛ inch, is selected to represent a unit of weight, such as 1 pound. A line is then drawn to scale in the direction that the force is applied, and the head of the arrow is placed at the appropriate end of the line to indicate whether the force is a push or a pull. In the case of muscular force it is always a pull. The arrowhead is therefore at the opposite end from the point at which the force is applied. The diagram in Figure 174 represents a pulling force of 10 pounds applied to point *A* in a horizontal direction from left to right. It is customary to indicate the direction of a muscular force in terms of the angle formed between

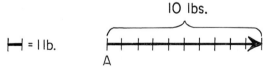

Figure 174. A straight line representing a 10-pound force which is applied to point *A*.

the line of force and the mechanical axis of the bone. Figure 172 shows a muscular force pulling on the radius, at an angle of 30 degrees to the bone's mechanical axis.

True Force and Resistance Arms of Lever; Perpendicular Distance.   In the discussion of levers in Chapter 13 it was assumed that both the force and the resistance were applied at right angles to the lever. Actually, such is seldom the case. We have seen how the direction, or angle of application, affects the function of the force. How does it affect the leverage?

In the earlier examples of leverage, in which the force was applied at right angles to the lever, the force arm was defined as the portion of the lever between the fulcrum and the point at which the force was applied. It might equally well have been defined as the perpendicular distance from the line of force to the fulcrum. Likewise, the resistance arm could have been defined as the perpendicular distance from the line, or direction, of the resistance to the fulcrum. These definitions hold true for all levers, regardless of the angle of application of force or the angle of application of the resistance. Whenever these angles are other than right angles, however, the perpendicular distance must be determined by measurement or by calculation, for it is no longer a portion of the lever itself.

The diagram in Figure 175 represents a muscle which is pulling at an acute angle to the mechanical axis of the bone. The fulcrum or axis of motion is marked *A,* and the point where the force is applied is marked *F*. The portion of the lever, *AF,* is not the true force arm, however, because the muscle's line of pull is not perpendicular to the mechanical axis of the lever. A line drawn from the fulcrum to the muscle's line of pull, at right angles to the latter, is known as the *perpendicular distance* or *true force arm* of the lever. Thus, in the majority of anatomic levers the true force arm is considerably shorter than one might suppose. Two factors determine this perpendicular distance, namely, (1) the angle of pull, and (2) the distance to the point of application of force from the fulcrum. The true resistance arm of a lever is determined in a similar manner.

In Chapter 3 it was stated that the effectiveness of a muscle in causing movement depended upon the leverage and angle of pull, as well as upon the actual force exerted by the muscle. This should now be apparent, since it is seen that the true force arm of the lever is determined by two factors, namely, the distance from the center of the joint to the muscle's line of pull (which in turn is determined by its angle of pull) and the distance from the center of the joint to the point at which the force is applied, i.e., the point at which the muscle attaches to the moving bone. The product of the

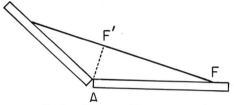

Figure 175. The perpendicular distance, *AF′*, represents the true force arm of the lever.

force, or tension, and the perpendicular distance (F × F′A) is known as the moment of force, or the torque. It is a measure of the muscle's ability to move the anatomic lever. Hence, if the muscle's force and the true force arm are known, the torque may be determined by multiplying them. Or if, on the other hand, the torque and perpendicular distance are known, the muscle's tension, i.e., force, may be found by dividing the torque by the true force arm of the lever, i.e., the perpendicular distance $\left(F = \dfrac{torque}{F′A} \right)$.
In many instances the shortening of a muscle as it moves an anatomic lever is accompanied by an increase in its angle of pull, and consequently in its perpendicular distance or true force arm. Thus an improvement in mechanical advantage compensates partially, at least, for a loss of force.

The reason for the additional questions about levers, which were suggested on page 288, should now be apparent.

The Composite Effect of Two or More Forces. Frequently two or more nonparallel forces are applied to the same object. For instance, a canoe may be acted upon by both the wind and the paddler, one force tending to send the canoe north and the other, east. In the body it is rarely, if ever, the case that an individual muscle acts by itself to move a segment. For example, there are at least four muscles that flex the forearm, and more than five that contribute to flexion of the leg at the knee joint. It might seem that if we knew the magnitude of each force which contributed to the movement in question, we could assume that the total effect of their combined force would be the sum of their respective forces. This is not the case, however, *unless the several forces are applied to the same point and are acting in identical directions.* Possibly there are two such examples in the body, the gastrocnemius and the soleus acting at the ankle joint, and the psoas and the iliacus acting at the hip joint. In each of these examples it will be noted that the two muscles have a common tendon for their distal attachments. In these cases it seems fair to assume that the total force acting upon the part is the sum of the forces exerted by the two muscles.

This is not true, however, when the forces are applied at different angles, that is, in different directions. In order to determine the composite effect of the forces in such cases it is necessary to use the method of finding the resultant of forces known in physics as the composition of forces. It must be pointed out that the method described here is for determining the resultant of two forces acting at an angle to each other and that it is therefore assumed that they have a common point of application. This is not true of the majority of muscles which act on the same bone. Nevertheless the principle of finding the composite effect of two or more forces, both as to magnitude and direction, is as true for forces acting on body segments as for forces acting on external objects. For purposes of illustration, therefore, let us assume that there are two muscles having a common point of attachment, but different angles of pull. Both the magnitude and the direction of the resultant force can be determined by the construction of a *parallelogram of forces* (see p. 319).

The essential facts for the student of kinesiology to learn from this discussion are summarized as follows:

1. The resultant magnitude of two forces is not their arithmetical sum unless the two forces are acting in exactly the same direction.

2. The resultant direction of two forces is not halfway between them unless the two forces are of equal magnitude.

3. The resultant of two forces depends not only upon the magnitude of each force, but also upon the angle of application, i.e., the direction of each force.

4. The same principles apply to muscular forces acting on body segments as apply to muscular and mechanical forces acting on external objects.

5. The multiple muscular action, characteristic of movements of the body segments, is an example of cooperation, not duplication. When several muscles act together to produce a single movement, they act at different points and at different angles. In this way they help to steady and guide the segment throughout its movement.

Work

Mechanically speaking, work is the product of the amount of force expended and the distance over which the force is applied. Thus $W = F \times D$, or more simply, $W = FD$. This equation applies not only to the work of machines, but also to muscular work when the latter is considered from the mechanical, rather than the physiologic, point of view.

If the force of the muscle is not known, it is computed from the muscle's physiologic cross section (see p. 307). The distance over which the force is applied is represented by the distance that the muscle fibers shorten. This has been found to be approximately one half of their resting length. The student is cautioned that neither the cross section nor the fiber length can be judged from the exterior of the muscle. In penniform and bipenniform muscles the physiologic cross section is considerably greater than the anatomic cross section, and the muscle fibers are considerably shorter than is the muscle as a whole. The internal structure of the muscle must be taken into consideration when one estimates the work that the muscle is capable of performing.

If the force of the muscle has not already been determined, a single formula may be used for computing the amount of work of which the muscle is capable. Assuming that a human muscle can exert 75 pounds of force to the square inch and that muscle fibers contract approximately one half of their resting length, the equation is as follows:

$W = 75 \times$ the physiologic cross section of muscle in square inches $\times$ ½ the length of the fibers in inches.

This will give work in terms of inch pounds. Since it is customary to measure work in terms of foot pounds, the number of inch pounds should be divided by 12.

Supplementary Material

Methods of Determining the Components of Force.   It is a simple matter to find the components of a muscular force when the muscle's total force and angle of pull are known. It can be found either by the use of trigonometry or by constructing a right triangle to scale.

Trigonometric Method.   Although this method requires the use of trigonometry, it is not necessary for the student to have any previous knowledge of this subject. A table of sines and cosines, and a few facts concerning the fixed relationships which exist between the sides and the angles of a right triangle, provide all the necessary information. These facts are as follows:

DEFINITIONS (see Fig. 176):

The "side opposite" is the side which faces the known acute angle in a right triangle.

The hypotenuse is the side which faces the right angle in a right triangle.

The "side adjacent" is the remaining side. It lies between the known acute angle and the right angle in a right triangle.

RELATIONSHIPS IN A RIGHT TRIANGLE:

The square of the hypotenuse equals the sum of the squares of the other two sides.

The sine of an angle is the ratio of the "side opposite" to the hypotenuse.

The cosine of an angle is the ratio of the "side adjacent" to the hypotenuse.

Hence, in Figure 176:

The sine of angle $Y = O/H$

The cosine of angle $Y = A/H$

APPLICATIONS TO MUSCULAR FORCE:

Problem: The muscle in the diagram (Fig. 177) has a force of 150 pounds acting at the distal attachment of the muscle and pulling at an angle of 30 degrees. Find the two components of force.

Method: Construct a right triangle, one angle of which is 30 degrees. This triangle may be superimposed on the original diagram. To do this, a perpendicular should be erected from any point along the long axis of the bone between the joint and the point of attachment. This perpendicular represents the rotatory component of force. The distance along the axis of the bone between the perpendicular and the point of attachment represents the nonrotatory component. The hypotenuse of the triangle, or the portion of the muscle's line of pull between the point of attachment and the perpendicular, represents the total force of the muscle (see Fig. 178, *A*). If desired, instead of superimposing the right triangle on the original diagram, a separate right triangle may be drawn (Fig. 178, *B*). The size of the triangle is immaterial, provided the proportions are correct.

Referring to a table of sines and cosines, we find that the sine of a 30-degree angle is .5, and the cosine, .866. If the sine of angle $Y = O/H$, then .5 = $O/150$, and O must equal 75. Since O represents the rotatory components, the latter must be 75 pounds.

If the cosine of angle $Y = A/H$, then .866 = $A/150$, and A must equal 129.9, or approximately 130. Hence the nonrotatory component equals approximately 130 pounds.*

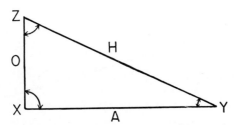

Figure 176. A right triangle in which $X =$ the right angle, Y and $Z =$ the two acute angles respectively, $H =$ the hypotenuse, $A =$ the side adjacent (to Y), and $O =$ the side opposite (to Y).

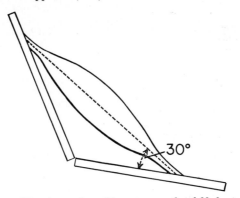

Figure 177. A muscle pulling at an angle of 30 degrees.

* It may surprise the student to discover that the sum of the components is greater than the total force. He should remember the facts concerning a right triangle, however. The square of the hypotenuse equals the sum of the squares of the other two sides.

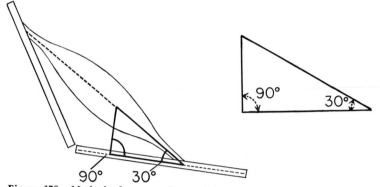

Figure 178. Method of constructing a right triangle for the purpose of determining the components of muscular force by the trigonometric method. Note that the hypotenuse coincides with a portion of the muscle's line of pull, and the side adjacent with the mechanical axis of the bone into which the muscle is inserted.

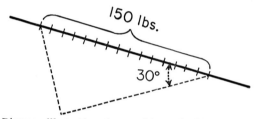

Figure 179. Diagram illustrating the graphic method of determining the components of muscular force.

Warning: The angle under consideration is the angle formed by the attachment of the muscle (that is, the muscle's line of pull) to the long axis of the moving bone. Pay no attention to the angle of the joint between the two bones, or to the angle between the muscle's line of pull and the stationary bone. Drawing a separate diagram, as in Figure 178, *B*, will help the student to avoid this pitfall.

Graphic Method.   Select a linear unit of measurement to represent a unit of force, such as ⅛ inch to represent 10 pounds of force. Draw a diagonal line to scale, the units of length representing the pounds of total force exerted by the muscle. At one end of this diagonal construct an angle equal to the angle of pull. Continue the side of this angle until it is nearly as long as the original line. From the other end of the diagonal drop a line which will be perpendicular to the second line. Measure the length of each of the two lines drawn from the ends of the diagonal. The line adjacent to the angle of pull represents the non-rotatory component of force, and the line opposite the angle of pull represents the rotatory component of force. This method is simple, but it requires accurate use of the ruler and protractor.

    EXAMPLE (see Fig. 179):
        The force of the muscle = 150 pounds
        The angle of pull = 30 degrees
        Let ⅛ inch = 10 pounds

Construct a diagram according to the directions. Measure the lower line. It is found to equal 13 units, that is, 13 × ⅛ inch. Now measure the up-and-down line. It is found to equal 7½ units, or 7½ × ⅛ inch. By computation we find that 13 × 10 = 130 pounds of nonrotatory or stabilizing force, and that 7½ × 10 = 75 pounds of rotatory force.

Method of Constructing a Parallelogram of Forces for Determining the Composite Effect of Two Forces.*   The composite effect of two forces is determined by the construction of a parallelogram, the sides of which are linear representations of the two forces. The first step is to mark a point on a piece of paper. This represents the point at which the two forces are applied. From this point two lines are drawn to scale, with the correct angle between them, that is, the same angle which actually exists between the two forces. By using these two lines as two sides of a parallelogram, the other two sides are constructed by a simple geometric method (Fig. 180). The diagonal is then drawn from the point of application to the opposite corner. This diagonal represents, both in magnitude and in direction, the composite effect of the two separate forces. It is known as the resultant of forces.

Note: The student should note that the angle between two muscular forces is the difference between their respective angles of pull.

Measurement of Muscle Strength Relative to Cross Section.   In 1948 Morris conducted a study for the purpose of measuring the strength of muscles per square centimeter of cross section. Using twelve college men and twelve college women as her subjects, she computed the areas of the flexor and extensor muscles of the forearm and lower leg by means of a formula based on width, depth and circumference measurements of the upper arm and thigh. These measurements were corrected for fat. To determine the approximate area of each muscle to be tested, she obtained the average proportion of each muscle from two sets of cross section drawings. By means of measurements made on x-rays she determined the leverage in which each muscle was involved. The mechanical efficiency of each muscle was computed by the use of the ratio, $\dfrac{FA}{RA}$. She then tested the forearm flexors, forearm extensors, leg flexors and leg extensors of each subject by means of the Martin breaking point test. From the data so obtained she computed the strength of each muscle per square centimeter of cross section. According to her findings, "the unweighted average of muscle strength was slightly above 9.2 K/cm.² for men and 7.1 K/cm.² for women." She concluded that, in general, her findings upheld those of Fick, but not those of Recklinghausen.

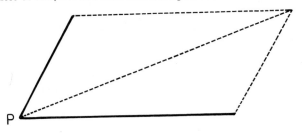

P = Point of application of two forces.

Figure 180.   A "parallelogram of forces" used for determining the composite effect of two forces.

* When one wishes to determine the resultant of three or more forces, a polygon, rather than a parallelogram, must be constructed. Directions for this procedure may be found in any standard physics text.

Figure 181. What is the approximate force that this muscle can exert? (Scale: ⅛ inch = 1 inch)

Figure 182. The humerus.

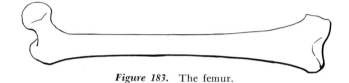

Figure 183. The femur.

Demonstrations, Laboratory Exercises and Problems

Note: Assume that the muscles can exert a force of 100 pounds per square inch of cross section.

1. How much force can each of the following muscles exert?
   Muscle A, having a cross section of 2 square inches.
   Muscle B, having a cross section of 4 square inches.
   Muscle C, having a cross section of 13 square inches.

2. Find the approximate force of which the muscle shown in Figure 181 is capable. Assume that the diagram is drawn to scale, ⅛ inch being the equivalent of 1 inch. The muscle is 1 inch thick.

3. Estimate the cross section of your own biceps muscle. Approximately how much force should it be able to exert?

4. Approximately how much force should your triceps be able to exert?

5. Measure the width of your gastrocnemius. Assume that it is 1 inch thick. Look at a picture of the muscle to see the slant of the fibers. Estimate the physiologic cross section of your muscle and calculate the amount of force it should be able to exert.

6. On each of the diagrams in Figures 182 and 183 draw a line representing the mechanical axis of the bone.

7. Referring to Figure 118 (p. 217), make a tracing of the femur and the adductor longus muscle. By using a ruler and a small protractor, find the angle of pull of the adductor longus in its resting position.

Suggestion: Draw a line representing the muscle's line of pull, also one representing the mechanical axis of the femur. Which is larger, the rotatory or the nonrotatory component? Is the latter a stabilizing or a dislocating component?

8. In the diagram of the biceps muscle in Figure 184, find the size of the angle of pull.

9. Using the data from question 5, draw an arrow (to a scale of your own choosing) which represents the magnitude and direction of the force exerted by your gastrocnemius muscle on the calcaneus bone. Assume that you are standing erect.

10. Using the scale, ⅛ inch = 1 inch, determine the true force arm of the forearm lever in Figure 184.

11. For each of the following anatomic levers estimate the approximate length of the true force arm, i.e., the perpendicular distance. Refer to anatomic illustrations or to a muscle manikin to help you estimate the angle of pull of the muscles. Unless otherwise stated, assume that the segments are in their normal resting position. (*Hint:* Use the mechanical axis of the segment for the lever.)

    a. The forearm lever with the biceps providing the force.

    b. The upper arm lever with the middle deltoid providing the force.

    c. The thigh lever with the adductor longus providing the force.

    d. The upper arm lever in the side-horizontal position with the entire pectoralis major providing the force. (*Hint:* Which view would show you the angle of pull for this movement, facing the subject or looking down from above?)

    e. Same lever as in *d*, with the anterior deltoid providing the force.

12. Referring to the diagrams in Figure 6 (p. 26), assume that a weight is suspended from the wrist. Find the true resistance arm of the forearm lever in positions *A, B* and *C*. Consider that the scale for these diagrams is 9 inches to the inch.

13. Assume that a muscle having a force of 300 pounds is pulling at an angle of 75 degrees. Find the components of force (*a*) by the trigonometric method; (*b*) by the graphic method.

14. Assuming that the weight used in question 12 is 8 pounds, determine the rotatory and nonrotatory components of the weight (*a*) by the trigonometric method; (*b*) by the graphic method.

15. Determine the amount of work (in foot pounds) performed by each of the following hypothetical muscles:

Muscle A, capable of a total force of 240 pounds and having fibers with an average length of 6 inches.

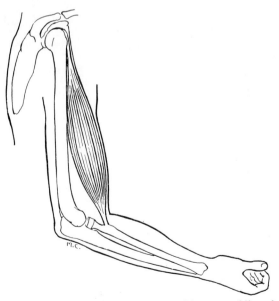

Figure 184. The forearm as a lever with the biceps providing the force.

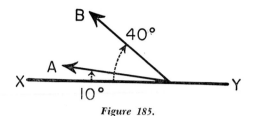

Figure 185.

Muscle B, capable of a total force of 150 pounds and having fibers with an average length of 24 inches.

Muscle C, having a cross section of 4 square inches and fibers with an average length of 12 inches.

16. Repeat problem 6 on page 320, this time estimating the angle of application and determining the true force arm of the lever from a diagram drawn to scale.

17. In Figure 185 muscle *A* has a force of 200 pounds and is pulling on the bone *X-Y* at an angle of 10 degrees. Muscle *B* has a force of 175 pounds and is pulling at an angle of 40 degrees. Find the composite effect of these two muscles in terms of (*a*) the amount of force; and (*b*) the direction, i.e., the angle, of pull. (*Hint:* Read the note on page 319.)

Bibliography

1. Amar, J.: The Human Motor. New York, E. P. Dutton & Co., 1920.
2. Arkin, A. M.: Absolute Muscle Power: The Internal Kinesiology of Muscle. Arch. Surg., *42:* 395–410, 1941.
3. Bowen, W. P., and Stone, H. A.: Applied Anatomy and Kinesiology. 7th ed. Philadelphia, Lea & Febiger, 1953.
4. Elftman, H.: Skeletal and Muscular Systems: Structure and Function. Medical Physics (1420–1430). Chicago, Year Book Publishers, Inc., 1944.
5. Fick, R.: Review of Literature on Mechanics of Joints and Muscles. Ztschr. f. Orthop. Chir., *51:* 320–337 (March 28) 1929.
6. Gray, H.: The Anatomy of the Human Body. 26th ed. Philadelphia, Lea & Febiger, 1954.
7. Luhr, O.: Physics Tells Why. 2nd ed. New York, Ronald Press, 1946, Chap. 2.
8. Morris, C. B.: The Measurement of the Strength of Muscle Relative to the Cross Section. Research Quarterly of Am. Assn. for Health, Phys. Ed. and Rec., *19:* 295–303 (Dec.) 1948.
9. Scott, M. G.: Analysis of Human Motion. New York, F. S. Crofts & Co., 1945, Chaps. 4, 6, 8.
10. Steindler, A.: Kinesiology of the Human Body. Springfield, Ill., Charles C Thomas, 1955, Lecture V.
11. Steindler, A.: What Has Biokinetics to Offer to the Physical Educator? J. Health and Phys. Educ., *13:* 507–509, 555, 556 (Nov.) 1942.
12. White, M. W., Manning, K. V., Weber, R. L., Cornett, R. O., and others: Practical Physics. 2nd ed. New York, McGraw-Hill Book Co., 1955.

Recommended Readings

Bowen, W. P., and Stone, H. A.: Applied Anatomy and Kinesiology. (See 3 above.) Chapter 1.
Luhr, O.: Physics Tells Why. (See 7 above.) Chapter 2.
Scott, M. G.: Analysis of Human Motion. (See 9 above.) Chapters 4, 6, 8.

Steindler, A.: Kinesiology of the Human Body. (See 10 above.)

Steindler, A.: What Has Biokinetics to Offer to the Physical Educator? (See 11 above.)

White, M. W., Manning, K. V., Weber, R. L., Cornett, R. O., and others: Practical Physics. (See 12 above.)

III · Underlying Principles of Basic Motor Skills

16 · Bases for the Development of Motor Skills

ONE OF THE FIRST requisites for the development of motor skills is the ability to recognize the elements of skillful performance. Teachers of physical education and therapists in the field of physical medicine are concerned not merely with performance in various activities, but with *skillful performance*. Hence, in a study of kinesiology, one rightly expects to learn how to recognize the qualities that distinguish between awkward and skillful movement, and to consider the basic principles which underlie motor skills.

There are a few general characteristics of skillful performance which are easily recognized. Efficient motion is one of the most important of these. Efficiency refers to the relationship between the amount of work accomplished and the force or energy expended. In mechanics we have seen that efficiency is expressed as the ratio of output to input. In human motion it is the ratio of the external work accomplished to the muscular energy expended. Whereas the greatest hindrance to mechanical efficiency is doubtless friction, in human motion it is unproductive muscular effort. The poorly coordinated person and the novice tend to make superfluous movements or to have unnecessary tensions. The characteristic of efficient bodily motion is the absence of waste movements, the use of the correct muscles with no more than the needed amount of force, and the relaxation of all muscles which do not contribute either directly or indirectly to the task. It results in smoothness and grace, in what is commonly called well coordinated movement. In relaxation terminology the same quality is known as "differen-

Figure 186. An example of skillful performance. (Courtesy of Springfield College.)

tial relaxation." This means simply the ability to relax the unneeded muscles while performing a motor skill. It is an important characteristic of skillful performance, since waste movements and unnecessary tensions not only make for awkward performance, but also hasten the onset of fatigue and increase its intensity. As Steindler has said, ". . . skillful or perfect motion always involves the least expenditure of effort . . ." for the work accomplished.[15] In rapid movements efficiency is characterized by a ballistic type of motion (see p. 46).

Another characteristic of skillful performance is *accuracy.* One may shoot at a basket with a beautifully coordinated and efficient movement, but unless the ball goes into the basket, the player is not considered skillful. Accuracy is based on a combination of factors, namely, good judgment of direction, distance and force, proper timing, and good muscular control. It is needed in simple acts such as lifting a forkful of food to the mouth, as well as in more complicated acts such as pole vaulting and pitching a baseball.

Closely related to the characteristics already mentioned are those of *adequate strength, speed* and *power*. Power implies the speed with which force is exerted. It is an important characteristic of skillful performance in such activities as high jumping, broad jumping, throwing, striking and kicking, and in speed events such as sprinting and swimming.

Judgment has already been mentioned as a factor in accuracy. It is more than that, however. In dual and team games and in boxing and wrestling, good judgment is one of the most important characteristics of skillful performance. It implies a sizing up of the situation and choosing wisely between several possible responses. It marks the difference between using one's head and acting blindly, between intelligent and unintelligent participation.

The general characteristics of skillful performance may therefore be summed up as *efficiency, accuracy, good judgment* and *ade-*

Figure 187. An example of skillful motion. (Anne Ross, Senior National A. A. U. Champion, 1941–1944; Senior National A. A. U. Highboard Champion, 1942–1944; Member of All-America Swimming Team, 1941–1944.)

Figure 188.   An example of skillful performance. (Courtesy of Springfield College.)

quate speed, strength and *power* for the task. There are of course the factors of *special aptitudes* which make one person a potential sprinter, and another a potential high jumper. These are related to build, to constitution and to temperament. It is a matter of common observation that greater skillfulness is achieved by individuals who happen to be endowed with greater aptitudes or innate

Figure 189. Examples of skillful performance. (Courtesy of Springfield College.)

Figure 190. An example of skillful performance. (Courtesy of Springfield College.)

capacities for certain kinds of accomplishments. Great individual differences are seen with respect to the various factors of motor ability such as hand-eye coordination, agility, reaction time and finger dexterity. To be sure, all these can be developed by practice, but not everyone can develop them to the same degree, for there is a wide range in native capacity.

The truly skillful performer is one who habitually obeys the principles of both the anatomic and the mechanical aspects of human motion. His neuromuscular coordination is at peak performance; his muscular function is highly efficient; his kinesthetic sense is well developed; his flexor and extensor reflexes are dependable; the movements of his joints are commensurate with his individual structure; and his techniques of motion are in accord with the laws of his physical environment. In short, he has learned how, and has made it his practice, to observe the principles of skillful motion.

It is hoped that this kinesiologic approach to the consideration of fundamental motor skills will help to give the physical education teacher, the athletic coach, the physical therapist, and the occupational therapist the proper background for applying the methods and techniques of his profession. Through a thorough understanding of the anatomic and the mechanical principles underlying the skills, of the demands made upon the body by the activities, and of the ways in which application of the principles may lead to more skillful performance, the kinesiologist becomes a true educator in the field of motor activities. Although it is possible to teach basketball or to give a massage without ever having studied kinesiology, just as it is possible to build a house without having studied architecture, it seems obvious that the average person will do a better job, be less likely to make costly mistakes, and be better prepared to solve unexpected problems if he is thoroughly grounded in the fundamental principles which apply to his particular field of interest. In physical education the well-prepared teacher is able to develop more skillful performance among his students, among the "dubs" as well as the stars. He is also more aware of the physical needs and limitations of each student and sees to it that all individuals are in better condition at the close of their season of instruction than they were at the beginning. The well-prepared therapist, likewise, is keenly aware of what he is doing when he attempts to increase the range of motion in a post-traumatic joint or to restore tonus to an atrophied muscle.

Anatomic Principles of Skillful Motion

Since the principles derived from anatomy and physiology apply to human motion in general, the most noteworthy of these are stated in this introductory chapter, rather than in the chapters on specific types of motor skills. They are listed briefly in the form of guiding principles. The list is by no means exhaustive. For further principles one should turn to the field of physiology of exercise.

Principles Relating to the Structure and Function of Joints

1. Since the range of motion may be limited by tight muscles, fasciae or ligaments, it may be increased by the stretching of these tissues.

2. The stretching of tight muscles, fasciae or ligaments should be done gradually and should be preceded by warm-up activities. The danger of rupturing soft tissues is minimized when they have been adequately "warmed-up."

3. Increase gained in the range of motion will be lost unless it is deliberately retained by means of continued exercise.

4. Flexibility of weight-bearing joints should not exceed the ability of the muscles to maintain the body segments in good alignment.

Principles Relating to the Muscular System and to Neuromuscular Function

1. All strenuous activity should be preceded by warm-up pro-

cedures, since these reduce the viscosity of the muscles. Reduction of viscosity not only helps to safeguard against tearing injuries, but also improves the efficiency of muscular function by reducing internal resistance. Muscles contract more rapidly after warm-up activities.

2. Muscles contract more forcefully if they are first put on a stretch, provided they are not overstretched. This principle and the preceding one suggest the function of the "wind-up" in pitching and of the preliminary movements in other sport skills.

3. Increase in muscular strength is brought about by increasing the demands made on muscles. This is known as the overload principle. It means that a muscle must be loaded beyond its customary load if strength is to be increased. This principle forms the basis for conditioning exercises and is the principle on which the system of "progressive resistance exercise" is based.[8] *Strength will not be progressively developed by the mere repetition of exercises of the same intensity.*

4. Unnecessary movements and tensions in the performance of a motor skill mean both awkwardness and unnecessary fatigue; hence they should be eliminated. This is achieved by first developing kinesthetic awareness of muscular tension, and then learning how to relax unneeded muscles.

5. Skillful, efficient performance in a particular technique can be developed only by practice of that technique. Only in this way can the necessary adjustments in the neuromuscular mechanism be made to assure a well coordinated movement.

6. Fatigue from overpractice diminishes skillful performance. It can be avoided by introducing properly spaced rest periods in the practice period.

7. The most efficient type of movement in throwing and striking skills is ballistic movement. Skills which are primarily ballistic should be practiced ballistically even in the earliest learning stages. This means that from the beginning the emphasis should be placed on form rather than on accuracy. Accuracy will develop with practice. If the emphasis is placed on accuracy in the learning stages, the beginner tends to perform the skill as a "moving fixation" or slow, tense movement. Once this pattern of movement is established, it is extremely difficult to change it later to a ballistic movement.

8. An important factor in the learning and perfecting of a motor skill is kinesthetic perception. A positive relationship between kinesthesis and certain motor skills has been demonstrated.[4, 9, 17] There is no evidence of a general kinesthetic sense, however.[16] Kinesthetic perception appears to be specific for the skill in question.

9. Reflex responses of the neuromuscular system should be recognized and should be utilized when such utilization is clearly indi-

cated. This statement is intentionally general because much more needs to be learned about some of the physiologic reflexes before specific principles can be derived from them and suggestions for their application recommended. While it seems appropriate to recommend the application of the well known extensor reflex to postural adjustments, as Dr. Royal S. Haynes has done, and to utilize the principle of reciprocal innervation in teaching ballistic motion, one needs to exercise extreme caution in applying less readily understood reflexes, such as the tonic neck and labyrinthine reflexes, to the treatment of patients suffering from disorders of the central nervous system. Brunnstrom, who has abstracted two articles by German investigators, warned the reader that applications of principles discovered in animal experimentation cannot be made to human beings without modification. That these and similar experiments have implications for treatment is doubtless true, but the findings of the laboratory need to undergo analysis and modification by experts before they can be adapted to the needs of the treatment room.

10. When there is a choice of anatomic leverage, the lever appropriate for the task should be used, i.e., a lever with a long force arm for movements requiring strength, and a lever with a long resistance arm for movements requiring range or speed. For example, kicking is an effective way of imparting force to a football because the leg provides a lever with a long resistance arm, but, for the same reason, it is a poor way of moving a heavy suitcase along the floor.

As an aid to studying the specific principles which pertain to the various types of activities, a classification of these activities is helpful. It not only provides a means of systemizing such study, but also enables one more readily to recognize the common elements in the different activities. For instance, chopping a tree, batting a baseball and putting the shot may seem like totally different kinds of skills, yet they are all forms of giving impetus to an external object, and hence are based on the same underlying principles. Familiarity with one skill in a group should facilitate the learning of any other skill in that group if the basic principles are recognized and applied. A classification of motor skills will often reveal such relationships which might not otherwise be apparent.

There are many possible classifications of activity skills. The student should select whichever one seems best suited to his purposes, or he may wish to devise his own. In suggesting the following classification the author acknowledges her debt to Glassow, Scott and Powell, each of whom has suggested an excellent classification.

Classification of Motor Skills

I. Skills of maintaining and regaining equilibrium
II. Skills of moving one's own body
    A. On land or other solid surface
        1. Arm, leg and trunk movements
        2. Locomotion
        3. Rotatory movements of the body as a whole
    B. In water
        1. Swimming
        2. Aquatic stunts
        3. Boating
    C. In the air
        1. Diving
        2. Trampoline and tumbling activities
    D. In suspension
        1. Swinging activities on trapeze, flying rings, etc.
        2. Hand traveling on traveling rings, horizontal ladder, etc.
III. Skills of receiving impetus
    A. Of own body
        1. Landing from jumps and falls
    B. Of external objects
        1. Catching and trapping
        2. Receiving with an implement
        3. Receiving and spotting in stunts and apparatus events
IV. Skills of giving impetus to external objects
    A. Pushing, pulling, thrusting, lifting
    B. Throwing with hand or implement
    C. Striking, hitting, kicking, etc.
V. The selection and classification of skills related to prevention of injury
    A. The maintenance of equilibrium and prevention of a fall
    B. The range of motion
    C. The intensity and duration of muscular exercise
    D. The transmission of weight through the bodily segments and the weight-bearing joints
    E. The reception of one's own weight
    F. The lifting and carrying of heavy objects
    G. The impact of external forces

Many activities involve several of these skills. For instance, a running high jump includes skills of locomotion, jumping, balance and safety. Likewise, the activities involved in carpentry may include skills of locomotion, balance and the giving and the receiving of impetus. The kinesiology student should be able to take any activity which can be classed as a motor skill, whether from the field of sport, of industry, of gardening or of homemaking—learn to break it down into its basic skills, analyze these both anatomically and mechanically, and finally identify the factors which contribute to or detract from, skillful performance in this activity. As an aid to analysis it is suggested that the student use an outline such as that given below. This is not intended as a rigid form, but merely as a guide to help the student in his analytical thinking. The form of the analysis used by the physical education student or by the student therapist should be adapted to his particular needs. The form used for the analysis of a therapeutic type of activity might well be different from that used for sports or for the dance. The outline presented here is a general one for the student of kinesiology. The items included in it are discussed in the remaining chapters of Part III.

Outline for the Kinesiologic Analysis of a Movement

Description of the movement
Purpose of the movement
Type of movement
  Translatory
    Rectilinear
    Curvilinear
  Rotatory (angular)
    Axis (axes) of rotation
    Approximate degrees of rotation
  Slow movement ("moving fixation")
  Ballistic movement
    How terminated?
    By the contraction of antagonistic muscles
    By the passive resistance of ligaments, muscles or fasciae at the limit of motion
    By the interference of an obstacle
Skill classification
  Maintaining or regaining equilibrium
  Postural
  Moving one's own body
    On land or other solid surface
    In water
    In the air without support
    Suspended
  Receiving impetus
    Of own body
    Of external object
  Giving impetus to external object
Anatomic analysis
  Joint and muscle analysis of essential parts of movement
  Anatomic principles
Mechanical analysis
  Mechanical problems and principles of essential parts of movement
Common faults and their correction
Precautions for avoiding strain and injury
Evaluation
  How well does the movement accomplish its purpose?
  Is the described form the best for fulfilling the objectives of efficiency, accuracy, and adequate strength, speed and power?

Demonstrations and Laboratory Exercises

Observe or practice the activities listed. Then, using as a guide the outline presented above, analyze them from the point of view of skill classification, mechanical aspects, and joint and muscle function.

1. Throwing a baseball
2. Bowling
3. Using a jigsaw
4. Weaving on a large loom
5. Rising from a chair
6. Walking on crutches with one good leg
7. Pushing a lawnmower or a hand snowplow

Bibliography

1. Brunnstrom, S.: Abstract of "Haltung" by Rudolph Magnus. Phys. Ther. Rev., *33:* 281–290, 1953.
2. Brunnstrom, S.: Abstract of "Head Posture and Muscle Tone" by A. Simons. Phys. Ther. Rev., *33:* 409–419, 1953.
3. Glassow, R. B.: Fundamentals in Physical Education. Philadelphia, Lea & Febiger, 1932.
4. Glassow, R. B.: A Laboratory Manual for Functional Kinesiology. Madison, Wis., Kramer Business Service, 1950.
5. Haynes, R. S.: Postural Reflexes in Relation to the Correction of Improper Body Position. Am. J. Dis. Child., *36:* 1095–1107, 1928.
6. Hoke, R. L.: Factors Conditioning Efficiency in Motor Skill. J. Exper. Psych., *15:* 316–330, 1932.
7. Morehouse, L. E., and Cooper, J. M.: Kinesiology. St. Louis, C. V. Mosby Company, 1950.
8. Morehouse, L. E., and Miller, A. T.: Physiology of Exercise. 2nd ed. St. Louis, C. V. Mosby Company, 1953.
9. Phillips, B. E.: The Relationship between Certain Phases of Kinesthesis and Performance during the Early Stages of Acquiring Two Percepto-Motor Skills. Research Quarterly of Am. Assn. for Health, Phys. Ed. & Recr., *12:* 571–586, 1941.
10. Powell, E.: Unpublished Syllabus of Kinesiology Course, Wellesley College, 1936.
11. Salit, E. Powell: The Development of Fundamental Sport Skills in College Women of Low Motor Ability. Research Quarterly of Am. Assn. for Health, Phys. Ed. & Recr., *15:* 330–339, 1944.
12. Scott, M. G.: Analysis of Human Motion. New York, F. S. Crofts & Co., 1945.
13. Scott, M. G.: Kinesiology Handbook; A Study Guide and Laboratory Manual. New York, F. S. Crofts & Co., 1947.
14. Seashore, R. H.: Individual Differences in Motor Skills. J. Gen. Psych., *11:* 38–66, 1930.
15. Steindler, A.: Mechanics of Normal and Pathological Locomotion in Man. Springfield, Ill., Charles C Thomas, 1935, p. 13.
16. Wiebe, V. R.: A Study of Tests of Kinesthesis. Research Quarterly of the Am. Assn. for Health, Phys. Ed. and Recr., *25:* 222–230, 1954.
17. Young, O. G.: A Study of Kinesthesis in Relation to Selected Movements. Research Quarterly of Am. Assn. for Health, Phys. Ed. & Recr., *16:* 277–287, 1945.

Recommended Readings

Glassow, R. B.: A Laboratory Manual for Functional Kinesiology. (See 4 above.)
Salit, E. P.: The Development of Fundamental Sport Skills in College Women of Low Motor Ability. (See 11 above.)

17 · Principles of Stability

BECAUSE MAN ordinarily holds himself in an upright position, and because the law of gravity is always in operation, the problem of stability is ever present. Probably the only time the human body is not adjusting itself in response to gravitational force is when it is in a position of repose, either lying down or reclining with all its parts completely supported. Either consciously or unconsciously, man spends most of his waking hours adjusting his position in order to resist the pull of gravity upon his body.

The ability to maintain one's balance under unfavorable circumstances is recognized as one of the basic motor skills. It is an indication of skill, for instance, to keep one's balance while walking a rail, landing from a jump, throwing and catching swift balls, and making quick changes of direction in a game situation. Hence stability is not limited to stationary positions of the body. It is an essential factor in many movements. In the giving and receiving of impetus the player's accuracy is largely dependent upon his stability preceding, during and following the act. In the giving of impetus, for instance, the magnitude and direction of force and the accuracy of applying it to the external object are influenced by the general control and stability of the body as a whole. The importance of the stance in this connection should be recognized. The stance represents the base of support, and this is one of the major factors in stability. The optimal stance for each sport is the one best adapted to the skill in question. It combines the requirements for stability with those for giving and receiving impetus, or with those for quick movements in a particular direction. Hence the stance is an important factor in pitching, batting, a tennis serve, forehand and backhand drives in tennis, and all strokes in golf. It is equally important in industries which involve manipulative activities in the standing position. One of the chief vocational problems of the amputee and the victim of paralysis is maintaining an adequate stance for the job in spite of the impairment of stability.

Familiarity with the following factors of stability will enable the student to analyze his balance problems and may suggest to the teacher the means of helping his less skillful students. It should also enable the therapist to help the amputee and the victim of paralysis to regain their lost sense of equilibrium.

The Height of the Center of Gravity.   Ordinarily the center of gravity is located approximately at the level of the upper third of the sacrum. Experiments have shown that in man the height of the center of gravity is about 56 per cent of his height;[8] and in woman, about 55 per cent of her height.[6] These figures hold true only for the normal standing position. If the arms are raised or if a weight is carried above waist height, the center of gravity shifts to a higher position, and equilibrium becomes more difficult to maintain. Activities and stunts, such as walking on stilts, canoeing, and balancing a weight on the head, are difficult or dangerous because of the relatively high center of gravity. Lowering the center of gravity will increase the stability of the body. If, for any reason, the equilibrium is too precarious in the standing position, assuming a crouching, kneeling or sitting position will lower the center of gravity and increase stability.

The Size of the Base of Support.   It is self-evident that a wide base of support adds to the stability of an object. Most of the difficulty experienced in walking on a balance beam, a railroad track or a tightrope, in ice skating and in toe dancing is due to the small base of support. The problem is to keep the center of gravity over the base of support, a requisite for maintaining equilibrium. The wider the base, the easier it is to keep the center of gravity directly above it.

In a man whose weight is supported entirely by his feet, the base of support includes not only his two feet, but also the intervening area. If the feet are separated, the base is widened and the equilibrium improved. An individual on crutches will be more stable if he places the crutches forward, making a triangular base instead of a linear one. There is another factor, however, that must not be overlooked. If one takes a stance that is wider than the breadth of the pelvis, the legs will assume a slanting position. This introduces a lateral component of force. If this is accompanied by insufficient friction between the feet and the supporting surface, as when standing on ice, obviously a widening of the base of support does not make for greater stability. In fact, the wider the stance, the less one can control the sliding of the feet. From this we see that we must observe *all* the principles which apply to a situation. Observance of only one may not bring the results expected.

The Relation of the Line of Gravity to the Base of Support. This factor is closely related to the preceding one. Since an object retains its equilibrium only so long as its line of gravity falls within its base of support, it follows that the nearer the line of gravity to the *center* of the base of support, the greater the stability (Fig. 191); conversely, the nearer the line of gravity to the *margin* of the base of support, the more precarious the equilibrium (Fig. 192). Once it passes beyond the margin, stability is lost and a new base must be established. It is this factor which constitutes the major problem in some modern dance techniques, in balance stunts, in walking a tightrope and in building pyramids. There is nothing that takes the place of repeated practice for developing the neuromuscular control necessary for acquiring such skills as these. There are, however, a few devices that help one to keep the center of gravity centered over the base of support. One of these we do almost unconsciously. If we carry a heavy weight at one side of the body (e.g., a suitcase or a pail of cement), *this constitutes a unilateral* load which, if uncompensated, would shift the center of gravity to that side, bringing it dangerously close to the margin of the base

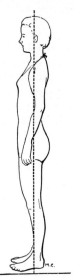

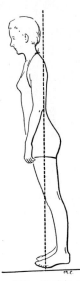

Figure 191. Position of the body in which the line of gravity falls approximately through the center of the base of support. This is a stable position.

Figure 192. Position of the body in which the line of gravity falls near the anterior margin of the base of support. This position is less stable than the one shown in Figure 191.

Figure 193. Compensating for a unilateral load by leaning to opposite side.

Figure 194. Compensation for a unilateral load by means of a slight shift of the entire body to the opposite side.

of support. By raising the opposite arm sideways, or by leaning to the opposite side, we counterbalance the external load and keep the line of gravity close to the center of the base of support (Figs. 193 and 194). Another application of the principle of keeping the line of gravity over the center of the base of support is seen in the tightrope walker who carries a balancing pole, or, to a less degree, in the gymnast walking on a balance beam with his arms extended sideward. The pole, or the arm, acts as a lever, and the reaction of a lever is in proportion to its length. Even a slight movement at the end of a long lever has a considerable reaction at the other end. Hence, if the tightrope walker starts to lean too far to the left, an almost imperceptible downward movement of the right end of the pole will be sufficient to help him regain his balance.

The Mass of the Body.   The mass or weight of an object is a factor in equilibrium only when motion or an external force is involved. It is a matter of common observation that an empty cardboard carton is more likely to blow down the street than one filled with canned goods. Likewise, a 250-pound fullback is less likely to be brushed aside than is a 130-pound one. In all sports involving physical contact, the heavy, solid individual stands a better chance of keeping his footing than does the lightweight one.

Momentum and the Impact of an External Force.   Whereas no individual can suddenly increase his weight in order to resist another individual charging into him at top speed, there are nevertheless two principles, the observance of which makes it possible to withstand this factor of external force. These are (1) inclining the body and (2) widening the base of support *in the direction of the oncoming force*. Leaning into the wind illustrates the first of these (Fig. 195); placing the feet in a forward-backward stance when catching a swift ball is an example of the second. When we stand in a bus or a subway train we resist the tendency to be thrown backward when the vehicle starts up either by standing sideways with the feet in a moderately wide stance, or by facing forward and leaning forward. We never face the back of the vehicle from choice, but if we must, we place one foot forward rather than incline the body backward, which would be the other alternative. These automatic reactions to external forces are all for one purpose, namely, to enable us to keep our center of gravity over our base of support in spite of the complicating factor of being acted upon by an external force.

Another form of the effect of external force is seen in the sudden cessation of motion. For instance, if a man is so foolish as to jump off a moving bus, he runs the risk of falling flat on his face. This is

Figure 195. Leaning into the wind to balance the force exerted by the wind.

because the forward-moving bus has imparted kinetic energy to his body, or, as we commonly say, he has received momentum from the moving bus. When he suddenly leaves the bus and ignores the factor of momentum, he loses the kinetic energy suddenly, very suddenly indeed, and finds himself thrown to the ground by an invisible force. He could have avoided this ignominious reaction if, upon jumping from the bus, he had faced forward, leaned backward and taken a few running steps in the same direction as the bus, thus assuring a gradual loss of kinetic energy, instead of an instantaneous one. Still better, he could have waited for the bus to stop.

Friction.   Friction as a factor in stability has already been suggested in relation to the size of the base of support. It has even greater influence when the body is in motion or is subjected to an external force. Lack of sufficient friction is what makes it difficult to keep one's equilibrium when walking on an icy pavement, particularly if a frisky dog tugs unexpectedly on its leash. When the supporting surface presents insufficient friction, the footgear can make up for it. The person who must walk on icy pavements can wear "creepers" on his shoes; the golfer and the field hockey player can wear cleats; and the gymnast and basketball player can wear rubber-soled shoes.

Segmentation.   If, instead of being in one solid piece, an object consists of a series of segments placed one on top of the other, its problem of retaining its equilibrium is a multiple one. Maximum stability of a segmented body is assured when the centers of gravity of all the weight-bearing segments lie in a vertical line which is centered over the base of support. In a column of blocks, this means that each block must be centered over the block beneath. In a jointed column, as in the human body, one segment cannot slide off another, but it is quite possible for the segments to be united in a zigzag line. Such is all too often the case in man's posture. In fact, the alignment of the body segments is a widely used criterion for judging standing posture. When the segments are aligned in a single vertical line, the posture is not only more pleasing in appearance to most of us, but there is less likelihood of strain to the joints and muscles. When one segment gets out of line, there is usually a compensatory disalignment of another segment in order to maintain a balanced position of the body as a whole. (In other words, for every "zig" there is a "zag"!) At every point of angulation between segments there is uneven tension thrown on the ligaments and uneven tonus in opposing muscle groups. This causes fatigue, if not actual strain.

Visual and Psychologic Factors.   Factors which belong in this category are less easily explained than the others, but are familiar to everyone. The giddiness that many experience when walking close to an unprotected edge high above the ground, or when crossing a swirling river on a foot bridge, is a real detriment to one's equilibrium. Even if the supporting surface is entirely adequate, the sense of balance may be disturbed. A common means of preserving the balance, both in this type of situation and when walking on a narrow rail, is to fix the eyes on a stationary spot above or beyond the "danger area." This seems to facilitate neuromuscular control by reducing the disturbing stimuli.

Physiologic Factors. Besides the visual and psychologic factors there are also physiologic factors related to the physical mechanism for equilibrium, namely, the semicircular canals. In addition to actual lesions of this mechanism, any disturbance of the general physical condition is likely to affect the sense of balance. Feelings of dizziness accompanying nausea, or any form of debility, reduce one's ability to resist other factors which threaten the equilibrium. These physiologic factors are largely beyond our control. One principle which can be derived from them, however, is that it is better to avoid situations which are likely to threaten the equilibrium when there is a temporary physiologic disturbance.

Summary of Principles

The principles of stability are stated here as simply and concisely as possible, and brief applications are suggested in each case.

1. Other things being equal, (1) the lower the center of gravity, (2) the larger the base of support, and (3) the more nearly centered the line of gravity with reference to the base of support, the greater will be the body's stability.

Applications:

a. The easiest and safest pyramids for beginners are those in which the participants are on their hands and knees. This position provides for a lower center of gravity, a larger base of support, and greater ease in centering the line of gravity than the kneeling or standing position.

b. In canoeing the kneeling position represents a compromise position which combines the advantages of stability and ease of using the arms for paddling. Kneeling is preferable to sitting on the seat because the lowering of the center of gravity makes the position a more stable one. While it is less stable than sitting on the floor of the canoe, it is a more convenient position for paddling.

c. An external load which is carried anywhere except on the head directly above the body's center of gravity will affect the relation of the line of gravity to the base of support adversely unless the body readjusts its alignment in order to compensate for the load. When carrying a heavy tray, suitcase or bag of cement, for instance, some portion of the body must be shifted in the opposite direction if the center of gravity is to be maintained above the center of the supporting base. If this is not done, the stability of the body will suffer and the muscles on the opposite side of the trunk will become tense in order to brace the body against the pull of the unbalanced load. A unilateral load may be counterbalanced by raising the opposite arm sideways, by bending to the opposite side, or by leaning to the opposite side from the ankles, while at the same time keeping the head erect (Figs. 193 and 194).

d. A person who has had both legs amputated above the knee is fitted to artificial legs which are somewhat shorter than his original limbs. Since this lowers his center of gravity, it helps to reduce the balance problem.

2. Other things being equal, the greater the mass of a body, the greater will be its stability.

Application: In sports in which resistance to impact is a factor, heavy, solid individuals are more likely to maintain their equilibrium than lighter ones. This provides one basis for selecting fullbacks in football.

3. In giving and in receiving an impetus with a strong horizontal component, greater stability is obtained if the base of support is widened in the direction of the line of force.

Applications:

a. In throwing and in catching a swift ball, in batting and in other activities involving the receiving or the giving of impetus to external objects, one can control his balance more readily if he widens his stance in the direction of the force.

b. Keeping one's balance when standing on a bus or train which is accelerating or decelerating is facilitated by widening the stance in the direction that the vehicle is moving, that is, in a forward-backward direction relative to the vehicle.

4. Other things being equal, the greater the friction between the supporting surface and the parts of the body in contact with it, the greater the body's stability will be.

Application: The wearing of cleats and rubber-soled shoes for sport activities not only aids in locomotion, but also serves to increase one's stability in positions held momentarily between quick or forceful movements, as in basketball, fencing, football, field hockey, lacrosse, etc.

5. Other things being equal, the most stable position of a vertical segmented body (such as a column of blocks or the erect human body) is one in which the center of gravity of each weight-bearing segment lies in a vertical line centered over the base of support, or in which deviations in one direction are exactly balanced by deviations in the opposite direction.

Applications:

a. This applies to postural adjustments for achieving a pleasing, well balanced alignment of the body segments, both with and without external loads.

b. In pyramid building and other balance stunts in which one person (or group of persons) supports the weight of another person or persons, the chief problem is one of either aligning or balancing the several centers of gravity over the center of the base of support.

6. Other things being equal, a person has better balance in locomotion under difficult circumstances when he reduces disturbing visual stimuli to a minimum and uses the vision as an aid.

Application: Beginners learning to walk on a balance beam or perform balance stunts, and others who for any reason have difficulty in keeping their balance, can minimize disturbing visual stimuli by fixing their eyes on a stationary spot in front of them, either at eye level or somewhat above eye level.

7. There is a positive relationship between one's physical and emotional state and his ability to maintain his balance under difficult circumstances.

Application: Persons should not be permitted to attempt dangerous balance stunts, or activities requiring expert balance ability, when their physical or emotional health is impaired.

8. The principles of maintaining equilibrium apply to the facility of regaining it following a temporary loss.

Applications:

a. After an unexpected loss of balance, as when starting to fall or after receiving impetus when "off balance," equilibrium may be more quickly regained if a wide base of support is established and the center of gravity is lowered.

b. Upon landing from a downward jump, stability may be more readily regained if the weight is kept evenly distributed over both feet, or over the hands and feet, and if a sufficiently wide base of support is provided.

c. Upon landing from a forward jump, the balance may be more readily regained if one lands with the weight forward, using the hands if necessary in order to provide support in the direction of motion. (See 3.)

d. Tightrope walkers use a balancing pole to help them regain their balance when they start to lose it. The pole serves as a long first class lever. Since the reaction of a lever is in proportion to its length, even a slight movement of the end of the lever has a considerable reaction at the fulcrum. Hence if the tightrope walker starts to lean too far to the left, an almost imperceptible downward movement of the right end of the pole will be sufficient to help him regain his balance. The gymnast walking on a balance beam uses his arms as a balancing pole by extending them sideward and dipping one or the other in order to counteract a loss of balance.

Supplementary Material

Method of Locating the Line of Gravity. It is a fairly simple matter to determine the relation of an individual's line of gravity to his base of support under experimental conditions. The student will find that it will repay him to do this because it will convince him better than words can do of the way the body automatically compensates for external loads and for segmental disalignment. It is revealing to see how the body compensates for the sideward raising of an arm, for the forward bending of the trunk, for a briefcase carried in one hand, or a load of books clasped against the chest (Fig. 196). No matter what the position, the relation of the line of gravity to the base of support is a remarkably stable one. Its relation to the body segments, however, shifts with every change in position. The segments automatically adjust themselves to maintain a balanced position—a position in which the center of gravity remains approximately over the center of the base of support.

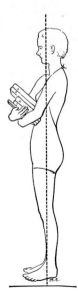

Figure 196. Compensatory adjustment of the body for an anterior load. Note that the line of gravity falls close to the center of the base of support.

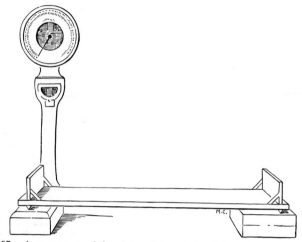

Figure 197. Apparatus used for determining the position of the line of gravity.

Directions for Determining the Position of the Line of Gravity
APPARATUS (Fig. 197):
1. Scales: preferably either the Toledo or the spring balance type.
2. A stool or block the same height as the platform of the scales.
3. A board about 40 cm. wide and a little over 100 or 200 cm. long—the latter if it is to be used for horizontal work. A knife edge should be attached to the under side of each end in such a way that when the board is placed in a horizontal position it will rest on the knife edges. For simplifying the calculations the distance from knife edge to knife edge should measure exactly 100 or 200 cm. The front edge of the board should be marked in centimeters. The board should be tested for accuracy. To do this, the experimenter should see whether it will balance exactly at the center.
DIRECTIONS:
1. Find the subject's total weight.
2. Put the board in place, with one knife edge on the scales platform and the other on the stool or block. Note the reading on the scales. This is the partial weight of the board (*B*).
3. Have the subject stand approximately in the center of the board, facing the scales and with the heels even. Note the reading on the scales. This is the partial weight of the subject and board together (*S & B*).
4. Use the following formula to solve for "*d*," this being the distance from the rear knife edge to the frontal plane in which the subject's center of gravity is situated:

$$d = \frac{(\text{Partial wt. of } S \text{ \& } B) - (\text{Partial wt. of } B)}{\text{Total weight of } S} \times \text{Length of } B \text{ (from knife edge to knife edge)}$$

5. Measure the distance "*d*" from the rear knife edge toward the end of the board resting on the scales. A perpendicular erected at this point represents the anteroposterior position of the subject's line of gravity. If desired, a mark may be made on the subject's foot to indicate the location of the line of gravity with reference to the anteroposterior aspect of the base of support. (*Note:* This is not a fixed point. It moves forward and backward as the subject sways forward and backward.)

6. The frontal or lateral position of the line of gravity may be found in the same manner by having the subject stand with his side toward the scales. In this case "*d*" represents the distance from the rear knife edge to the sagittal plane in which the subject's center of gravity is located.

7. If it is desired to find the single point representing the spot where the line of gravity intersects the base of support, a piece of paper should be placed under the subject's feet for the side-view measurement. The outline of the feet should be traced on the paper. When the first "*d*" is found, the distance should be measured and marked on both the left and right sides of the paper. The paper should then be removed and the two points connected by a straight line. When the subject faces forward for the second measurement, the paper should be placed on the board so that the subject's feet will fit in the foot prints. When the second "*d*" is found, the distance should be measured and marked on both edges of the paper and the two points connected by a straight line. The point at which the two lines intersect represents the approximate position of the point where the line of gravity strikes the base of support. This is a crude method of locating this point and is not strictly accurate, since the subject may not be standing in exactly the same posture for both measurements. Furthermore, the element of swaying always introduces a source of error. A more accurate method for determining the position of the line of gravity has been described by Hellebrandt.

Directions for Determining the Height of the Center of Gravity. The same equipment is used as for determining the position of the line of gravity, except that the longer board must be used for this. Also there should be a perpendicular foot rest at each end of the board, directly over each knife edge. These must not destroy the balance of the board. The subject lies on the back with the head toward the scales and the feet at right angles against the foot rest at the other end. The foot rest should be high enough to support the feet in the proper position. The position the subject assumes should be as much like the standing position as possible. The measurements and calculations are made as before. In this case "*d*" represents the distance from the foot rest to the horizontal plane in which the subject's center of gravity is situated. This is comparable to the distance from the center of gravity to the ground, when the subject is in the standing position. The center of gravity itself is located at the point where the line of gravity intersects this horizontal plane.

Photographic Method. This method of determining the position of the line of gravity may easily be adapted to use with photographs. This has several advantages. Photographs of the subject in several positions can be taken in succession and the computations and measurements be made later. Several prints of the same photograph can be made and used for the entire class. The subject can assume positions it would be difficult to hold long enough for the computations and measurements to be made directly. In adapting this method to photographs the length measurements (i.e., total length of board and distance "*d*") are made on the photograph instead of on the board itself. This means that the photographed length of the board must be substituted for the actual length in the formula. Computations will be made easier if the distance of the camera from the board is adjusted so that the photographed length of the board will be a round number, such as 5 or 10 cm. It is possible to do this by taking the back off the camera and looking through a piece of ground glass held behind the camera. The dimensions of the image on the glass will be the same as those on the film.

Center of Gravity Experimentation. A number of experiments relating to the center of gravity were made by Hellebrandt at the University of Wisconsin. She found the height of the center of gravity in women to be 55 per cent of their standing height. She studied the way in which the body sways when a person attempts to stand still and observed that although the center of gravity of the body as a whole shifts incessantly during relaxed and effortless standing.

the patterns formed by a trajectory of the shifting center of weight and the mean position of the vertical projection of this theoretical point (i.e., the line of gravity) are relatively constant. She found that the average area of maximal sway for a group of men and women was only 4.09 sq. cm. and that the differences between the men and the women were not statistically significant. It was noted that although the line of gravity was close to the center of the base of support, in the majority of subjects it was slightly to the left and behind the exact center. In a study on the influence of shoes on the position of the center of gravity Hellebrandt found that shoes of low and of moderate heels had a negligible effect upon postural stability and the position of the line of gravity, but that high heeled shoes tended to cause a forward shifting of the line of gravity and to increase the amount of swaying, apparently indicating a decrease in stability.

In a series of studies on the relation of age to the height of the center of gravity, Palmer found that the latter maintained a fairly constant ratio to the height of the individual at all ages, ranging from 55 to 59 per cent. From the age of 6 fetal months to 70 years the center of gravity was found to descend gradually from the level of the seventh thoracic vertebra to the level of the first sacral segment.

In 1922 Croskey, Dawson, Luessen, Marohn and Wright reviewed methods of determining the position of the center of gravity and then used an improved seesaw method in their own experiment. Using fifty men and fifty women as their subjects, they found the center of gravity in men to be 56.18 per cent of their height, and in women 55.44 per cent. They also found that the height of the center of gravity was considerably more variable in women than in men. They found no correlation between the height of the center of gravity and body weight or height.

A few investigators have been interested in the possibility of a relationship between the line of gravity and standing posture. In their historical survey of this subject Cureton and Wickens noted that no quantitative studies have been found which related the center of gravity to the area of the base as a diagnostic test for posture. Using the Reynolds and Lovett technique for determining the position of the line of gravity and their own method of analyzing anteroposterior posture, they made a number of correlation studies. They concluded that there was a definite relationship between the position of the line of gravity and posture, strength, physical fitness and athletic ability. The coefficient of correlation between their measure of kyphosis and the line of gravity measurement was .256. The relationship between body lean and the line of gravity was indicated by a coefficient of .864. This denotes a high degree of positive relationship, but on the other hand, body lean *is* the position of the body which is associated with the anteroposterior shifting of the line of gravity. They are one and the same thing. In fact, one wonders why the relationship was only .864 instead of 1.0. In correlating body lean with kyphosis, Cureton and Wickens obtained a coefficient of .363. They interpreted this as an indication of a trend for men who habitually stood with their weight more forward to have straighter upper backs. The authors apparently did not investigate the relationship between the anteroposterior position of the line of gravity and the alignment of body segments.

Crowley and Johnston in two separate studies could find no relationship between the anteroposterior position of the line of gravity and total anteroposterior posture as measured by the MacEwan-Howe objective method.[7, 11]

Likewise, Hellebrandt and her co-workers, using this method on a larger number of subjects, could find no relationship between the objective posture score and the anteroposterior shifting of the line of gravity. They suggested that this surprising failure to find a relationship between the two might indicate that the posture criterion in common use is based on an esthetic concept of posture rather than on a physiologic one.

Demonstrations and Laboratory Exercises

1. Try to carry a load, first without compensating for it, and then compensating as completely as possible. Check the degree of compensation each time by locating the position of the line of gravity with reference to the center of the base of support. Describe the kinesthetic sensation in the trunk muscles in each case. Do you notice greater tension in one position than in the other?

2. Walk on a balance beam:

a. Looking ahead at the wall.

b. Looking at a person who is in front of the balance beam doing a vigorous exercise such as the jumping jack.

c. With the eyes closed. What is your reaction in each case? Explain.

3. Walk along with a partner beside you. Without warning, the partner is to give you a sudden, but not overforceful, sideward push. How do you react? If you did not succeed in "catching your balance," can you explain the reason for your failure?

4. Describe or find references for five pyramids and list them in their order of difficulty. Explain the reasons for the order you have chosen.

5. Do the same for five dual balance stunts.

6. Build two columns of blocks, one with the blocks carefully centered one over the other, the second column with the blocks staggered but balanced. Grasping the lowest block of each column, slide the columns back and forth, changing the speed frequently and suddenly until the blocks tumble. Which column is the first to topple? Why?

7. Determine the anteroposterior position of the line of gravity for three different subjects standing in their natural posture.

8. Determine the position of the line of gravity for a subject in each of the following standing positions:

a. Facing the scales and leaning as far forward as possible with the body in a straight line from the top of the head to the ankles.

b. Facing the scales and leaning as far backward as possible with the body in a straight line.

c. Facing the scales and leaning as far to the side as possible with the body in a straight line.

9. Determine the lateral aspect (front or back view) of the line of gravity in a subject who is standing on one foot.

10. Determine the height of the center of gravity in a subject (a) with the arms at the sides, and (b) with the arms raised overhead.

11. Do several original center of gravity experiments.

Note: You may identify some principles which are not described in this chapter. If so, discuss them with your classmates and formulate a statement that expresses them clearly.

Bibliography

1. Amar, J.: The Human Motor. New York, E. P. Dutton & Co., 1920, Book VI, Chap. I.

2. Croskey, M. I., Dawson, P. M., Luessen, A. C., Marohn, I. E., and Wright, H. E.: The Height of the Center of Gravity in Man. Am. J. Physiol., 61: 171–185, 1922.

3. Cureton, T. K., and Wickens, J. S.: The Center of Gravity of the Human Body in the Antero-posterior Plane and Its Relation to Posture. Supplement to Research Quarterly of the Am. Assn. for Health and Phys. Ed., 6: 93–105, 1935.

4. Fick, R.: Handbuch der Anatomie und Mechanik der Gelenke. Jena, G. Fischer, 1910.

5. Hellebrandt, F. A., Riddle, K. S., Larsen, E. M., and Fries, E. C.: Gravitational Influences on Postural Alignment. Physiotherapy Rev., *22:* 143–149, 1942.
6. Hellebrandt, F. A., and Franseen, E. B.: Physiological Study of Vertical Stance of Man. Physiol. Rev., *23:* 220–225, 1943.
7. MacEwan, C. G., and Howe, E. C.: An Objective Method for Grading Posture. Research Quarterly of Am. Assn. for Health and Phys. Ed., *3:* 144–157, 1932.
8. Palmer, C. E.: Studies of the Center of Gravity in the Human Body. Child Development, *15:* 99–180, 1944.
9. Reynolds, E., and Lovett, R. W.: Method of Determining the Position of the Center of Gravity in Its Relation to Certain Bony Landmarks in the Erect Position. Am. J. Physiol., *24:* 286–293, 1909.
10. Steindler, A.: Kinesiology of the Human Body. Springfield, Ill., Charles C Thomas, 1955, Lecture 7.
11. Wellesley College Studies in Hygiene and Physical Education: Factors in Anteroposterior Posture. Supplement to Research Quarterly of Am. Assn. for Health and Phys. Ed., *9:* 89–96, 1938.

Recommended Reading

Steindler, A.: Kinesiology of the Human Body (see 10 above). Chapters 3 and 4.

18 · Postural Principles

In this section on Underlying Principles of Basic Motor Skills it has been the purpose of the author to bring together and to state concisely the various principles, discovered either by scientific experiment or by experience, which would serve to guide both the teacher and the student in developing desirable motor skills. In the field of posture this has been particularly difficult to do. The reasons for this will be discussed later. Although posture is thought by many to be a factor in all motor skills, rather than a motor skill in itself, so much attention is focused on it by the three professions —physical education, physical therapy and occupational therapy— that it would seem appropriate to devote a chapter to the principles which apply to it.

There are innumerable concepts of human posture, and innumerable interpretations of its significance. Posture may well claim to be "all things to all men." To the physical anthropologist posture may be a racial characteristic, or it may be an indication of phylogenetic development; to the orthopedic surgeon it may be an indication of the soundness of the skeletal framework and muscular system; to an artist it may be an expression of the personality and the emotions; to the actor it serves as a tool for expressing mood or character; to the physician, the biologist, the fashion model, the employer, the sculptor, the dancer, the psychologist—to each of these, posture has a different significance. Each sees posture within the framework of his own profession and interest. This is no less true of the kinesiologist. To him, posture is a gauge of mechanical efficiency, of kinesthetic sense, of muscle balance, and of neuromuscular coordination.

Part of the difficulty in identifying postural principles lies in

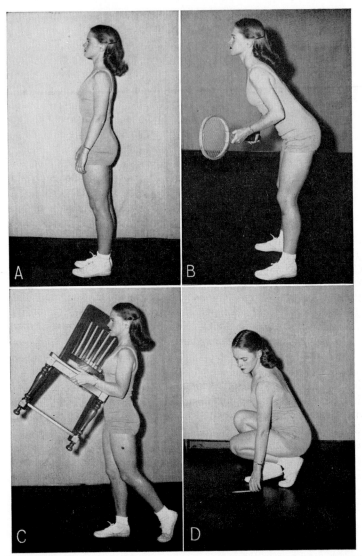

Figure 198. The erect standing posture is the point of reference for other postural patterns. *A,* Erect standing posture; *B,* adaptation of posture to a sport activity; *C,* adaptation of posture to carrying a large object; *D,* adaptation of posture to picking up a small object from the floor. (Photos by MacLaurin.)

the fact that no individual's posture can be adequately described. Posture means position, and a multisegmented organism such as the human body cannot be said to have a single posture. It assumes many postures and rarely holds any of them for an appreciable time. To be sure, certain characteristic patterns become apparent as we have the opportunity to observe an individual over an extended period, but it is difficult, if not well nigh impossible, to measure, or even record, characteristic postural patterns. Another difficulty in identifying postural principles is due to the many varieties of human physique. In recent years these have been brought to our attention by Sheldon. The importance of considering these individual differences of build when evaluating posture has been emphasized by Frost.

Thus we see the dual fallacy upon which posture norms are based. Posture norms are appropriate only for the mythical average figure, and apply only to the static standing position, which does not necessarily represent habitual postural patterns. Nevertheless an attempt is made here to present specific postural principles whenever there is objective justification for so doing. When specific principles cannot be stated, tentative ones are suggested if the clinical evidence or common experience seems to warrant their inclusion. In some instances ideas which are commonly accepted as principles are mentioned for the sole purpose of pointing out the fact that there is no evidence to support them. This does not preclude the possibility of such evidence being presented some time in the future, however.

In view of the fact that activity postures are of greater concern to the teacher and the therapist than static postures, it may be well to say a word in defense of examining and photographing the posture of subjects in the erect standing position. It is admitted that the posture in such a position is of little importance in itself. It becomes significant, however, when it is taken as the point of departure for the many postural patterns assumed by the individual, both at rest and in motion (Fig. 198). Since there is an almost endless variety of activity postures, and since these are extremely difficult to judge, it is a convenient custom to accept the standing posture as the individual's basic posture from which all his other postures stem. Hence, as a reflection of the individual's characteristic postural patterns, the standing posture takes on an importance it would not otherwise have. Its importance, however, *is in direct proportion to the extent that it represents the individual's habitual carriage.*

Principles Related to the Mechanism for Maintaining and Adjusting Erect Posture.   Posture is regulated in part by reflex action and in part by volitional effort. Since these have both been discussed elsewhere (pp. 42 and 43), they are but briefly mentioned here.

1. Stimuli arising from vision, from the semicircular canals, from the stretching of antigravity muscles, and from pressure on

the soles of the feet elicit an increase in the tonus of the antigravity muscles and thus provide the body with a means of remaining upright without the necessity for conscious control.

2. Temporary postural adjustments can be made volitionally by means of the same mechanism by which all volitional movements are made (p. 42). These adjustments are necessarily within the structural limitations of the individual.

3. The gradual changing of habitual postural patterns can be brought about by the same means by which any neuromuscular habits are changed. This is a slow process of reconditioning the neuromuscular pathways. The specific method for accomplishing this forms the basis for the different schools of thought that exist in the field of posture education and corrective exercise. Some believe that it can be accomplished by the frequent repetition of carefully selected exercises performed with control and with constant attention to correct form.[11, 13, 24, 30, 32] Others believe that the rebuilding of the necessary neuromuscular pathways can be accomplished only by the indirect method, that is, by influencing the individual's neuromuscular response by means of his thought processes. Mental concepts are utilized for this purpose.[34, 35] Still others seek to establish new postural habits by practicing movements which are believed to develop the natural postural reflexes.[12, 14] All groups recognize the fact that the establishing of new postural patterns can take place only within the limits of the individual's structural heritage.

4. The kinesthetic sense would seem to be a vital factor in the mechanism for establishing and adjusting postural patterns, but this has not yet been demonstrated. It is believed that if valid tests could be found for habitual carriage and for kinesthetic awareness of head and trunk positions, a relationship between posture and kinesthesis could be established.

Principles Related to Stability

1. Hellebrandt demonstrated that even the erect standing posture is not literally static. "Standing," she concluded, "is, in reality, *movement upon a stationary base.*"[15] Her experiments revealed that the center of gravity did not remain motionless above the base of support no matter how still the subject attempted to stand, but moved forward, backward and sideward. This motion indicated that the subjects were constantly swaying. When the swaying was prevented by artificial means, there was a strong tendency to faint. Hence the involuntary swaying was seen to serve the purpose of a pump, aiding the venous return and assuring the brain of adequate circulation for retaining consciousness.

2. In the same experiments Hellebrandt found that the oscillations of each individual were balanced so exactly that the average

position of the line of gravity, relative to the base of support, was remarkably constant. From this it would seem that we can assume the presence of a controlling factor in our tendency to sway. Apparently the stretch reflex, the kinesthetic sense and vision all operate here to confine the oscillations to a limited area, an area well within the boundaries of the base of support.

3. Some experimenters have investigated the possibility of a relationship between the position of the line of gravity, relative to the base of support, and the quality of posture. The findings of the different investigators do not agree, however. Hence there would seem to be insufficient evidence to support a claim for such a relationship. (See the summary of investigations by Cureton and Wickens, Crowley, and Johnston in the Supplementary Material for Chapter 17.)

4. In informal class experiments the author found that the relation of the line of gravity to the base of support was not affected significantly or consistently when the subject assumed different positions of the upper extremities or held external objects such as books, a suitcase or a tray. This would seem to provide evidence of the body's tendency to compensate for deviations of some of its parts from the fundamental standing position. The principle would appear to be established that, under ordinary circumstances, the disalignment of one segment of the body, whether anteroposteriorly or laterally, is accompanied by a compensatory disalignment of another segment or segments. If the disalignment is not exactly balanced, excessive tension in certain muscle groups results. This is particularly apparent when external loads are not adequately compensated. To the best of the author's knowledge there has been no large-scale investigation of this matter of compensatory alignment. Objective evidence is suggested, but is as yet inconclusive.

Principles Related to the Alignment of Body Segments

1. In much of the literature on posture, statements are made that in the ideal standing posture the line of gravity bears a definite relation to certain anatomic landmarks, such as the mastoid process, the acromion process, the junctions of the anteroposterior curves of the spine, the hip joint (greater trochanter of the femur), the knee joint and the lateral malleolus. In a class study made on only six subjects at Wellesley College the relation of the line of gravity to some of these landmarks was investigated. The variation among these six subjects is shown by the following measurements:

Distance from Line of Gravity to:	*Total Range*
Ankle joint......3.80 cm. in front to 6.65 cm. in front	2.85 cm.
Knee joint......0.46 cm. behind to 2.85 cm. in front	3.31 cm.
Hip joint.......6.65 cm. behind to 0.95 cm. in front	7.60 cm.
Shoulder joint...1.80 cm. behind to 6.65 cm. in front	8.45 cm.
Mastoid process..0.95 cm. behind to 5.23 cm. in front	6.18 cm.

Figure 199. Vertical alignment of the body.

In evaluating this study the reader should not fail to take into account the influence of body sway and the difficulty of locating the anatomic landmarks on the accuracy of the measurements. The students who conducted the study found it particularly difficult to locate the surface point which corresponded to the midpoint of the hip joint. It might be of interest to repeat an investigation of this sort, using a large number of subjects, representing both sexes and a variety of physique types. In determining the location of the line of gravity it would be well to take the mean of several measurements in order to minimize the influence of sway. The results of such a study might indicate what could be accepted as a "normal zone" of the line of gravity in the erect standing position. It might help also in analyzing the alignment of the body segments, and thus lend itself to diagnostic purposes.

2. It has frequently been stated that a standing posture in which each weight-bearing segment was balanced vertically upon the segment beneath it made less demand on the muscles than a posture in which the segments formed a zigzag alignment.[2, 32] Good posture, they say, takes less muscular effort to maintain than poor. They offer the explanation that when a segment is not in vertical alignment, the force of gravity is not parallel with its long axis, and hence exerts a rotatory component of force. This reasoning seems entirely logical, but overlooks the fact that even in the most ideal posture rotatory components of force are present, owing to the facts that (1) the supporting column of the trunk (i.e., the spine) is not centrally located anteroposteriorly; (2) the supporting base (the feet) projects forward from the lower extremities instead of being centered beneath them; (3) the spinal column is curved anteropos-

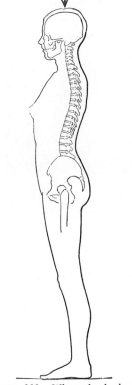

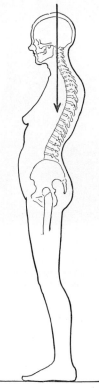

Figure 200. When the body is in good standing posture, the rotatory effect of the force of gravity is minimized.

Figure 201. When the body is in a poor standing posture, the force of gravity has an exaggerated rotatory effect on the weight-bearing segments.

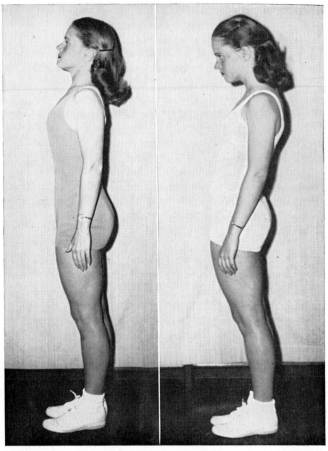

Figure 202. The relation of posture to metabolic economy. *A,* An overtense posture is more costly. *B,* An overrelaxed posture is economical, but it subjects the ligaments to strain.

An easily erect posture, as shown in Figure 198, *A,* which involves no unnecessary tension, is best from all points of view. (Photo by MacLaurin.)

teriorly; and (4) the chest forms an anterior load upon which gravity is constantly exerting a rotatory force. The weight of the breasts in women constitutes an additional anterior weight, causing an even greater rotatory component of gravitational force.

The question of the energy cost of standing posture has been investigated by both Hellebrandt and McCormick. Both concluded that the increase of metabolic rate in standing over the basal rate was so small, compared with the metabolic cost of moving and exercising, that it could be considered negligible. McCormick included both anteroposterior and lateral measurements of body alignment. From these she concluded that the type of posture which involved a minimum of metabolic increase appeared to be one in which the knees are hyperextended as completely as the joints permit, the hips are pushed forward to the limit of extension, the thoracic curve is increased to the maximum, the head is projected forward, and the upper trunk is inclined slightly backward in a posterior list (see Fig. 202, *B*). As one might expect, this is a typical picture of fatigue posture. A common variation of it is a shift of the weight to one foot with accompanying asymmetric adjustments in the spine and lower extremities.

From these two studies it would seem that minimum energy expenditure cannot be accepted as a criterion of posture. Metabolic economy is desirable up to a point, since it indicates absence of hypertonicity, but good alignment should not be sacrificed for it. An investigation which might prove of interest would be a comparison of the energy cost of good alignment among individuals whose habitual alignment represented a wide range. A second phase of such a study might involve a period of posture instruction for the "poor alignment group" with metabolism tests at the completion of the instruction. It is a matter of common observation that good alignment is achieved with varying degrees of effort by different individuals. One person maintains good alignment with no apparent effort, while another cannot assume it even momentarily without great effort and excessive tension. It would be of interest to learn whether practicing a better alignment until it became habitual would be accompanied by a drop in the energy cost of that alignment.

There appears to be a definite relationship between the alignment of the body segments and the integrity of the joint structures. It is generally accepted that prolonged postural strain is injurious to these structures. Ligaments which are repeatedly subjected to stretch become permanently stretched, and cartilages which are subjected to uneven pressures and to abnormal friction become damaged. There is adequate clinical evidence to support the contention that prolonged postural strain is a factor in the arthritic changes which take place in the weight-bearing joints. Objective evidence may be lacking, but it might not be difficult to secure if postural records and x-rays of the weight-bearing joints could be obtained for an adequate number of subjects over a ten- or twenty-year period. Such an investigation might prove or disprove the claim that the human machine functions more efficiently when the weight-bearing segments are in "proper" alignment, with a minimum of stress and strain on them.

Principles Related to Evolutionary and Hereditary Influences

1. In tracing the evolution of the human structure and its posture, Morton has shown the influence that the force of gravity has had on the morphologic development, first of the terrestrial quadrupeds, then of the arboreal primates, and finally of man. The evolution from horizontal to vertical posture was achieved, he claimed, by the force of gravity pulling on the suspended body of the arboreal primates when they engaged in brachial locomotion. The changes which developed in man's structure, he stated, were the direct result of the shift from a vertically suspended position to a vertically supported one. This shift was responsible not only for the changes in the weight-bearing parts of the musculoskeletal structure, but also for changes in the upper extremities, which were now freed for the development of a great variety of manipulative skills. While no specific principle is derived from this explanation of the role played by the force of gravity in the evolution of man's structure, an awareness of it might be of help in our analyses of individual postures.

2. Attention has already been called to individual variations in posture (p. 355). Rogers' claim that these are due in large part to heredity, and McCloy's evidence of a hereditary factor in the posture of the spine, were mentioned in the Supplementary Material for the Chapter on the Spinal Column (p. 84). In attempting to correct a person's posture one must be realistic and accept the limits imposed by this hereditary factor. Improvement can doubtless be made, but one must not expect to effect a radical change in the basic shape of the spine.

3. Certain pathologic conditions, such as congenitally dislocated hips, tuberculosis of the spine, cerebral palsy, and poliomyelitis with resultant paralysis of trunk muscles, may cause such changes in an individual's posture that the usual hereditary and environmental influences are obscured.

Principles Related to Organic Function.   One frequently mentioned criterion of good posture is the relationship of the alignment of the body to organic function.[11, 32] Postural patterns are not thought to be good unless they both permit and encourage normal function of the vital physiologic processes, particularly those of respiration, circulation, digestion and elimination. Considerable clinical evidence has been presented to substantiate this belief, but experimental evidence is scarce.[7, 16, 20]

In this regard, Hellebrandt commented that the concept of the harmful effect of poor posture on visceral function was "based on more or less tenuous evidence without regard for the wide margin of safety under which all organ systems function and the paucity of proof that the anatomical position of a viscus is a valid criterion of the adequacy of its physiologic behavior."[16] And Karpovich has remarked, ". . . . except for the fact that lordosis may be associated with orthostatic albuminuria, there is no scientific proof that improvement of slight irregularities in posture leads to definite improvements in the physiologic functions of the body."[20] There is, however, some evidence of a relationship between menstrual function and posture. Hoffman studied the findings of the routine orthopedic examination for two groups of college women, one group known as the "dysmenorrhea group," the other as the "no-pain group." The two groups were found to differ significantly with respect to two postural traits, namely, anteroposterior pelvic tilt and bilateral hip asymmetry.

Fox also studied the relation of certain aspects of posture to dysmenorrhea. She investigated the incidence of dysmenorrhea in three groups of young women, one a control group, one a group characterized by sway back (posterior list of the trunk), and one group characterized by faulty pelvic tilt (increased inclination). She found that dysmenorrhea occurred with greater severity among the sway back group than among the control group. Unlike Hoffman, however, she did not find a significant relationship between pelvic tilt and dysmenorrhea.

Principles Related to Strength and Flexibility.   That strength and flexibility are factors in posture would seem to be a universally accepted thesis, judging by the preponderance of strength and flexibility exercises included in the majority of corrective programs, also by the strength and flexibility measurements included in posture tests. Interest has been shown particularly in the strength of the abdominals, scapular adductors and spine extensors, and in the flexibility of the pectorals and the hamstrings. There seems to have been little scientific investigation of the relation of these strengths and flexibilities to posture. It would seem that the universal acceptance of such a relationship may have been responsible for the attitude that there was no need for such investigation. Yet nowhere in the literature can the author find a clear statement as to what constitutes optimal strength or optimal flexibility for the maintenance of good posture. Possibly it is a matter of balance between opposing muscle groups, rather than of strength or flexibility *per se,* or it may be a matter of relative muscle length. These aspects would seem to bear investigation.

In comparing the abdominal strength of a control group with that of two faulty posture groups—one characterized by sway back, and the other by faulty pelvic tilt—Fox did not find that abdominal strength was a differentiating factor. She recommended that further study be made of this problem, especially since her sway back group was much smaller than the others.

Principles Related to Psychologic Aspects of Posture.   A kinesiology text scarcely seems an appropriate place for discussion of psychology. Nevertheless there are certain psychologic aspects of posture which it is well for the person involved with posture instruction not to overlook. The observance of anatomic, physiologic and mechanical principles will be to no avail if the implications of psychologic factors are ignored.

In the first place, a person's posture is not merely a matter of his neuromuscular and musculoskeletal systems. It is frequently indicative of his personality and his emotions.[5, 6] Head and shoulder exercises will do little for a shy girl whose posture gives the impression that she is trying to withdraw into herself and make herself as inconspicuous as possible. Nor will abdominal exercises correct the lordosis of the small man whose posture obviously indicates overcompensation for the inferiority feelings engendered by his small stature. Many posture problems are essentially problems for the psychiatrist or the guidance expert, rather than for the physical educator or physical therapist. The ideal solution to these double-barreled problems might well be provided by the cooperative efforts of these specialists.

In the second place, a conspicuously abnormal posture may be the cause of emotional disturbance in a person who already tends to be overself-conscious. Like any other physical handicap, it may interfere with the individual's personal and social development unless he learns to see it in its right perspective.

An important role of psychology in posture education is that of motivation. No matter how well the teacher or the therapist has selected the exercises, and no matter how conscientiously the student or the patient practices them, they will have little effect in improving the individual's habitual postural patterns unless he is motivated to *want* to improve them.

And finally, psychology is used as a technique of treatment by those who use the method of mental concepts to change neuromuscular pathways (see p. 356). For success in this method they depend completely upon the cooperation of the individual in mental participation, for it is by this means that the changes in the neuromuscular pathways are effected.

Summary

A summary of this chapter emphasizes the dearth of actual objective support for specific principles relating to posture. The following areas appear to be the only ones for which there is such support:

1. Postural reflex action
2. Stability of the erect standing position as evidenced by the relationship of the line of gravity to the base of support

3. The influence of heredity and environment on posture

4. The relationship between certain postural faults and two manifestations of faulty organic function, namely, orthostatic albuminuria and dysmenorrhea.

Since so much emphasis is placed on posture, it is indeed unfortunate that there is so little objective evidence that our efforts are being made in the right direction. The author is inclined to be sympathetic toward Miller's conclusions:

> ... although orthopedists and physical educators have been working actively for the past fifty years with the problems involved in posture, there is still a seemingly unwarranted lack of agreement among practitioners of both fields. Three basic differences of opinion are implicated in this bewildering lack of unanimity: (1) whether any particular posture is more advantageous physiologically than any other posture; (2) whether prescribed physical activity can actually modify posture; and (3) whether it is possible to agree upon a definition of "good" posture and upon a method of accurately measuring such a concept. Eminent authorities in both physical education and medical circles can be found to support either side of any of these questions.[26]

In view of this lack of evidence and these differences of opinion, what stand shall the kinesiologist take in regard to posture? Shall he ignore it, or shall he formulate tentative principles to guide him in posture education and correction, and shall he adhere to these until they are definitely disproved and indications for other principles have become apparent? The author believes that, either consciously or unconsciously, the physical educator, the physical therapist and the occupational therapist are bound to be guided by *some* principles of posture, whether they are founded on fact or conjecture. Since it appears that the difficulty of devising an accurate measure of habitual posture will always be a problem in posture research, the formulation of some guiding principles, based on the best knowledge we have available, incomplete though it be, seems to the author to be justifiable. It seems not only justifiable, but also imperative, if we are to continue to teach body mechanics in our schools and clinics. In full recognition of their limitations, and knowing that they may be superseded as new evidence is revealed by further research, the following postural principles are suggested:

1. The weight-bearing segments of the body are so aligned in good standing posture that the line of gravity passes through these segments within certain "normal" limits, yet to be defined. Such a definition should either be applicable to all physiques, or should indicate to what types of physique it is, or is not, applicable.

2. Since Hellebrandt found that, in every individual she had observed, the average location of the center of gravity was close to the geometric center of the supporting base, it would seem that the relation of the line of gravity to the base of support is not necessarily indicative of good posture.

3. Good standing posture is a position of extension of the weight-bearing joints. This should be an easy extension and should not be accompanied by strain or tension.

4. From the point of view of energy expenditure, good posture would seem to be a position which requires a minimum expenditure of energy *for the maintenance of good alignment.* Excess energy expenditure indicates hypertonicity or poor neuromuscular coordination, or both. A posture requiring an absolute minimum energy expenditure does not fulfill the requirements of good posture because it is characterized by "hanging on the ligaments," that is, a dependence upon the ligaments of the weight-bearing joints, rather than upon muscle tonus, for resisting the downward pull of gravity.

5. Good posture, in repose and in activity, permits mechanically efficient function of the joints. In other words, friction in the joints is minimized, tensions of opposing ligaments are balanced, and pressures within the joints are equalized. Hence the skeletal structure is architecturally and mechanically sound and there is a minimum of wear and tear on the joints.

6. Good posture, both static and dynamic, requires normal muscle tonus. This implies adequate development of the antigravity muscles to resist the pull of gravity successfully and to maintain good alignment without excessive effort or tension. It also implies a balance between antagonistic muscle groups. There is no indication, however, that "the stronger the muscles the better the posture."

7. Good posture, both static and dynamic, requires sufficient flexibility in the structures of the weight-bearing joints to permit good alignment without interference or strain. Poor flexibility may be caused by tight ligaments or fasciae, by short muscles or by hypertrophied muscles. The flexibility should not be so great, however, that excessive muscular effort is needed to keep the weight-bearing joints in alignment.

8. Good posture requires good coordination. This implies good neuromuscular control and well developed postural reflexes.

9. Adjustments in posture can be made more readily by individuals who have a good kinesthetic awareness of the postures they assume and of the degree of tension in their muscles.

10. Good posture, both static and dynamic, is not detrimental to any organic function.

11. A relationship exists between habitual posture and personality, also between habitual posture and emotional states.

12. In view of the great variety of human physiques and individual differences in structure, due either to heredity or to early environmental influence, there can be no single detailed description of good posture.

13. In the last analysis, both the static and the dynamic posture of any individual should be judged on the basis of how well it meets the demands made upon it.

Demonstrations and Laboratory Exercises

1. To demonstrate the alignment of the body segments take from five to seven large wooden blocks, each having a vertical line painted in the center of one side. A layer of thick felt should be glued to the top and bottom of each block, and a small hook screwed into each of two opposite sides.

a. Arrange the blocks in a straight column with the painted lines in front. Connect the hooks on the sides with elastic bands. The elastic "ligaments" will be under equal tension, and the felt "cartilages" under equal pressure when the column is in perfect alignment.

b. Now insert wedges between the blocks in such a way that every other block tips to the left, and the alternate blocks tip to the right. The elastic "ligaments" will now be under unequal tension, and the felt "cartilages" under unequal pressure. The zigzag alignment of the painted lines illustrates graphically the poor alignment of the segments.

2. To demonstrate good and poor alignment of a single weight-bearing joint, such as the knee, two blocks arranged like those described above may be used in a similar manner.

3. Demonstration and practice of the postural reflexes described by Haynes:

a. Lying face down, contract the gluteal muscles by pinching the buttocks together. Note the involuntary extension of the spine, knees and ankles, the supination of the feet, and the increased tension in the abdominal muscles.

b. Lying face down, raise one leg slightly and extend it completely. Notice the increased tension in the muscles on the back of the other leg.

4. Using the method described in the preceding chapter, take anteroposterior line of gravity photographs of several subjects representing various postures. After drawing the line of gravity on each photograph observe them carefully and note the relation of the line to the head, shoulders, upper trunk, lower trunk, pelvis, knees and ankles.

5. Take ten anteroposterior line of gravity photographs of one subject within a period of one week. Compare these.

6. Take anteroposterior line of gravity photographs of several subjects representing different physique types. Can you make any generalizations about the relation of physique to posture?

7. Do an original posture study with a small number of subjects.

Bibliography

1. Billig, H. E.: The Release of Fascial Ligamentous Contractures in Physical Rehabilitation. Industrial Medicine, *14:* 270–273, 1945.
2. Bowen, W. P., and Stone, H. A.: Applied Anatomy and Kinesiology. 7th ed. Philadelphia, Lea & Febiger, 1953.
3. Brunnstrom, S.: Center of Gravity Line in Relation to Ankle Joint in Erect Standing. Phys. Ther. Review, *34:* 109–115, 1954.

4. ———: The Changing Conception of Posture. Phys. Ther. Review, *20:* 79–84, 1940.

5. Campbell, D. G.: Posture: A Gesture toward Life. Physiotherapy Rev., *15:* 43–47, 1935.

6. Cowell, C. C.: Bodily Posture as a Mental Attitude. J. Health & Phys. Ed., *1:* 14–15, 56, 1930.

7. Deaver, G. G.: Posture and Its Relation to Mental and Physical Health. Research Quarterly of Am. Assn. for Health and Phys. Ed., *4:* 221–228, 1933.

8. Dorland, W. A. N.: The American Illustrated Medical Dictionary. 23rd ed. Philadelphia, W. B. Saunders Co., 1957.

9. Fox, M. G.: The Relationship of Abdominal Strength to Selected Posture Faults. Research Quarterly of Am. Assn. for Health, Phys. Ed. and Recr., *22:* 141–144, 1951.

10. Frost, L. H.: Individual Structural Differences in the Orthopedic Examination. J. Health and Phys. Ed., *9:* 90–93, 122, 1938.

11. Goldthwait, J. E., Brown, L. T., Swaim, L. T., and Kuhns, J. G.: Essentials of Body Mechanics in Health and Disease. 5th ed. Philadelphia, J. B. Lippincott Company, 1952.

12. Haller, J. S., and Gurewitsch, A. D.: An Approach to Dynamic Posture Based on Primitive Motion Patterns. Arch. Phys. Med., *31:* 632–640, 1950.

13. Hawley, G.: Kinesiology of Corrective Exercise. 2nd ed. Philadelphia, Lea & Febiger, 1949.

14. Haynes, R. S.: Postural Reflexes in Relation to the Correction of Improper Body Position. Am. J. Dis. Child., *36:* 1095–1107, 1928.

15. Hellebrandt, F. A.: Physiology and the Physical Educator. Research Quarterly of Am. Assn. for Health, Phys. Ed. and Recr., *11:* 12–29, 1940.

16. ———: Postural Adjustments in Convalescence and Rehabilitation. Fed. Proc., *3:* 243–246, 1944.

17. ——— and Franseen, E. B.: Physiological Study of the Vertical Stance of Man. Physiol. Rev., *23:* 220–255, 1943.

18. Hoffman, E.: Certain Physical and Physiological Characteristics as Related to the Incidence of Severe Dysmenorrhea. Unpublished M.S. Thesis, Wellesley College, 1942.

19. Huddleston, O. L.: Postural Reflexes. Arch. Phys. Therapy, *21:* 282–289, 1940.

20. Karpovich, P. V.: Physiology of Muscular Activity. 4th ed. Philadelphia, W. B. Saunders Company, 1953, p. 279.

21. Keith, A.: Man's Posture—Its Evolution and Disorders. Brit. M.J., *1:* 451, 454, 499, 502, 545, 548, 587, 590, 624, 628, 669, 672, 1923.

22. Kendall, H. O., Kendall, F. P., and Boynton, D. A.: Posture and Pain. Baltimore, Williams & Wilkins Company, 1952.

23. McCormick, H. G.: The Metabolic Cost of Maintaining a Standing Position, with Special Reference to Body Alignment. New York, King's Crown Press, 1942.

24. Mensendieck, B.: Mensendieck System of Functional Exercises. Portland, Me., Southworth-Anthoensen Press, 1937.

25. Metheny, E.: Body Dynamics. New York, McGraw-Hill Book Company, Inc., 1952.

26. Miller, K. D.: A Physical Educator Looks at Posture. J. Sch. Health, *21:* 89–94, 1951.

27. Morton, D. J.: Human Locomotion and Body Form. Baltimore, Williams & Wilkins Company, 1952.

28. Ober, F. R.: Relation of the Fascia Lata to Mechanical Disability of the Spine. Surgery, *4:* 21–32, 1938.

29. Phelps, W. M., et al.: The Diagnosis and Treatment of Postural Defects. 2nd ed. Springfield, Ill., Charles C Thomas, 1956.

30. Rathbone, J. L.: Corrective Physical Education. 6th ed. Philadelphia, W. B. Saunders Company, 1959.
31. Sheldon, W. H., Stevens, S. S., and Tucker, W. B.: The Varieties of Human Physique. New York, Harper & Brothers, 1940.
32. Stafford, G. T., and Kelly, E. D.: Preventive and Corrective Physical Education. 3rd ed. New York, Ronald Press, 1958.
33. Steindler, A.: Kinesiology of the Human Body. Springfield, Ill., Charles C Thomas, 1955, Lecture XIV.
34. Sweigard, L. E.: Body Mechanics and Posture in Modern Iife. Symposium on Posture. Printed by Phi Delta Pi, 1938.
35. Todd, M. E.: The Thinking Body. Boston, Charles T. Branford Company, 1949.
36. Wellesley College Studies in Hygiene and Physical Education: Factors in Anteroposterior Posture. Supplement to the Research Quarterly of Am. Assn. for Health and Phys. Ed., 9: 89–96, 1938.
37. Wells, K. F.: What We Don't Know about Posture. J. Health, Phys. Ed. and Recr., 29: 31, 32, 1958.
38. Wiebe, V. R.: A Study of Tests of Kinesthesis. Research Quarterly of Am. Assn. for Health, Phys. Ed. and Recr., 25: 222–230, 1954.

Recommended Readings

Campbell, D. G.: Posture: A Gesture toward Life. (See 5 above.)
Frost, L. H.: Individual Structural Differences in the Orthopedic Examination. (See 10 above.)
Hellebrandt, F. A.: Physiology and the Physical Educator. (See 15 above.)
Metheny, E.: Body Dynamics. Chapter 7. (See 25 above.)

19 · Principles of Moving One's Body

WE WALK down the street, we run to catch a bus, we swim, dance, jump and do gymnastic exercises. These are but a few of the many ways in which we move our own bodies. Perhaps we nod to an acquaintance, wave to a friend, rub our hand over our head, shake a foot that has gone to sleep—these are common examples of moving parts of our bodies. There is no movement we perform, no matter how small or inconsequential, that is not governed by specific principles. The basic mechanical principles are derived, on the whole, from Newton's three laws of motion and from the principles of leverage. These laws apply to all motion, but the specific behavior of the body in its obedience to these principles may vary according to the environment in which it is moving and to the nature of its support. Before considering these laws, however, it may be well to review briefly the basic principles which apply in all circumstances.

General Principles of Moving One's Own Body

1. According to the Law of Inertia, a body will not move until a force is applied to it. There must be a constant or regularly repeated application of such force when opposing forces are acting on the body. The force of gravity, friction, air resistance and water resistance are common opposing forces. Whenever possible, momentum should be used in movements that involve continuous motion in order to avoid the necessity of repeatedly overcoming inertia.

Examples:

a. In walking, the inertia of the body has to be overcome at each step because of the opposing forces of gravity, air resistance, and the restraining push of the forward foot as it makes contact with the ground.

b. In swimming and boating, the chief opposing force is that of water resistance. Strokes must be repeated regularly if movement is to continue. Of the three, the human body, the rowboat and the canoe, the canoe meets the least resistance from the water because it displaces the least water and is the most streamlined in shape. Hence it will glide the farthest before its motion is stopped.

c. When coasting on a sled, once the level ground is reached, the sled soon comes to a standstill because of the opposing force of friction.

d. In activities that require a pull-up followed by a push-up, as in the pole vault and the breast-up on a horizontal bar, there should be no pause between the pull and the push, in order to avoid the necessity of overcoming the body's inertia a second time.

2. According to the Law of Inertia, force is needed to change the direction of a moving body.

Example: In walking and running, exaggerated up-and-down movements mean that additional force is being used unnecessarily. The same is true of exaggerated up-and-down movements preparatory to throwing for distance, putting the shot, and so on. It is more efficient to use one's energy for productive movement.

3. According to the Law of Inertia, a body in motion will continue to move until it is acted upon by an external force.

Example: When running, although opposing forces are constantly acting upon the body, an additional force must be introduced in order to make the body lose its momentum in a relatively short space. This is done by inclining the body backward and extending the leg forward at the end of the swinging phase in order to increase the restraining force of the forward leg when the foot strikes the ground.

4. According to the Law of Action and Reaction, every action is accompanied by an equal and opposite reaction.

Examples:

a. In walking, running, jumping, and so on, the foot is pushed against the ground. The ground pushes back with equal and opposite force, causing the body to move forward or upward, as the case may be. For instance, in walking, running and broad jumping, the foot pushes primarily backward, and because of the counterforce of the ground, the body moves forward. In vertical jumping, the feet push directly downward, and the body moves upward.

b. In attempting to walk on smooth ice, the foot tries to push backward, but is unable to do so because of the absence of friction. Consequently the body does not move forward. When the feet fail to give support, gravity takes over.

c. In walking on sand or deep snow, although much energy is expended, the feet succeed in exerting only slight backward force against the loose and shifting substance under them, and in return there is a proportionately slight reaction to send the body forward.

d. When the body is not supported by a solid surface, the "equal and opposite reaction" to the action of its parts occurs within the body itself. For instance, a person who has jumped off the high board, or who is floating in the water, will find that when he swings both legs forward from the hips, the trunk will move forward to meet them. Or, when he swings one arm at shoulder level from a sideward to a forward position, the whole body will turn on its longitudinal axis toward the moving arm.

5. When the body as a whole is set in motion, either it will undergo translatory movement as in locomotion, or it will rotate. If it is in contact with the ground, it will either rotate about its own vertical axis, or will rotate about successive points of contact with the ground. In the latter instance this will result in translatory movement of the body as a whole.

Examples:

a. Walking and running represent translatory movement of the body as a whole brought about by angular movements of the lower extremities. In the supporting phase of walking, the lower extremity partially rotates about its point of contact with the supporting surface, that is, the point where the foot is in contact with the ground. In a series of cartwheels it rotates about each hand and foot in succession. In a forward roll it rotates about the hands, shoulders, back, buttocks and feet (Fig. 203).

b. In fancy dives, such as the one-and-a-half, half or full gainor, the body rotates about its center of gravity at the same time that it is moving in a parabolic pathway.

There appear to be four basic environments in which the human body moves. These are as follows:

1. The body is supported by the ground or other surface which simulates the ground.
2. The body is supported by water.
3. The body is unsupported, i.e., it is projected or is falling through space.
4. The body is suspended.

There may, of course, be various combinations of 1, 2 and 4.

Principles of Moving One's Own Body When It Is Supported by the Ground or Similar Surface

Movements of the Body as a Whole. When the body as a whole is set in motion, it is participating either in locomotion by self-propulsion, or in rotation. Locomotion is a form of translatory motion produced by angular motion of the extremities. In order for the body to propel itself it must be able to push against a resistant surface. In accord with the Law of Action and Reaction, its action is dependent upon the reaction of the supporting surface. The principles listed below apply specifically to walking. Applications to other forms of locomotion should be made by the student.

1. Since propulsion of the body is effected by the diagonal pressure of the foot against the supporting surface, the efficiency of locomotion depends upon counterpressure and friction.

2. A body at rest will remain at rest unless acted upon by a force. Since walking is produced by a pendulum-like motion of the limbs, the inertia of the body must be overcome at every step.

3. A body in motion will continue in motion unless acted upon by a force. Since motion is imparted to the trunk by the backward thrust of the leg, the trunk has a tendency to continue moving forward, even beyond the base of support. A brief restraining action of the forward limb acts as a check on the momentum of the trunk.

4. Force applied diagonally consists of two components, horizontal and vertical. The vertical component in walking serves to counteract the downward pull of gravity. The horizontal component serves (1) in the restraining phase, to check forward motion, and (2) in the propulsive phase, to produce forward motion. The horizontal component of force in the propulsive phase must exceed that in the restraining phase if the end result is to be progressive forward motion.

5. The speed of the gait is directly related to the magnitude of the pushing force and to the direction of its application. This force is provided by the extensor muscles of the hip, knee and ankle joints, and the direction of application is determined by the slant of the lower extremity when the force is being applied.

6. The economy of the gait is related to its timing with reference to the length and weight of the limbs. The most economical gait is one which is so timed as to permit a pendulum-like motion of the lower extremities.

7. Translatory movement of a lever is achieved by the repeated alternation of two rotatory movements, the lever turning first about one end, then about the other.[7]

8. Walking has been described as an alternating loss and recovery

Figure 203. The body rotating around its points of contact with the supporting surface. (Redrawn from LaPorte and Renner: The Tumbler's Manual, by courtesy of Prentice-Hall, Inc.)

of balance.[7] This being so, a new base of support must be established at every step.

9. Stability of the body is directly related to the size of the base of support. In walking, the lateral distance between the feet is a factor in balance.

a. A negative lateral distance between the feet, such as occurs when one foot is placed directly in front of the other, increases the difficulty of maintaining balance, since it decreases the width of the base of support.

b. A wide lateral distance between the feet increases stability, but tends to cause a weaving gait and to make the body sway from side to side.

c. The optimum position of the feet appears to be one in which the inner borders fall approximately along a single straight line. This gives adequate stability and minimizes lateral motions of the body.

Rotatory Movements of the Body as a Whole.   When the body is supported by a solid surface, it can rotate either about its own vertical axis, as when pirouetting on the toes or on skates, or about its successive points of contact with the supporting surface, such as the hands and feet in a cartwheel; the hands, shoulders, back, buttocks and feet, in a forward roll (Fig. 203). Two principles which apply specifically to rotatory movements of the body are as follows:

1. Rotatory motion may be accelerated by shortening the radius, and decelerated by lengthening the radius. For instance, pulling the arms in close to the body while pirouetting on ice skates will increase the speed, and extending the arms horizontally will decrease it.

2. A long lever has greater velocity at the end than does a short

lever, moving at the same angular velocity. For instance, the hands and feet have greater velocity in a cartwheel than they do in a forward roll.

Movements of Segments of the Body. The following principles apply to movements of bodily segments, movements in which the body as a whole remains in approximately the same location.

1. Since a long lever has greater velocity at the end than a short lever moving at the same angular velocity, in movements of the arm, the hand has greater velocity when the elbow is kept straight, and in movements of the leg, the foot has greater velocity when the knee is kept straight.

2. Centrifugal force is developed in circular movements of bodily segments, as in strenuous arm circling. This should be recognized as a potential source of injury to the shoulder joint, since the centrifugal force creates a dislocating tendency.

3. The momentum of any part of a supported body can be transferred to the rest of the body. For instance, if one stands with one arm extended forward and then vigorously flings it horizontally sideward-backward, the whole body will tend to follow the arm. This transfer of momentum could not take place were it not for the reaction of the supporting surface.

Principles of Moving One's Own Body When It Is Supported by Water

The problem of moving the body through the water is fundamentally not so different from that of moving it on land. As in walking, it is necessary to push against something in order to move the body from one place to another. The chief differences between locomotion in the water and locomotion on land are that (1) in the water the body is concerned with buoyancy rather than with the force of gravity; (2) the substance against which it pushes affords less resistance to the push; (3) the medium through which it moves affords more resistance to the body; and (4) as a means of getting the greatest benefit from the buoyancy and of reducing the resistance afforded by the water, it is customary to maintain a horizontal, rather than a vertical, position.

Buoyancy differs with individuals and, on the whole, is greater in women than in men. The average person has sufficient buoyancy to float close to the surface of the water. The buoyancy of a body is indicated by the amount of water it displaces. Corresponding to the center of gravity on land, immersed bodies have a center of buoyancy. This is a center of balance in the water. A human body so lacking in buoyancy that it sinks to the bottom is a rarity. The practical problem in swimming is not to keep from sinking, as beginners are inclined to think, but to get the mouth out of the water at rhythmic intervals in order to permit regular breathing. This is a matter of coordination, not buoyancy.

In swimming, as in all motion, the initial mechanical problem is to overcome the inertia of the body. Once the body is in motion, the problem is to overcome the forces which tend to hinder it. In terrestrial locomotion the body exerts its force against the supporting surface, that is the ground, in order to overcome inertia. The forces resisting the progress of the body are the force of gravity and air resistance. In aquatic locomotion the water is both the supporting medium and the source of resistance. In swimming, the hands and feet depend upon the counter pressure of the water in order that the force may be transmitted to the body. Yet, at the same time, the body must overcome the resistance afforded by the water.

Thus the major problems in the mechanics of swimming are the minimizing of resistance and the advantageous application of force. The swimmer reduces the resistance by streamlining his body position, by relaxing in the recovery phase of the stroke and by eliminating useless motions and tensions. There are many different strokes in swimming, but they all involve either a pulling or a pushing motion of the arms, and either a pincer or a thrusting action of the legs. In order to get maximum horizontal propulsion from the arm and leg movements it is necessary to eliminate upward, downward and sideward components of force as much as possible. Swimming with ease, power and efficiency requires a precise coordination of arm and leg motions, of breathing and of use of the trunk muscles in maintaining an optimum position.

The major principles which apply to swimming are as follows:

Principles Relating to the Application of Force

1. The body will move in the opposite direction from that in which the force is applied. For instance, a backward thrust will send the body forward; downward pressure will lift it; pressure to the right will send it to the left. Hence, in the crawl stroke, too much force at the beginning of the arc will have too great a downward component, thereby tending to lift the body. This increases resistance and is a needless expenditure of energy. In the breast stroke, the two arms balance each other; hence too great an outward force at the beginning of the stroke, or inward force at the end of the stroke, does not produce lateral motion, but results in a waste of energy.

In many aquatic stunts and lifesaving techniques the swimmer deliberately pushes himself up or down by pushing his hands and feet against the water in the direction opposite to that in which he wishes to move. No matter how complicated the movement in a synchronized swimming technique, it is brought about by observing the principle that a body moves in the opposite direction from that in which the force is applied.

2. Maximum force is attained by presenting as broad a surface as possible in the propulsive movements of the limbs and by exerting a backward pressure through as great a distance as possible, provided undesirable forces are not inadvertently introduced. This implies that the full surface of the hand should be used and that the hand should not enter the water so soon that it shortens the stroke unduly. In the crawl stroke care must be taken not to reach too far, however, since this involves lifting the shoulder and is likely to introduce a lateral force acting on the trunk.

Principles Relating to the Reduction of Resistance

1. A rapidly moving body in the water leaves a low pressure area immediately behind it. This creates a suction effect and tends to pull the body back. Although this backward pull cannot be entirely eliminated, it can be reduced in the crawl stroke by keeping the feet close together.

2. The sudden or quick movement of a swimmer's body, or one of its parts, at the surface of the water tends to cause whirls and eddies. These create low pressure areas which have a retarding effect on the swimmer. They can be reduced by slicing the hand into the water and by eliminating movements which do not contribute to forward progression. In the flutter kick, movement of the feet in the air does not contribute to the propulsion of the body; hence the feet and legs should be kept just below the surface of the water.

3. The more streamlined the body, the less the resistance to progress through the water. The streamlining of the body in the crawl stroke is accomplished by

> a. Carrying the head so that the water level is somewhere between the hairline and just below the eyes, depending upon the buoyancy and speed of the swimmer;
>
> b. Carrying the body parallel with the surface of the water;
>
> c. Carrying the buttocks just below the surface of the water;
>
> d. Keeping the legs, ankles and feet close together.

Application to Boating and Canoeing.*   On the whole, the principles which apply to swimming apply also to boating and canoeing. This is particularly obvious in canoeing, for the paddle

---

* Some readers may object to the inclusion of boating and canoeing in a chapter devoted to principles of moving one's own body. They argue that these activities are examples of giving impetus to an external object. To the author, the argument that they are forms of locomotion by self-propulsion is just as valid as the other. In her opinion the primary purpose of boating and canoeing is locomotion of the self on the water, and the locomotion of the craft is of secondary importance. An additional argument in favor of including the discussion of rowing and paddling in this chapter is that the principles of locomotion in the water are the same, regardless of whether the locomotion is caused by movement of the hands and feet or of oars and paddles.

is used in much the same way as are the arms in swimming. The use of the oars in rowing is more limited, since they must be kept in the oarlocks at all times. In paddling, as in the arm movement of the crawl stroke, too much force at the beginning of the stroke has too great a downward component, and hence too great a lifting effect. Conversely, too much force at the end of the stroke has too great an upward component, and hence a depressing effect on the canoe. In order to make the canoe move smoothly in a horizontal direction, without unnecessary bobbing up and down, it is essential to reduce these two components to a minimum and to put the emphasis on the backward movement of the blade.

The techniques of steering the canoe are based on this same principle. Assuming that there is only one paddler and that he is paddling from the center of the canoe, if he wished to move the canoe broadside to his paddling side he would put his paddle in the water, blade parallel to the keel, directly opposite the center of the canoe, as far out as he could conveniently and safely reach, and then draw the blade squarely toward him at right angles to the keel of the canoe. If he wished to move broadside away from his paddling side, he would slice the blade into the water opposite the center of the canoe and close to it, with the blade parallel to the keel, and then push it directly away from him at right angles to the keel. In order to turn the canoe, he would have to reach either forward or backward and press the blade toward or away from the canoe at a point as far from the canoe's center of buoyancy as he could conveniently reach. A drawing stroke nearer the bow would make the canoe turn toward the paddling side; a drawing stroke nearer the stern would make the canoe turn away from the paddling side. (The direction taken by the canoe as a whole is stated in terms of the bow. As the stern of the canoe moves toward the paddling side, the bow moves away from it.) Steering a canoe is logical and simple when one remembers the principle that movement occurs in the direction opposite to that in which the force is applied, and, at the same time, remembers that a canoe tends to rotate about its center of buoyancy when force is applied at any point other than in line with this center.

Principles of Moving One's Own Body When It Is in the Air, Free of Support

The unsupported body is eventually drawn to the earth by the force of gravity. Its initial movement through space, however, may be one of projection, the direction usually being horizontally forward, vertically upward, or somewhere between the two. In diving and in high jumping the projection is essentially in an upward direction; in broad jumping and in dismounting from a moving vehicle, it is more nearly horizontal. There are two essential principles which apply to moving the body when it is unsupported.

1. When the body is unsupported, momentum of the body as a whole cannot be developed. This means that its center of gravity cannot be displaced from its path of motion, this pathway having been determined by the force of gravity and the force of its projection into space. Once the body is in the air, its center of gravity will follow the same pathway as that of any inanimate object which has been projected at a similar angle by a corresponding force. *Nothing the diver can do will alter the pathway of his center of gravity, once he has left the diving board.*

2. The only total movement which can be initiated in the unsupported body is rotation around its center of gravity. It can be made to rotate around a vertical, frontal-horizontal or sagittal-horizontal axis, or any intermediate axis. Whereas either translatory motion or rotatory motion can be initiated in both the earth-supported and the water-supported body, in the unsupported body there can be no translatory movement other than that caused by gravity and by the initial projection. The implication of this principle is that

Figure 204. Front somersault dive in layout position. An example of rotatory movement of the body as a whole when it is unsupported. (Courtesy of H. E. Edgerton.)

the diver must have his center of gravity ahead of the board at the moment of take-off if he is to clear the board when he comes down.

Principles of Moving One's Own Body When It Is Suspended

Climbing, hanging, swinging and other suspension activities were more commonly engaged in by our early ancestors than by more recent generations. In the days of primitive man and his forebears they were a common form of locomotion. The modern version of these brachial activities is seen in the trapeze activities of the aerial artist at the circus, and in exercises and stunts on the flying rings, traveling rings, horizontal bar, high boom, stall bars, ropes and various forms of hanging ladders in the gymnasium and on the playground. Ladder climbing and brachial locomotion without swinging are modifications of locomotion on the ground. All swinging movements of a suspended body are governed by the principles of the pendulum and of circular motion.

Principles Relating to the Movements of a Pendulum

1. The movement of a pendulum is produced by the force of gravity. This presupposes a starting position in which potential energy is present. In other words, the pendulum must be moved from its resting position before the force of gravity can make it swing downward.

2. The upward movement of a pendulum is effected by the momentum developed in the downward movement.

3. The amplitude of a pendulum, i.e., the range of its swing, depends upon the height from which its movement is initiated. The amplitude may be increased by the application of external force to the pendulum, but at the moment of such application the pendulum is temporarily not being allowed to act as a pendulum.

4. The time taken by the pendulum to make a single round trip excursion (known as its *period*) is related to the length of the pendulum. The longer the pendulum, the more slowly it swings. Specifically, the period of the pendulum is proportional to the square root of its length.

5. The period of the pendulum is not influenced by its weight. A heavy body will swing no faster than a lighter one, or vice versa. This is consistent with the behavior of freely falling bodies.

6. As the pendulum swings downward, its speed increases; as it swings upward, its speed diminishes until the zero point is reached. Hence the pendulum's speed is greatest at the bottom of the arc, and least (zero) at each end of the arc.

7. The swinging body moves through an arc, first in one direction, then in the reverse direction. Thus it undergoes partial rotation about a center of motion. Since this rotation takes place in a

vertical plane, the influence of gravitational pull must be taken into consideration. Whereas the force of gravity *produces* the downward swing, it *opposes* the upward swing. Nevertheless it is indirectly responsible for the latter, since the upward swing is caused by the momentum which was built up in the preceding downward swing. Rotation of a body in the vertical plane can be accelerated by shortening the radius (i.e., distance between the body's center of gravity and the center of rotation) on the up-swing, and lengthening it on the down-swing. Since, in the movement of a pendulum, speed is greatest at the bottom of the arc, shortening the radius at this point accelerates its speed (i.e., its angular velocity) more than in any other position.

Observation of this principle provides the means for attaining greater height in swinging on the flying rings or trapeze. As the body passes under the point of support (i.e., the center of rotation) on its forward swing, the knees should be brought up in front of the body. Toward the end of the up-swing the legs should be extended as high as possible. On the entire back-swing, and on the forward down-swing, the body should be relaxed in the extended position.

8. When a pendulum reaches the end of its arc, just before it reverses its direction, it reaches a zero point in velocity. At this precise moment the force of gravity is momentarily neutralized by the upward momentum. Also centrifugal and centripetal force neutralize each other at this moment. The performer can take advantage of this situation by using this moment to perform "trick" movements such as reversing the grasp and facing in the opposite direction, performing cut-offs on the traveling rings, and others.

9. Since the movement of a pendulum is circular, the characteristics of circular motion apply. The grasp of the hands must constantly combat the tendency of centrifugal force to pull the body off the apparatus. If the body does break loose, it will fly off at a tangent to the arc of its swing, and there is danger of injury.

Additional Applications of the Principles Which Pertain to the Movements of a Pendulum

1. The initial problem of the child on the swing and of the gymnast on the flying rings is that of being given potential energy. Ruling out the help of an accomplice, he must find a way of putting himself into a position in which he will have potential energy. He does this usually in one of three ways. He may move the apparatus to some position other than its normal position of rest before he suspends himself from it (i.e., he pulls the rings or swing as far back as he can reach before getting on); his feet may be able to reach the supporting surface when he is on the apparatus, in which case he can push his feet against the floor or take little run-

ning steps; or he may use a pumping action to get started. For the man swinging on the rings, this involves bending the legs up in front of the body and then extending them as high as possible. This puts them in a position in which gravity will act on them and the downward movement of the legs causes momentum to be developed, which in turn is transferred to the rest of the body. The range of the arc of motion may be increased by the repetition of this procedure on the forward-upward phase of the swing. The child in the swing accomplishes the same result by inclining the trunk backward and raising the feet forward. He can start the swing even more effectively if he can pull the ropes toward his body and, at the same time, press forward against the seat.

2. Initiating a pendulum swing on the traveling rings is achieved by flexing each arm alternately. Because of the wide distance between the traveling rings, this procedure moves the body a considerable distance from its resting position, and thus puts it in favorable position for the force of gravity to act on it.

3. Progression on the traveling rings is achieved by releasing the "rear" hand at the "rear" end of the arc, flinging the extended arm sideward-downward slightly in front of the body, and then forcefully upward in a continuous arc of motion. The momentum developed by the arm turns the body toward the other arm, and, as the hand reaches for its new point of suspension, the body has made a half-turn and is facing in the opposite direction. This process is repeated first with one arm, and then with the other, and with the body turning first one way and then the other, but always as it is moving in the direction of the ultimate goal. Unless sufficient momentum is developed, the performer will have difficulty in reaching the new point of suspension with his free hand.

This activity depends for its success upon the development of adequate potential energy, or energy of position, to assure sufficient kinetic energy to enable the body to rise to the same height at which it started. When the body is suspended by one hand, the only force producing the swing is the force of gravity. Attempts to use muscular force to increase the height of the swing result in jerky, unproductive movements which interfere with the smooth, pendulum-like motion of the body. For effective hand traveling, the principle of the pendulum needs to be kept in mind, namely, that the motion of a pendulum depends upon the force of gravity.

4. The timing of such activities as the cut-off on the traveling rings, uprises on the horizontal bar, changing hands and turning the body around on the flying rings or trapeze, is governed by the fact that the force of gravity and the upward momentum of the body momentarily neutralize each other at the moment when the

pendulum reaches the end of its arc, just before it reverses its direction.

5. If it is desirable to control the speed of swinging for any reason, the supporting ropes should be lengthened for a slower swing and shortened for a faster swing.

6. Centrifugal force increases the difficulty of maintaining one's grasp on the rings or trapeze. If the performer loses his grasp, his body obeys Newton's first law of motion and flies off at a tangent to its previous arc of motion. For this reason great care must be taken with beginners and children. The instructor should watch their hands for indications of slipping and should teach them to dismount on the forward swing, preferably just before the base of the arc is reached. The experienced performer, however, will find it more desirable to dismount toward the end of the forward swing, once he has learned how to receive the impact of his own body by losing his kinetic energy gradually (see p. 387).

Principles Other Than Those Relating to the Movements of a Pendulum. In hand traveling without swinging, the body is not moving like a pendulum. Locomotion by this means is similar to locomotion on the ground or in the water in that it depends upon the principle of action and reaction. As in walking, force applied against a supporting surface in one direction will cause the body to move in the opposite direction. The movement is similar to side stepping in that the body moves sideways. The lateral application of force may seem to be imperceptible, yet without it the body would not progress laterally. Hand traveling without swinging on a boom or horizontal ladder is achieved by alternately moving first one hand away from the other hand, and then moving the second hand toward the first. As the first hand moves, the second hand pushes laterally against the apparatus. Both hands share the weight equally for a moment; then the second hand is released and brought toward the first hand, while at the same time the first hand is pulling laterally on the apparatus. This process is repeated.

Demonstrations and Laboratory Exercises

1. Perform, or observe someone else perform, each of the following, and in each case identify the force that stops the motion of the body:

   a. Slide on the ice or slippery floor.

   b. Jump vertically upward.

   c. Plunge for distance in the pool.

2. Observe someone performing a vertical jump, (*a*) with and (*b*) without the help of his arms. Compare the height of the two jumps by noting the level of the top of his head. A chart consisting of numbered horizontal lines should be suspended behind the subject, and the observer should stand on a bench, squarely facing the subject and chart. This experiment should be repeated several times and with several subjects in order to minimize chance variations in the power of the leg action.

3. *a.* Twirl on the toes (preferably on ice skates) with the arms held close to

the body; then extend the arms sideward before the angular momentum is spent.

b. Repeat this experiment, starting with the arms extended sideward at shoulder level; then pull them in close to the body before the angular momentum is spent.

What is the effect of extending the arms in *a,* and of pulling them close to the body in *b*? What principle is illustrated?

4. If you are a reasonably skillful performer, do a backward roll (*a*) starting from a squat position and (*b*) from a standing position. What is the advantage of the latter method, and what are the chief problems? What principles are illustrated?

5. Do the arm movement of the crawl stroke and deliberately press hard with the hand as soon as it enters the water, and, at the end of the stroke, instead of taking the hand out of the water at the proper time, continue the movement of the arm until the hand has pressed upward against the water. What is the effect on the body of these two errors in the crawl stroke?

6. Observe or perform the following swimming stunts and analyze them in terms of the direction in which the body is moved and the direction of the application of force:

    a. Dolphin

    b. Side sculling

    c. Foot foremost surface dive

    d. Little man in a tub

7. Observe or perform a somersault dive in (*a*) the tuck position; (*b*) the pike position; and (*c*) the full layout position. What is the difference in the speed of rotation and the number of turns possible in a given space? What principle is illustrated?

8. Study diagrams or sequence photographs of several different dives and note the position of the pelvis at the instant of take-off in each of these. This provides the basis for a rough estimate of the position of the center of gravity. What do you estimate to be the position of the center of gravity relative to the end of the board?

9. In the same illustrations note the direction of the application of force just prior to the take-off. Is it vertically downward? If not, how does it deviate from the vertically downward direction?

10. Lie on the side in the water and swing both legs forward vigorously, keeping both knees straight. Does the trunk move? If so, how? What principle is illustrated?

11. Observe an experienced diver make the following jumps and note any movement of the trunk:

    a. Jump feet first from a high board and on the way down turn both feet to the left.

    b. Jump feet first from a high board with both arms extended sideward at shoulder level and on the way down swing the right arm horizontally forward.

12. Hang from a pair of flying rings which are high enough to enable you to clear the floor with your feet. Hang motionless for a moment, and then start swinging without help from anyone else. How did you initiate the swinging movement?

13. Swing on the flying rings. At the end of the forward swing, at the moment when the momentum of the swing and the force of gravity neutralize each other, reverse the grasp of one hand. The ability to do this easily is an indication that you have timed the movement correctly.

14. Swing on the flying rings or trapeze without attempting to get much height. Practice dismounting from various positions and notice the effect on the body. As a safety precaution be sure that there are no pieces of furniture or apparatus in your way, and have plenty of mats on the floor.

Bibliography

1. Bowen, W. P., and Stone, H. A.: Applied Anatomy and Kinesiology. 7th ed. Philadelphia, Lea & Febiger, 1953.
2. Glassow, R. B.: Fundamentals in Physical Education. Philadelphia, Lea & Febiger, 1932, Sections I and II.
3. Glassow, R. B.: A Laboratory Manual for Functional Kinesiology. Madison, Wis., Kramer Business Service, 1950.
4. McCloy, C. H.: Mimeographed material and class notes for course in Mechanical Analysis of Motor Skills, State University of Iowa.
5. Morehouse, L. E., and Cooper, J. M.: Kinesiology. St. Louis, C. V. Mosby Company, 1950.
6. Scott, M. G.: Analysis of Human Motion. New York, F. S. Crofts & Co., 1945.
7. Steindler, A.: Kinesiology of the Human Body. Springfield, Ill., Charles C Thomas, 1955.

20 · Principles of Receiving Impetus

IMPETUS, in the words of Webster's Dictionary, is "the property possessed by a moving body in virtue of its mass and its motions; . . . applied commonly to bodies moving suddenly or violently." Thus both the human body itself, and the objects it handles, may possess impetus. If two men of unequal weight are running at equal speed, the heavier man has greater impetus than the lighter. Conversely, if two men of the same weight are running at different speeds, the faster runner has the greater impetus. These are examples of impetus associated with horizontal motion, particularly that of self-propulsion. Horizontal motion is experienced also by a man who is riding on a horse, train or other vehicle, even though he appears to be motionless. The motion of the vehicle is imparted to him, as is seen if he falls off the horse or jumps from the moving train. Added to the impetus of the horizontally moving vehicle is the impetus of the downward motion resulting from the fall or jump. No wonder, then, that broken bones are likely to result from falls off horses and jumps from moving trains.

Impetus from vertical motion is experienced by anyone who falls through space. Such motion, which occurs subsequent to a downward jump, a dive or an accidental fall, has a rapidly increasing velocity due to the effect of gravitational force. Falling bodies are known to increase their velocity at the rate of 32 feet per second, each second. When the body lands on a supporting surface, its impetus is said to have been received. Likewise, the impetus of a horizontally moving body is received when its motion is stopped as the result of contact with a resisting surface, such as a wall or other obstacle.

Examples of receiving the impetus of external objects are commonly seen in sports. Baseballs are caught or fielded with the hands; hockey balls and pucks are received with a stick; soccer balls are trapped with the feet; and blows from an opponent's fists are received by various parts of the body. Examples of receiving the impetus of external objects are also seen in industry and in daily life. Cartons and tools are tossed from one man to another; red hot rivets are tossed and caught with tongs; victims from a fire are caught in nets.

Problems and Principles. What are the particular problems involved in these diverse forms of receiving impetus, and what are the principles which enable us to solve these problems satisfactorily? Considering first the reception of the body's own impetus, the chief problems would seem to be those of avoiding injury and of regaining equilibrium promptly. It is the abrupt loss of motion resulting from collision with an unyielding surface that is likely to cause an injury. To use more technical terms, and hence more exact ones, all moving bodies have what is known as kinetic energy —the energy of motion. Like impetus, and like momentum, kinetic energy is related both to the mass of the body and to its velocity. (Momentum $= mv$; kinetic energy $= \frac{1}{2} mv^2$.) In order to avoid injury from too abrupt a loss of kinetic energy it is necessary to find some means of losing it more gradually. This is achieved only by increasing the distance over which the kinetic energy is lost. The various devices we use for absorbing the shock of impact serve this purpose.

Another factor in injury which should not be overlooked is the relation of the force of impact to the size of the area which bears the brunt of the impact. A force of 100 pounds concentrated on 1 square inch of body surface, for instance, is likely to cause more serious injury than is the same amount of force spread over an area of 36 square inches. The problem here is clearly to increase the size of the area which receives the force of impact. This is especially important when there is limited opportunity for increasing the distance over which the kinetic energy is lost.

The problem of regaining equilibrium is largely a problem in controlling the placement of the limbs in preparation for landing, for equilibrium is regained when an adequate base of support is established. This implies sufficient control to place the feet, or perhaps both the hands and the feet, in a position which will provide a favorable base. The problem of regaining equilibrium is closely related to that of avoiding injury, since the esablishing of an adequate base is dependent upon the integrity of the bones and joints which receive the force of impact.

Various methods of falling are taught in classes of tumbling and modern dance. Perhaps one of the most effective measures for the prevention of injury in accidental falls is this kind of instruction, followed by the practice of a variety of falls until the techniques have been mastered. This helps more than anything else to establish the right patterns, patterns which will be followed automatically when accidental falls occur.

The problems involved in receiving the impetus of external objects appear to be threefold: namely, avoiding injury, maintaining equilibrium, and receiving the object with accuracy and control. As in the case of receiving the impetus of one's own body, avoidance of injury in catching or receiving external forces is achieved by increasing the distance over which the object's kinetic energy is lost. When catching a swift baseball, the experienced player will not hold his hands rigidly in front of him, but will "give" with the ball. By moving his hands toward his body through a distance of 10 to 20 inches as he receives the ball, he is making it possible for the ball's kinetic energy to be lost gradually. This same principle is likewise true for the player who is reaching for a high ball with one hand. The extended arm acts as a lever, the force being applied by the impact of the ball on the palm. The "moment of force" is therefore the product of the force of impact and the length of the arm. In the case of a fast ball, this can put a tremendous strain on the shoulder joint, as well as endanger the bones of the hands. To avoid injury the player should "give" by reaching somewhat forward for the ball and drawing his arm back at the moment of impact, also by rotating his body and by stepping back if the force is sufficiently great. If he lets the elbow flex slightly, he will shorten the lever of his arm and thus reduce the "moment of force."

Another factor in avoiding injury when catching swift balls is the position of the hands. Beginners often reach with outstretched arms and point their fingers toward the approaching ball. This leads to many a "baseball finger." The fingers should be pointed either down or up, according to whether the ball is below or above waist level.

The maintenance of equilibrium is an important problem in receiving the impetus of external forces. A swift ball or a sudden blow can easily catch us "off balance" and cause us to lose our equilibrium. There is little advantage to catching a swift ball with accuracy and safety if, in the process of catching it, we fall over backward. The stance is of great importance here. Widening the stance, i.e., the base of support, in a direction at right angles to the flight of the approaching ball does little to increase the catcher's stability. The base needs to be widened in the direction of the ball's flight, and thus make it possible for the catcher to shift his weight from the forward to the rear foot at the moment of impact. This not only increases his chances of maintaining his equilibrium, but also contributes to the gradual reduction of the ball's motion.

Skillfulness in receiving a swiftly moving object is characterized by accuracy and control. These qualities are achieved in part by a gradual loss of kinetic energy, the same factor that is responsible for avoiding injury. This contributes to accuracy and control by serving as a safeguard against rebound. Additional factors in accuracy include vision, judgment, and adjustment of the position of the body as a whole, as well as of the part directly concerned with receiving the object. "Keeping the eye on the ball" is essential to judging its speed and direction, and hence to adjusting the position of the body. Thus accurate judgment depends upon accurate vision, and accurate adjustment of the body depends upon both, as well as upon agility and smoothness of neuromuscular response. Together, these factors make up what is known as "hand-eye and foot-eye coordination." To a certain extent this is innate, but it is also developed and improved by practice.

In receiving both the impetus of one's body and that of external objects, an important factor to be considered is the subsequent movement one expects to make. It may be the determining factor in deciding on the stance to assume. For instance, if a run is anticipated, a forward-backward stance will be more favorable than a lateral one. Furthermore, it will be desirable to have the weight over the forward foot. If a catch is to be followed immediately by a throw, the movements used for "giving" may be blended into the preparatory movements of the throw. These are fine points which have much to do with the degree of one's skill in an activity.

In summary, the principles to observe in receiving impetus, both that of one's own body and that of external objects, are stated below, together with some representative applications of these principles.

Summary of Principles of Receiving Impetus

Principles Related to Avoiding Injury

I. The more gradually the kinetic energy of a moving body is lost, the less likely is the loss to cause injury.

  A. Applications to receiving the impetus of one's own body:

    1. For landing from jumps wear rubber-soled shoes and use landing pit or gymnasium mat.

    2. When landing from a fall, attempt to land on the more heavily padded parts of the body.

Figure 205. Effecting a gradual loss of kinetic energy by bending the knees upon landing from a jump.

3. When landing from a jump, attempt to land on the balls of the feet and immediately let the ankles, knees and hips flex, controlling the action by means of eccentric contraction of the extensor muscles of these joints (see Fig. 205).
4. When horizontal motion is terminated by a fall or jump, as in the case of falling off a horse, tripping and falling when running, jumping off a moving vehicle, and so on, attempt to diminish the horizontal motion gradually by rolling, somersaulting, taking a few running steps or doing a series of "frog jumps."
5. When landing from a jump, if the suggestions in *3* are not adequate, attempt to transfer the downward motion of the body to horizontal motion by rolling or somersaulting.
6. When landing from a fall following horizontal motion, if the suggestions in *4* are not feasible, attempt to take some of the weight on the hands, letting the arms "give" at the wrists, elbows and shoulders. When falling forward in an extended position, attempt to arch the back as the hands take the weight, turn the face to the side, and rock down on the front of the body. This method is especially applicable to tripping and falling when running.

B. Applications to receiving the impetus of external objects:
1. Wear a thickly padded glove when catching fast balls. This reduces the shock of impact by effecting a slightly more gradual reduction of the ball's velocity. The greater the mass of the ball, the thicker the padding needed.
2. When catching a ball with both hands, "give" with the arms by pulling them in toward the body at the moment of impact, and, if necessary, shift the weight backward and take a backward step or two.
3. When catching a high ball with one hand, allow the arm to move horizontally backward and rotate the body in the same direction. By bending at the elbow the likelihood of straining the shoulder will be reduced. By placing oneself in a favorable position in the first place, the need for overreaching will be prevented.
4. The method of reducing kinetic energy gradually when catching a ball may be adapted in such a way that it will serve as the preparatory movement for throwing. In catching a basketball, for instance, swinging the arms down to one side and rotating the body not only assure

a gradual loss of the ball's velocity, but also serve to put the hands and ball in a favorable position for throwing. The transition from catching to throwing is thus made with one continuous motion.

5. The principle of "giving" when catching balls applies also to "spotting" and to receiving in apparatus work in the gymnasium. In receiving the weight of another person the "giving" is effected by a lowering and bending of the arms and bending of the knees, or by taking several steps, according to whether the motion is chiefly vertical or horizontal.

II. The larger the area of the body which receives the force of impact, the less will be the force per unit of surface area. The applications of this principle are limited to the act of landing from a fall.

1. When falling forward, rocking onto the front of the body serves to increase the area which receives the force of impact, as well as to effect a gradual loss of kinetic energy.

2. When one seems to be in danger of falling on the elbow, a slight twist may make it possible to roll onto the upper arm and shoulder and thus increase the area receiving the force of impact.

3. When one seems to be in danger of falling on one knee, it may be possible to twist onto the side of the leg and rock onto the side of the thigh, perhaps using one arm to help absorb the shock.

Principles Related to Maintaining and Regaining Equilibrium. Other things being equal, the larger the base of support and the better centered the center of gravity above this base, the greater will be the body's equilibrium.

A. Applications to receiving the impetus of one's own body:

1. In any jump or fall the body's equilibrium is temporarily lost. In order to gain prompt control of the body upon landing, a favorable base of support can be established by adjusting the position of the feet *before landing* in such a way that they will provide a base of adequate width when the landing is made.*

2. In connection with the above, the position assumed by the feet should be such that it will facilitate the equal distribution of body weight over them.

3. External aids to making a controlled landing include a smooth landing surface and appropriate footwear. These help to prevent turned ankles and stubbed toes which might spoil an otherwise good landing.

4. When one lands with so much force that it is difficult to establish an adequate base of support with the feet alone, one or both hands should be used to establish a temporary base large enough to assure a quick recovery of equilibrium.

5. In order to provide an adequate base of support for the recovery of balance following forceful horizontal movements, the larger dimension of the base should be parallel with the direction of the horizontal movement. This will necessitate a forward-backward stance if one is facing in the direction of the horizontal motion. It will necessitate a sideward stance if one lands facing sideward with reference to the direction of motion. This adjustment of stance is particularly applicable to vaulting and tumbling activities. When one trips while running, the body automatically uses this method in its attempt to prevent a fall.

* The practice of teaching landing with the feet together when vaulting over gymnastic apparatus is not in keeping with this principle. This method of landing is not to be condemned for that reason, but it should be recognized as a test of skill. The skillful gymnast can regain his balance in spite of a narrow base of support. Beginners should be permitted to land with their feet separated.

B. Applications to receiving the impetus of external objects and forces:

1. In preparation for catching a swift ball, especially a heavy one such as a medicine ball, assuming a moderately wide stance with the feet separated in the direction of the approaching ball will enable the catcher to keep his balance. It also enables him to increase the distance for stopping the ball's velocity.

2. When standing in a moving train or bus, balance is maintained more readily as the vehicle accelerates and decelerates if one takes a moderately wide stance parallel with the long axis of the vehicle, in other words, with the direction of movement.

3. If the body is subjected to pushes, pulls or blows, it can maintain and regain balance more readily if the feet are separated in a stance which is parallel with the direction of the force.

Principles Related to Accuracy and Control in Receiving External Objects

1. The more gradually the velocity of an external object is reduced, the less likely is the object to rebound when its impetus is received.

All the methods suggested for avoiding injury when receiving the impetus of external objects also apply to preventing rebound.

2. "Keep the eye on the ball." Whether the object whose impetus is about to be received is a ball, a carton or a fist, keeping the eyes on it will enable one to judge its speed and direction and to respond accordingly. The tendency of some novices to shut the eyes should be checked at the outset.

3. Catching an external object with accuracy and control is largely dependent upon the position of the catcher relative to the direction of the approaching object. Putting oneself in the most favorable position possible is an essential objective for accurate catching. This is basic to the prevention of injury and to the maintenance of equilibrium.

Demonstrations and Laboratory Exercises

1. Jump from a low bench to the floor, landing on both feet.

   a. Landing with minimum "give," that is, with as little flexion at the ankles, knees and hips as possible.

   b. Landing with maximum "give," that is, allowing the ankles, knees and hips to flex to a full squat position. The head should be kept erect.

   c. Landing as in b, but looking down at the feet.

   Which method is preferable? Why?

2. Trip on the edge of a mat and fall forward, landing first on the knees, then on the hands.

   a. Keeping the arms rigid, elbows straight.

   b. Letting the elbows flex, arching the back, rocking down onto the abdomen and chest, with the head turned sideways.

3. Jump down from a table or gymnasium box, using the parachute landing technique, that is, landing on the toes with the feet together, bending the knees slightly and turning sideward, rolling onto the side of the leg, thigh and hip, then onto the back of the shoulder, keeping the arms close in front of the chest and the head flexed forward.

4. Catch a medicine ball thrown straight toward your chest.

   a. With your arms rigidly outstretched.

   b. With your hands held close in front of your chest.

   c. With your arms outstretched at first, but brought in toward your chest at the moment of impact.

   Which method is preferable? Why?

5. Receive a hard drive in field hockey, (a) with, and (b) without, "giving"

with the stick. Compare the results both as to control of the ball and sensation in the hands.

Bibliography

1. Glassow, R. B.: Fundamentals in Physical Education. Philadelphia, Lea & Febiger, 1932.
2. McCloy, C. H.: Mimeographed material and class notes for course in Mechanical Analysis of Motor Skills, State University of Iowa.
3. Morehouse, L. E., and Cooper, J. M.: Kinesiology. St. Louis, C. V. Mosby Company, 1950.
4. Price, H C.: Tumbling and Stumbling Safely. J. Health and Phys. Ed., *13*: 531–4, 566–7, 1942.

21 · Principles of Giving Impetus to External Objects

A MAN PUSHES a lawnmower across his lawn, an archer shoots an arrow from his bow, a baseball pitcher throws a basebal across the plate and the batter hits it into center field, a camper paddles his canoe upstream, a school teacher opens the window, a housewife shuts the sliding door of her closet, a porter lifts a suitcase and puts it up onto the rack. As widely diverse as these activities may seem, they have a common denominator. Each involves the giving of impetus to an external object, whether this is done directly by some part of the body, as the hand or the foot, or through the medium of an implement such as a baseball bat. Together with activities of receiving the impetus of external objects, they comprise the group of activities referred to as manipulative skills. With possibly a few exceptions, the activities in this group may be classified into the following three major categories:

1. Activities characterized by the continuous application of force, e.g., pushing, pulling and lifting.
2. Activities characterized by the development of kinetic energy in a movable object, followed by the release of the object at the moment of maximum velocity. All throwing activities are included in this category, including throwing with an implement as in lacrosse.
3. Activities characterized by a momentary contact made with an object by a moving part of the body, or by an implement

held by or attached to a moving segment of the body. The object itself may be either stationary or moving. This category includes all forms of striking, such as hitting with the hand (as in handball), striking with a club or racket (as in baseball, golf and tennis), kicking and heading (as in soccer).

The two activities which do not seem to belong specifically to any of the categories described, but which combine the characteristics of two or three of them, are archery and the use of a sling shot. In these activities the body indirectly applies force to a movable object through the use of an elastic structure with which the object is in contact. Potential energy is imparted to the elastic structure by means of a pull. When the elastic structure is suddenly released, the potential energy becomes kinetic energy, and this is immediately transferred to the movable object.

In the chapter on force it was seen that a force could be described in terms of its magnitude, its direction, and the location of the point at which the force was applied. These three aspects of force form the basis of most of the principles of giving impetus to external objects. Supplementing these are the factors which relate to the stability of the body at the moment of giving impetus and those which relate to the interaction between the body and the surface which supports it. Unless the body has good stability when it is giving impetus to an object, much of the force is wasted.

One should remember that all projected objects, such as balls and arrows, are being acted upon by the force of gravity as well as by the force imparted by the person responsible for projecting them. If one wished to calculate the resultant force acting upon the object, he could do it by the method of constructing a parallelogram of forces, one side of which would represent the force of the impetus and the other side the force of gravity (see p. 319).

The value of a classification such as the one for skills of giving impetus to external objects is that it enables one to see the relation-

Figure 206. Giving impetus to an external object. *A*, Putting the shot; *B*, batting a baseball.

ships between activities. This is particularly helpful in the learning of new skills because the principles learned in connection with one skill can be applied to all skills in the same category. One need only recognize the factors common to both the old skill and the new in order to select the principles which apply to the latter. The factors and the principles which pertain to the giving of impetus to external objects are presented below. Anatomic and mechanical principles pertaining to specific forms of these skills are included in some instances.

Principles of Giving Impetus to an External Object

1. Relating to the magnitude of the force:

The object will move only if the force is of sufficient magnitude to overcome the object's inertia. The force must be great enough to overcome not only the mass of the object, but all restraining forces as well. These include (1) friction between the object and the supporting surface, (2) resistance of the surrounding medium (e.g., wind or water), and (3) the effect of leverage. By the latter is meant the product of the object's weight (or the resistance force) and the weight arm (or resistance arm) of the lever. Other things being equal, the shorter the weight arm of a lever, the less force required to move it.

2. Relating to the direction of force:

a. The direction in which the object moves is determined by the direction of the force applied to it. If the force consists of two or more components, the object will move in the direction of the resultant of those components (see p. 311).

b. If an object is free to move only along a predetermined pathway (as in the case of a window or sliding door), any component of force not in the direction of this pathway is wasted and serves to increase friction.

3. Relating to the point at which the force is applied:

a. Force applied in line with an object's center of gravity will result in linear motion of the object, provided the latter is freely movable.

b. If the force applied to a freely movable object is not in line with the latter's center of gravity, it will result in rotatory motion of the object.

c. If the free motion of an object is interfered with by friction or by the presence of an obstacle, rotatory motion may result, even though the force is applied in line with the center of gravity.

4. Relating to the interaction between the body and the supporting surface:

Force exerted by the body will be transferred to an external object in proportion to the effectiveness of the counterforce of the feet (or other parts of the body) against the ground (or other supporting surface). This effectiveness depends upon the counter-pressure and the friction presented by the supporting surface.

Applications to Pushing, Pulling and Lifting.   The chief concern in these activities is economy of effort and avoidance of strain. Economy of effort is assured when the force is applied in line with the object's center of gravity and in the desired direction of motion. If friction tends to impede the movement of the object, this must be taken into consideration also. For instance, suppose one is confronted with the task of pushing a tall cabinet across the room. If the cabinet has casters and if the floor is uncarpeted, the most efficient way to push the cabinet is by placing the hands at the midpoint (assuming the weight of the cabinet to be equally distributed between the top and the bottom) and to apply a horizontal push against it. If the floor is carpeted, however, or if the cabinet has no casters, there will be a tendency for the cabinet to tip when the push is applied in line with its center of gravity. In order to assure linear motion, the hands must be placed lower down at a point found by experimentation.

If one's purpose is to cause rotatory rather than linear motion, the effectiveness of the force depends upon the distance of the point of its application from the object's center of motion. In the case of the steering wheel of an automobile or the helm of a ship, the center of motion would be the center of the wheel, and the ideal point for applying force would be at the rim of the wheel or the outer end of a spoke. In the case of a wardrobe trunk which

Figure 207. Ways of giving impetus to an external object. *A,* Pushing; *B,* puliing; *C,* lifting; *D,* throwing; *E,* striking; *F,* striking.

is tipped onto one edge and is being moved by a series of partial pivots on alternating corners, the center of motion is the point of contact with the floor, in other words, first one corner, then the other. The force is applied at the corresponding upper edge of the trunk, the ideal point for maximum efficiency being the corner diagonally opposite the one serving as the point of contact.

The influence of the resistance arm of the lever is seen in a pull used for opening a window or a sliding door. For instance, if one attempts to open a window by standing facing it and flexing the forearms at the elbows, the forearms are used as levers and the weight of the window serves as a resistance to the turning of the lever. The total amount of resistance may be expressed in terms of the weight of the window multiplied by the length of the forearm. In other words, the weight of the window is exerting a rotatory force against the forearm. On the other hand, if one stands close to the window with the arms extended downward in a near-vertical position and with the feet turned sideways so as to permit slight flexion at the knee joints, the window may be opened by pushing the feet downward against the floor and extending the legs at the knee and hip joints. In this way there is practically no lever action, therefore no rotatory force exerted by the resistance of the window. The resistance is represented by the weight of the window alone.

The principle of reducing the resistance or weight arm to a minimum in order to reduce the amount of force required is also seen in lifting a weight from the floor. For instance, it takes less force to lift and hold a heavy package close to the body than it does to lift and hold it at arm's length. Likewise it takes less force to lift a package by stooping than it does by bending at the waist with the knees straight. In stooping, the weight-arm is the horizontal distance from the center of the knee joint to the body's line of gravity; in bending from the waist the weight-arm is the horizontal distance from the center of the hip joint to the body's line of gravity. There are other factors involved here too, but the relative length of the weight-arm is an important one. Also, because of the shorter weight-arm, it takes less force to lift by stooping with the trunk inclined slightly forward than with the trunk held vertically. This is discussed more fully in Chapter 27.

An example of applying the force not exactly in the direction of motion is seen in drawing a low cart by a rope. If the body is erect, the rope will slant upward from the cart to the hand. The pull on the cart therefore consists of two components, forward and upward. Since the purpose is to draw the cart horizontally forward, this upward component of force is wasted. While stooping in order to keep the rope horizontal would assure a single horizontal force, this can hardly be recommended because of the inconvenience and discomfort of maintaining such an unnatural position. A better solution is to use a longer rope. Although this does not eliminate the upward component of force, it serves to make it relatively smaller and the horizontal component relatively greater.

The importance of a solid supporting surface and of the presence of friction between the feet and the supporting surface is readily seen in all the pushing, pulling and lifting activities. One need only imagine attempting a tug-of-war on a muddy field or pushing a car on an icy road to appreciate this.

Applications to Throwing.   The efficiency of imparting force to a ball is judged in terms of the speed, distance and direction of the ball after its release. The purpose of the throw determines which of these is given the greater emphasis. Both the speed and the distance of the thrown ball are directly related to the magnitude of the force used in throwing it and to the speed of the hand at the moment of the release. The speed the hand can acquire depends upon the distance through which it moves in the preparatory part of the act (Fig. 208, *A* and *B*). Hence the longer the preparatory backswing, and the greater the distance that can be added by means of rotating the body, shifting the weight, and perhaps even taking a step, the greater the opportunity for accelerating. These preparatory movements, in order to be effective, must be coordinated. Each one must be added to the preceding movement at just the right moment in order for them to contribute to maximum speed.

Greater speed and distance can be attained if internal resistance is reduced to a minimum. This is accomplished partly by a warm-up immediately preceding the throwing event, and partly by a gradual increase of the range of motion in the joints involved, achieved by preliminary training.

The distance the ball will travel depends upon the angle of elevation as well as the magnitude of the force applied to it. When pushing an object, the force is more effective if applied in a horizontal direction. In throwing a ball for distance, however, the effect of gravity must be considered. As soon as the ball is released, gravitational force starts to operate on it. The effect of this becomes noticeable as soon as the speed of the ball is materially reduced (because of air resistance). Hence greater distance can be obtained if the propulsive force contains an upward as well as a horizontal component. This serves to keep the ball in the air longer and permits longer horizontal travel before the ball hits the ground. Too much elevation is not desired, however, because the upward and the horizontal components of force are in inverse proportion

Figure 208. Contrasting styles of throwing. *A,* With a long lever and a long backswing. *B,* With a short lever and a short backswing.

to one another. The optimum angle of elevation for distance throwing is approximately 45 degrees.

It might seem that for maximum distance all the force should be applied in line with the ball's center of gravity. This is not the case, however. If a slight rotatory force is imparted in such a way that a back spin (Fig. 209, *B*) results, the ball will travel farther, provided the rotatory force is not sufficient to cut the propulsive force materially. The explanation is that the lower part of the ball meets more air resistance than the upper when it is spinning backward. This tends to lift the ball and to keep it in the air longer. Conversely, top spin (Fig. 209, *A*) decreases the distance the ball travels. When back spin is used, the ball may be released at an angle slightly less than 45 degrees from the horizontal.

While not directly related to the imparting of force, there are three qualities of the ball itself which influence the distance it will travel when thrown. These are the mass and size of the ball and the nature of its surface. A heavy ball will travel farther than a light one of the same size and thrown at the same speed because it is less affected by air resistance. Likewise, a small ball and a smooth-surfaced ball will travel farther than a large or rough-surfaced one because it meets with less air resistance.

The direction taken by a thrown ball depends primarily upon the

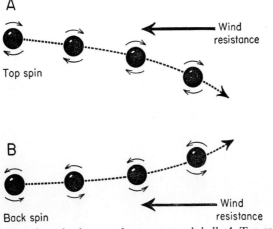

Figure 209. The effect of spin on a thrown or struck ball. *A,* Top spin; *B,* back spin.

direction of the force applied to it. If a lateral rotatory force is applied, some lateral spin will result. A clockwise spin (as seen from above) makes the ball go somewhat to the thrower's right; a counterclockwise spin makes it go to his left. Wind also influences the direction of the ball. It imposes an additional force; hence the direction of the ball will be the resultant of the propulsive force and the force imparted by the wind.

Applications to Striking, Hitting, Kicking, and the Like. As in the case of throwing, the effectiveness of striking, hitting and kicking is judged in terms of the speed, distance and direction of the struck ball. All the factors that apply to these aspects of a thrown ball apply similarly to a struck ball. There appear to be six major factors which apply to the speed of a struck ball. These are (1) the speed of the oncoming ball, (2) the mass of the ball, (3) the speed of the striking implement at the moment of contact, (4) the mass of the striking implement, (5) the coefficient of restitution (i.e., the elasticity) of the ball, and (6) the coefficient of restitution of the striking implement. At least two of these factors, namely, the speed of the approaching ball and the speed of the striking implement, may be further analyzed into secondary factors. For instance, the speed of the striking implement is determined by the magnitude of the force exerted; and the magnitude of the force is dependent upon the distance of the preparatory back swing and upon the speed of muscular contraction. The distance of the preparatory back swing is further dependent upon the range of motion in the joints and upon the timing of the swing. Furthermore, the effective-

Figure 210. Tennis serve. The entire body acts as a lever to impart maximum force to the ball. (Photo by Loder.)

ness of the force exerted by the body is completely dependent upon a strong grip and a firm wrist for transmission of the force from the body to the striking implement.

Returning to the six major factors in the speed of a struck ball, the following applications are of interest to the sports instructor.

1. The greater the velocity of the approaching ball, the greater the velocity of the ball in the opposite direction after it is struck, other things being equal. If at first this seems contradictory to the reader, he should think of a ball being thrown against a resisting surface such as a wall. The reader will agree that the faster the ball is traveling when it hits the wall, the faster it will travel on the rebound from the wall. Now, if in addition to the element of rebound, the wall itself moves forward to meet the ball, it is providing an additional force. This is in effect what happens when a pitched ball makes contact with a forward-swinging bat.

2. The greater the velocity of the striking implement at the moment of contact, the greater the velocity of the struck ball, other things being equal. Obviously, a full-powered swing will send the ball farther and faster than will a bunt.

3. The greater the mass of the ball, *up to a point,* the greater its velocity after being struck, other things being equal. A hard baseball will travel farther and faster than a soft ball. Nevertheless an iron ball would offer too much resistance for the average batter using an average bat.

4. The greater the mass of the striking implement, *up to a point,* the greater the striking force, and hence the greater the speed of the struck ball, other things being equal. A good baseball player usually selects a heavy bat. Too heavy

a bat, however, is inadvisable because of the difficulty of swinging it with sufficient speed and control.

5. The higher the coefficient of restitution (i.e., the elasticity) of the ball and the striking implement, the greater the speed of the struck ball, other things being equal.

As to the distance of the struck ball, other things being equal, the greater the ball's speed of departure, the greater its distance. As in the case of a thrown ball, the optimum angle of elevation is approximately 45 degrees. This angle is slightly less when back spin is imparted to the ball, and greater when top spin is imparted.

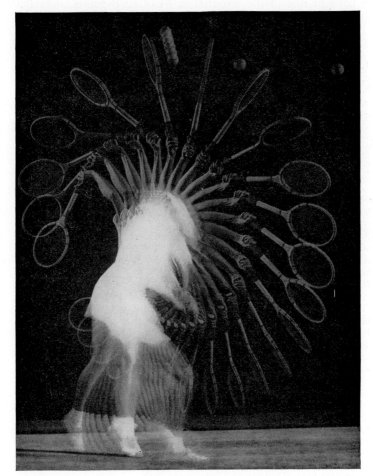

Figure 211. Tennis serve. An example of giving impetus to a ball. (Courtesy of H. E. Edgerton.)

The direction taken by the struck ball is influenced by four factors: namely (1) the direction of the striking implement at the moment of contact; (2) the relation of the striking force to the ball's center of gravity (an off-center application of force causes spin, and spin affects direction); (3) degree of firmness of grip and wrist at moment of impact; and (4) the laws governing rebound. According to the last, the angle of rebound equals the angle of incidence, except in the case of a soft ball (that is, a ball which compresses greatly when hit), in which case the angle of rebound is slightly less than the angle of incidence. An understanding of the angle of rebound is of particular importance in the racket games. It forms the basis of one of the essential skills of such games, namely, the skill of accurate placing of the ball.

Demonstrations and Laboratory Exercises

1. Raise a window from the bottom:
a. Standing at arm's length.
b. Standing close, facing the window and using both hands.
c. Standing close, side to the window and pushing it up with one hand with the elbow bent and the forearm in a vertical position.
Which is the best method for a heavy window or a window that sticks? Explain in terms of components of force and the direction of application of force.
2. Open (or close) a sliding door:
a. Standing at arm's length.
b. Standing close, facing the door.
c. Standing close, facing in the direction that the door is to move, using a pushing motion with the forearm parallel with the door.
Which is the best method? Explain in terms of direction of application of force, and of components of force.
3. Push a heavy piece of furniture. Experiment to find the most efficient method.
a. At what point on the object did you apply the force? Explain the underlying principles.
b. What was the position of your arms? Explain the advantage.
c. What was the position of your body? Explain the advantage.
4. Throw a tennis ball or baseball for distance:
a. Standing still, facing in the direction of the throw.
b. Standing with the left side toward the direction of the throw, with the feet apart and the weight evenly distributed, getting a full arm swing and body twist with the throw.
c. Same as in b, except with the weight on the right foot to begin with, shifting to the left as the ball is thrown.
Compare the three methods for distance. Explain in terms of length of back swing, speed at moment of release, and total distance used in applying force to ball before releasing it.
5. If possible, observe a small child or an untrained girl, and then a trained boy or girl, throw a small ball at a target 20 or 30 feet away. Analyze the motions of each with reference to the pathway of the hand immediately preceding, at the moment of, and following the release. Explain the factors differentiating the good throws from the poor.
6. Observe slow motion films of throwing, striking and other forms of giving

impetus. Look for the application of the principles stated in this unit, or for the lack of such application.

Bibliography

1. Glassow, R. B.: Fundamentals in Physical Education. Philadelphia, Lea & Febiger, 1932, Sections I and II.
2. Hartley, D. L.: Kinesiological Analysis of Shotput. Thesis, State University of Iowa, 1939.
3. McCloy, C. H.: Mimeographed material and class notes for course in Mechanical Analysis of Motor Skills, State University of Iowa.
4. Morehouse, L. E., and Cooper, J. M.: Kinesiology. St. Louis, C. V. Mosby Company, 1950, Chaps. 19, 20, 21 and 22.
5. Scott, M. G.: Analysis of Human Motion. New York, R. S. Crofts & Co., 1945, Chaps. 9 and 13.

Recommended Readings

Glassow, R. B.: Fundamentals in Physical Education. (See 1 above.)
Morehouse, L. E., and Cooper, J. M.: Kinesiology. (See 4 above.)
Scott, M. G.: Analysis of Human Motion. (See 5 above.)

22 · Selection and Classification of Principles Pertaining to the Prevention of Injury

IN ALL PHYSICAL activities there is some likelihood of injury. Whether such injury is due to an accident or whether it is due to structural limitations, it can usually be avoided if the proper precautions are taken. Chance plays a relatively small part in injuries resulting from physical activities. "Hindsight" frequently reveals the fact that either a mechanical or a physiologic principle was disregarded. Hence familiarity with the principles relating to safety provides the means for preventing such injuries. Acquainting the student with these principles should be as important a part of the physical education program as teaching the activity skills themselves. It is not enough to incorporate the observance of the principles in the technique of the skill; the student should be aware of the principles themselves in order that he may apply them in other situations—in industry, on the street, in the home—wherever and whenever the occasion arises.

The major principles pertaining to the prevention of injury are presented below. They are stated in the form of directions which, if observed, will help to minimize the likelihood of strain and injury.

Principles Relating to the Maintenance of Equilibrium and Prevention of Falls

1. Maintain an adequate base of support.
2. Lower the center of gravity when this is feasible.
3. Keep the center of gravity well centered over the base of support.
4. Increase the size of the base of support in the direction of force or motion.

Principles Relating to the Range of Movement

1. Keep within the normal range of motion for each joint in order to avoid ligamentous and fascial strain. (This requires an understanding of anatomic structures and their limitations.)
2. Strengthen the muscles in order to lessen the likelihood of exceeding the normal range of motion. (For example, strengthen the abdominal muscles in order to help prevent an overthrow in diving.)
3. If attempting to increase the range of motion in a joint or muscle, do it gradually and only after an adequate warm-up.
4. Observe the principles of receiving one's own weight and the impact of external objects in order to avoid joint sprains.

Principles Relating to the Intensity and Quantity of Muscular Exercise

1. Do not exercise past the point of excessive fatigue.
   a. Accidents often occur when muscles are fatigued and when the individual is too tired to be alert.
   b. Excessive fatigue products in the muscles frequently cause soreness, especially in individuals who are not in good condition.
2. Provide adequate training before permitting participation in specific sports. An untrained individual is likely to use his body poorly under the stress of the moment. There should be a careful progression of instruction and practice.
3. Avoid sudden, violent movements whenever possible, and precede all strenuous activity with a warm-up. (Sudden exertion, especially if the muscles are cold, is likely to cause muscle tears.)
4. Observe the principles of receiving, lifting and supporting weights, in order to prevent muscular strain.

Principles Relating to the Transmission of Weight through the Body Segments and Weight-Bearing Joints

1. Provide adequate protection for weak joints.
   a. Individuals who have poorly aligned or previously injured joints may have to be excluded from certain activities. (For example, an individual who has knock-knees is likely to have his knees injured in strenuous activities involving running, jumping and bodily contact.)
   b. Individuals who have poorly aligned or previously injured joints probably need to wear some form of support or protection.

2. Reduce the rotatory components of force to a minimum. (This requires an awareness of positions which put certain segments under rotatory stress.)

a. If on the hands and knees supporting others, as in a pyramid, the thighs should be perpendicular to the floor.

b. If being supported by another, the weights should be placed in line with the other individual's supporting structures. (For example, a person who is standing on the back of another who is on his hands and knees, should place one foot over the other's shoulders and one over the pelvis.)

3. Only individuals with adequate strength and maturity should support the weight of others.

a. Avoid too great a discrepancy between the strength of the lower man and the weight of the upper man in stunts and pyramids.

b. Avoid using physically immature boys and girls for supporting heavy weights, as in the base of pyramids. (Many of the epiphyses are still not united in teen-aged boys and girls.)

Principles Relating to the Reception of One's Own Weight

1. When landing from a *downward* jump:

a. Ensure a gradual loss of kinetic energy by landing on the balls of the feet and immediately letting the ankles, knees and hips bend, controlling the action by means of eccentric contraction of the muscles.

b. Reduce the force of the impact by wearing rubber-soled shoes and by having a soft landing surface.

c. Regain stability by keeping the center of gravity over the center of the base of support on landing. (This may be done by keeping the weight evenly distributed over both feet, or over the hands and feet, and by providing a sufficiently large base of support on landing.)

2. When landing from a *forward* jump and when participating in any activity which involves forward momentum:

a. Ensure a gradual loss of the forward kinetic energy by continuing in a roll, run, hop, slide or "frog jump," unless landing in a soft pit, in which case this will not be necessary.

b. Regain stability by providing support in the direction of motion. This is done by landing with the weight forward, using the hands if necessary, in which case the elbows as well as the leg joints should "give."

c. Reduce the force of impact by wearing rubber-soled shoes and by having a soft landing surface.

3. When falling:

a. Ensure a gradual loss of the forward kinetic energy by continuing in a roll, slide, and the like, whenever feasible.

b. Absorb the shock of impact (i.e., ensure a gradual loss of kinetic energy) by letting the arms "give" as they receive the weight. When falling forward on the knees and catching oneself on the hands, arching the back and turning the face sideward make it possible to rock down on the front of the body without injury. The elbows should bend as soon as the hands touch the floor. This method of self-protection is especially applicable to falling after tripping.

c. Receive the weight on the padded parts of the body, attempting to land on the various parts in a progressive sequence. For example, after falling on the knee, attempt to fall sideways on the thigh, then onto the side of the arm or the hand which promptly slides out, with the head falling on the extended arm. (This applies particularly to intentional falls in modern dance.)

d. Attempt to land on as large an area of the body as possible in order to minimize the force per square inch.

Principles Relating to Lifting and Carrying External Weights

1. Reduce the rotatory components of weight to a minimum.

a. Get close to the heavy object which is to be lifted from the floor.

b. Carry heavy burdens close to the body.

(1) A suitcase, with the arm hanging straight down.

(2) A tray, with elbow bent, forearm vertical, and hand close to shoulder.

(3) A basket, in the crotch of the elbow with the upper arm in a vertical position.

c. Stoop to reach an object on the floor by bending the knees and inclining the trunk slightly forward.

2. Use the muscles best suited to the task.

For example, when lifting a heavy box from the floor, by stooping as described in *c* above, the strong thigh and buttock muscles will be used, instead of the weaker spine extensors.

3. Avoid lifting excessive weights.

a. Girls of average strength should not lift weights of more than one quarter or one third of their own body weight, and boys should not lift weights of more than one half of their body weight. These amounts can be increased through training.

b. If an individual wishes to learn to lift heavier weights, he should train gradually.

Principles Relating to Receiving the Impact of External Forces

1. When catching balls and other objects, and when receiving individuals in tumbling and apparatus work:

a. Observe the principles of reducing kinetic energy gradually instead of suddenly.

(1) "Give" with the arms.

(2) Shift the weight back from one foot to the other, or take a step backward.

(3) Move along with the individual when receiving or "spotting" in tumbling and apparatus events.

b. Wear adequate protection, such as a baseball mitt, shin guards, and so on.

c. Put yourself in a favorable position in order to prevent the necessity for overreaching.

d. Point the fingers upward, outward or downward, but not forward.

2. Being hit by a moving body, e.g., a person or a ball:

a. Try to receive the force and ease the shock the same as when catching a ball.

b. Guard against being caught off balance.

c. Wear adequate protection, e.g., shin guards for hockey and padded clothing for football.

d. If possible, avoid lateral blows on the knee, especially when the knee is bearing weight in a flexed position. (This is a common cause of injury to the ligaments and cartilages.)

e. Move along with the striking object. (In boxing this is known as "riding a punch.")

Principles Relating to Circular Motion

1. Since centrifugal force develops in all circular movements, activities such as "snapping the whip," swinging on the flying rings, and so on, should be engaged in only by those who are known to have sufficient strength to keep from being snapped off.

2. Individuals who have a tendency toward chronic dislocation of the shoulder should not be allowed to do strenuous arm circling or swinging movements because of the centrifugal force which develops in such activities.

Bibliography

1. Lloyd, F. S., Deaver, G. G., and Eastwood, F. R.: Safety in Athletics. Philadelphia, W. B. Saunders Company, 1936.
2. Lowman, C. L.: The Vulnerable Age. J. Health and Physical Education, *18:* 635–636, 693 (Nov.), 1947.
3. Lowman, C. L.: Physical Educational Counseling. J. Health and Physical Education, *13:* 510, 554–555 (Nov.), 1942.
4. Price, H. D.: Tumbling and Stumbling Safely. J. Health and Physical Education, *13:* 531–534, 566–567 (Nov.), 1942.
5. U. S. Department of Labor, Division of Labor Standards: A Guide to the Prevention of Weight-Lifting Injuries. Special Bulletin No. 11, Washington, D. C., Supt. of Doc., Gov. Printing Office, 1943.

IV · Applications of Kinesiology

23 · Locomotion: Walking and Running

BECAUSE WALKING is man's most common activity, it is presented here as the first example of the application of kinesiology to familiar motor skills. In the over-all classification of these skills (see p. 336) it belongs under locomotion, which in turn belongs to the category of skills referred to as "moving one's own body."

Locomotion means the progressive movement of the entire body from one place to another by means of self-propulsion. Ordinarily the propulsion is provided by the lower extremities, but it is occasionally provided by all four extremities, as in creeping, or by the upper extremities alone, as in walking on the hands and hand traveling on a horizontal ladder. Locomotion may involve the use of wheels, blades, skis, and so on, attached to the feet, or it may involve a vehicle such as a bicycle or wheel chair, or a small craft such as a boat, canoe or surfboard propelled by means of the arms or legs, with or without the use of a propelling implement (e.g., oars, paddles, poles). Locomotion by self-propulsion may be on the ground or in the water, but, at the present writing, not in the air except by means of suspension.

Aside from the locomotor skills which are used primarily for taking a person to a specific location, there are the skills in which man indulges for sport and pleasure. These include walking, running, swimming and dancing. For purposes of systematizing the study of locomotor skills the following classification is suggested.

Forms of Locomotion by Self-Propulsion

1. **On Foot**
   Walking
   Running
   Climbing (inclined plane, stairs, ladder, etc.)
   Descending (inclined plane, stairs, ladder, etc.)
   Jumping, leaping, hurdling
   Skipping, hopping, sliding, side-stepping, etc.
   Progressive dance steps, e.g., polka, mazurka, etc.
   Snow shoeing
   Skiing on level or up hill
   Walking on stilts
2. **On Wheels and Blades**
   Bicycling*
   Roller skating
   Ice skating
   Propelling self in wheel chair*
3. **On Hands**
   Walking on hands
   Hand traveling on boom, horizontal ladder, traveling rings, etc.
4. **On Hands and Knees or Hands and Feet**
   Creeping
   Crutch walking*
   Stunts, e.g., dog running, rabbit hopping, etc.
5. **Rotatory Locomotion**
   Cartwheels
   Forward, backward and sideward rolls
6. **Aquatic Locomotion**
   Swimming
   Boating (rowing, paddling, punting, etc.)*
   * These activities are also forms of manipulative skills.

Only two forms of locomotion are considered in this chapter, namely, walking and running. These are examples of terrestrial locomotion. Swimming, which is a form of aquatic locomotion, is analyzed in Chapter 24.

Walking

To the casual observer the movements involved in walking appear to be relatively simple, yet kinesiologic analysis shows them to be exceedingly complex. The dovetailing of muscular action and the synchronization of joint movements illustrate beautifully the teamwork present in all bodily movements. Not even the most complex piece of machinery designed by the most skillful engineers of our time exceeds the movements of the human machine in perfection of detail or in smoothness of function.

Recent research on the gait, such as that conducted at the University of Californa as part of the Prosthetic Devices Research Project, has served to emphasize the complexity of human locomotion and the magnitude and difficulty of the task of synthesizing

all its elements.[1, 13] Therapists confronted with the task of helping
to restore the coordination of walking to those who have lost it—
because of amputation or paralysis—would do well to study Steindler's chapters on the gait in his book, "Kinesiology of the Human
Body," and to acquaint themselves with the findings of recent research in this area. The average student of kinesiology, however,
may find the following more simplified analysis of the gait adequate
for his purposes.

Neuromuscular Considerations.   Walking is a reflex action.
No conscious control is necessary. On the contrary, if attention is
focused on any part of the gait, a tension is likely to develop and
the natural rhythm and coordination are disturbed. Reflexes are
responsible not only for the movements of the limbs, but also for
the extension of both the supporting leg and the trunk in resisting
the downward pull of gravity. This extension serves to give stability
to the body in the supporting phases of locomotion, a stability
which provides for effective muscular action in producing the
necessary movements. Thus, in walking, as in all the motions of the
body, smooth, coordinated movement requires properly functioning
reflexes, normal flexibility of the joints, and optimum stability of
the body as a whole in the weight-bearing phases of the act.

Mechanical Analysis of Walking.   Walking is effected by the

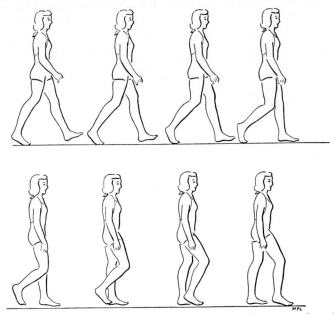

Figure 212. A normal gait at moderate speed. (Traced from a motion picture
film.)

alternating action of the two lower extremities. It is an example of translatory motion of the body as a whole brought about by means of the angular motion of some of its parts. It is also an example of a periodic movement, that is, a pendulum-like movement in which the moving segment (in this case, the lower extremity) may be said to start at zero, pass through its arc of motion, and fall to zero again at the end of each stroke. In walking, each lower extremity undergoes two phases, the swinging or recovery phase and the supporting phase. The supporting phase is further divided into a restraining phase (from the moment the foot touches the ground until it is directly under the center of the body) and the propulsion phase (from the moment when the foot is under the center of gravity until it leaves the ground). The beginning of the restraining phase of one leg overlaps with the end of the propulsive phase of the other leg, thus constituting a brief phase of double support when both feet are on the ground. This is characteristic of the walk and serves to differentiate it from the run. In the swinging phase of the walk the action of the lower extremity may be likened to that of the pendulum of a clock; in the supporting phase, to that of the inverted pendulum of a metronome. Gravity and momentum are the chief sources of motion for the swinging phase; hence this phase represents a ballistic type of movement (p. 46), particularly when the individual is walking at his natural pace. The source of motion for the supporting phase is, for the first half, the momentum of the forward-moving trunk (provided by the recent propulsive action of the other leg) and, for the second half, the contraction of the extensor muscles of the supporting leg. Whether or not the supporting phase can also be classed as ballistic movement is open to question. Even the swinging phase varies in its ballistic quality, according to the speed of the gait, the skill, flexibility and build of the walker. A tense individual will tend to substitute muscular action for the pendulum swing of the lower extremity, and an individual with tight hamstrings will have to exert additional muscular force in order to overcome the restraining action of the short hamstrings. An individual who has decided knock-knees or fat thighs will also have difficulty in getting a natural, pendulum swing because of friction and interference between the two limbs. The only way he can avoid this interference is by increasing the lateral distance between his limbs, thus introducing an undesirable lateral component of motion.

Walking and other similar forms of locomotion involve a balancing of forces. Only the most obvious of these are mentioned here.

1. The inertia of the stationary body is overcome by the horizontal component of force. Since periodic movement is characterized by an alternating increase and decrease of speed, it is inevitable

that inertia must be overcome at every step. As the center of gravity moves forward, it momentarily passes beyond the anterior margin of the base of support, and a temporary loss of balance results. At this point the downward pull of gravity threatens a complete loss of equilibrium. A timely recovery of balance is brought about, however, by the contact of the swinging leg with the ground, thus establishing an adequate base of support and starting a new supporting phase.

2. When forward motion has been imparted to the trunk by means of the backward thrust of the leg and foot, it tends to continue unless restrained by another force. Once the center of gravity passes beyond the base of support, it is essential to restrain the action of the trunk until a new base of support is established. Hence, as the foot is brought to the ground in front of the body at the close of its recovery phase, a restraining phase is constituted. This diminishes as the leg approaches a vertical position. As long as the foot is in front of the center of gravity, there is a *forward* component of force in the thrust of the foot against the ground, resulting in a *backward* counterpressure of the ground against the foot which is transmitted to the leg and thence to the trunk.

3. In the same phase of the step as that discussed above in section 2, the trunk is acted upon by the downward pull of gravity as well as by momentum. This downward force is counteracted by the vertical component of force of the supporting leg. During the phase of double support each leg exerts some vertical force. If the vertical force exceeds that needed to balance the gravitational force, it results in an exaggerated lift of the body, causing a gait characterized by a bounce or unusual spring.

4. The forward-moving trunk meets with air resistance, which tends to push it backward. By inclining the body forward, the pull of gravity is utilized to balance the force of the air resistance. When walking against a strong wind, it is necessary to incline the body farther forward in order to effect a balance. If the air resistance is not balanced by the force of gravity, it must be balanced by the contraction of the abdominal and other anterior muscles of the neck and trunk. On the other hand, if the body is inclined too far forward, the force of gravity acts too strongly on it and must be counteracted by tension of the posterior muscles. Thus the proper degree of forward inclination is a factor in muscular economy.

5. The degree to which the pressure of the foot actually imparts motion to the body in the propulsive phase, and restrains it in the restraining phase, is in direct proportion to the counterpressure of the supporting surface. If the surface lacks solidity, as in the case of mud, soft snow, and sand, it offers too little resistance to give the needed counterpressure. The pressure of the foot results in

slipping or sinking, and more pressure must be applied in order to achieve even a slow forward progress. Hence the efficiency of the gait depends upon the right balance between the pressure of the foot and the counterpressure of the supporting surface.

6. Like counterpressure, friction is also an essential factor in the effective application of the forces needed in walking. Because of the diagonal thrust of the leg at the beginning and end of the supporting phase, friction between the foot and the ground is essential in order that the counterpressure of the ground may be transmitted to the body. For efficient walking, friction must be sufficient to balance the horizontal component of force. If it is insufficient, the thrust of the foot results in a slipping of the foot itself, rather than in the desired propulsion of the body. The greater the horizontal component of force (as when walking with a long stride), the greater the dependence upon friction for efficient locomotion.

Anatomic Analysis of Walking.*   The action taking place in the joints of the lower extremity is essentially that of flexion and extension. But in much the same way that the shoulder girdle co-operates with the arm movements of the upper extremity, the pelvic girdle cooperates in movements of the lower extremities. The pelvis has the double task of transmitting the weight of the body alternately first over one limb, then over the other, and of putting each acetabulum in a favorable position for the action of the corresponding femur. The adaptations of pelvic position are made in the joints of the thoracic and lumbar spine as well as in the hip joints. Thus as first one foot and then the other is put forward, the flexion and extension movements of the thigh are accompanied by slight movements of rotation and of abduction and adduction at the hip joints, and by slight lateral flexion and rotation of the spine.

The joint analysis, as presented below, is systematic rather than chronologic; that is, the action of each joint is analyzed separately, without regard for the chronologic sequences or the timing of the various movements in walking as they relate to one another.

Joint Analysis

Swinging Phase

HIP.   Flexion; outward rotation (due to rotation of pelvis toward other limb); adduction at beginning and abduction at end of phase, especially if long stride is taken (due to rotation of pelvis and length of stride).

KNEE.   Flexion during first half; extension during second half.

ANKLE AND FOOT.   Dorsal flexion; prevention of plantar flexion.

* The anatomic analysis of walking which appeared in the first edition of this text was based chiefly on original observations and palpations, supplemented by analyses found in the literature. The analysis, as now presented, has been modified to include pertinent findings of the Prosthetic Devices Research Project conducted at the University of California.

PELVIS AND SPINE.   Rotation toward opposite side; prevention of dropping of pelvis toward unsupported side.

UPPER EXTREMITIES.   Unless restrained, the arms tend to swing in opposition to the legs, the left arm swinging forward as the right leg swings forward, and vice versa. This is usually accomplished without obvious muscular action and serves to balance the rotation of the pelvis. It is a reflex action. When the arm swing is prevented, the upper trunk tends to rotate in the same direction as the pelvis, causing a tense, awkward gait.

Supporting Phase

HIP.   Extension; reduction of outward rotation, followed by slight inward rotation; prevention of adduction of thigh and dropping of pelvis to opposite side.

KNEE.   Slight flexion at moment of contact, followed immediately by extension.

ANKLE AND FOOT.   Slight plantar flexion, followed by slight dorsal flexion; prevention of further dorsal flexion which weight of body tends to cause. Plantar flexion at end of propulsive phase, especially in vigorous walking.

PELVIS AND SPINE.   See comments under Swinging Phase.

UPPER EXTREMITIES.   See comments under Swinging Phase.

TOES.   Hyperextension at metatarsophalangeal joints at end of propulsive phase, especially in vigorous walking.

Muscular Analysis (Fig. 213)

Swinging Phase

MUSCLES OF SPINE AND PELVIS.   Semispinalis, rotatores, multifidus and external oblique abdominal muscle on side toward which the pelvis rotates. Sacrospinalis and internal oblique abdominal muscle on opposite side. (Note: Rotation of the pelvis to the right constitutes rotation of the spine to the left. See p. 226.) The psoas and quadratus lumborum help to support the pelvis on the side of the swinging limb.

MUSCLES OF HIP JOINT.   The tensor fasciae latae, sartorius, pectineus and iliopsoas contract during the first part of the swinging phase. The rectus femoris also contracts slightly at the very beginning, but soon relaxes. Whether it is acting chiefly at the hip joint or at the knee joint in this phase is difficult to say, but it seems likely that its action is primarily at the knee joint, since it roughly parallels the action of the vastus intermedius. In the latter part of this phase there is no appreciable action of the flexors of the thigh in normal walking on level ground. Since this is a ballistic movement, none would be expected. In rapid walking the actions of the sartorius and rectus femoris are noticeably increased, and that of the tensor fasciae latae slightly so.

During the latter part of the swinging phase the hamstrings, particularly the long head of the biceps femoris, contract with moderate intensity, and the gluteus maximus and medius contract slightly at the very end of the swing. The adductors longus and magnus, and presumably brevis, contract slightly after the swinging limb has passed the halfway mark. Just what the function of the adductor magnus is, is not clear. It may help to steady and guide the forward-swinging limb. In any event its action is extremely slight, even in rapid walking.

It is assumed that the six deep outward rotators are responsible for the slight outward rotation of the thigh which compensates for the rotation of the pelvis in the opposite direction. These muscles are too deeply located, however, for our present methods of testing.

If the pelvis were allowed to drop on the unsupported side, abduction would occur on that side. That this does not occur in normal walking is due to the

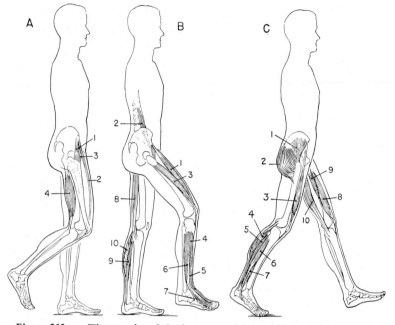

Figure 213.   The muscles of the lower extremity used in walking. *Key: A: 1,* Tensor fasciae latae; *2,* sartorius; *3,* pectineus; *4,* biceps femoris. *B: 1,* Rectus femoris; *2,* iliopsoas; *3,* vastus lateralis (medius and intermedius are not shown); *4,* tibialis anterior; *5,* extensor hallucis longus; *6,* extensor digitorum longus; *7,* peroneus tertius; *8,* semitendinosus and semimembranosus; *9,* soleus; *10,* gastrocnemius. *C: 1,* Gluteus medius; *2,* gluteus maximus; *3,* rectus femoris; *4,* gastrocnemius; *5,* soleus; *6,* peroneus longus; *7,* peroneus brevis; *8,* vastus medialis and intermedius (lateralis not shown); *9,* adductor longus; *10,* semitendinosus and semimembranosus; (tibialis posterior on right leg is not shown).

action of the abductors on the supported side and to that of the quadratus lumborum on the unsupported side. Action of the adductors on the swinging side appears to be negligible. The abduction which occurs at the end of a long stride is apparently produced by the gluteus medius and gluteus maximus.

MUSCLES OF KNEE JOINT.   At the beginning of the swinging phase when the foot is lifted from the ground, the action of the flexors is surprisingly slight in normal walking. The short head of the biceps femoris and the sartorius appear to be responsible for this action. Contraction of the popliteus is assumed, but cannot be tested. The rectus femoris and the vastus intermedius contract briefly at the very beginning of the swinging phase. Their contraction, which began toward the end of the supporting phase, appears to be tapering off during the beginning of the swinging phase. Since the leg is flexing at the knee joint at this time, their action must be eccentric contraction. Although the gastrocnemius is in a position to help flex the leg, it is not found to contract during this phase.

As the leg extends during the second half of the swinging phase, the short head of the biceps femoris increases its action and is joined by the long head, and later by the semimembranosus and semitendinosus. Since these are flexors of the leg and extensors of the thigh, it is assumed that they are contracting eccentrically. Their function here may be to prevent hyperextension of the knee at the end of the swinging phase.

In normal walking the quadriceps extensors contract slightly at the end of the swinging phase. The action of these muscles, as well as that of the medial hamstrings, increases in rapid walking. In an easy gait the movement appears to be initiated by gravitational force and continued by momentum. This force is sufficient to extend the leg at the knee, but in more vigorous walking the quadriceps femoris provides the force for leg extension.

MUSCLES OF THE ANKLE AND FOOT. The tibialis anterior, extensor digitorum longus, extensor hallucis longus, and probably the peroneus tertius contract with slight to moderate intensity at the beginning of the swinging phase, then taper off somewhat during the middle portion of this phase and increase considerably toward the end of it. The plantar flexors are completely relaxed throughout this phase.

Supporting Phase

MUSCLES OF THE HIP JOINT. During the first part of the supporting phase all three gluteal muscles contract with moderate intensity; then maximus and medius taper off during the middle part. Gluteus minimus continues to contract moderately during the middle portion. The only muscles of the hip which contract appreciably during the last part of the supporting phase are the adductors magnus and longus. In rapid walking the gluteus maximus and minimus contract with appreciable intensity during the first part of the supporting phase, and the adductor longus contracts with appreciable intensity during the last part. The hamstrings apparently have but a small part in the supporting phase of normal walking. Only the long head of the biceps contracts at all, and it contracts only slightly at the very beginning of this phase. In rapid walking both the long head of the biceps and the semitendinosus contract with moderate intensity during the first half of the supporting phase.

In considering the function of these muscles which act at the hip joint during the supporting phase of walking it would seem that the gluteus maximus, adductor longus, and the long head of the biceps femoris are responsible for extending the thigh; gluteus medius and minimus for reducing outward rotation and producing slight inward rotation, also for preventing a tilt of the pelvis to the opposite side during the middle portion of the supporting phase. In this function they are aided by the quadratus lumborum. Just what the function of the adductor longus is, is not clear. It may well be for the purpose of steadying the femur against the pull of the abductors, thus enabling them to act on the pelvis rather than on the femur.

MUSCLES OF THE KNEE JOINT. The quadriceps extensors contract moderately in the early part of the supporting phase, then gradually relax. They appear to control the slight flexion which occurs in the knee at the moment of contact. The vastus intermedius continues to contract throughout the first half of this phase. As the leg reaches the vertical position, the knee apparently locks and makes contraction of the extensors unnecessary. The tension of the stretched hamstrings at the end of the swinging phase, especially when a long stride has been taken, may well be the factor which initiates the slight flexion at the moment of contact. The rectus femoris and vastus intermedius contract slightly again at the end of the supporting phase. In rapid walking all these muscles contract more strongly and for a longer duration. There is an abrupt increase in their action in the second half of the supporting phase which would seem to indicate that the extension of the leg at the knee is much more forceful in rapid walking than in normal walking.

MUSCLES OF THE ANKLE AND FOOT. Action current studies show that there is considerable action of the tibialis anterior in the early part of the supporting phase. It seems likely that this takes place chiefly before the anterior portion of the foot is bearing its full share of the weight of the body. Any action after that is probably associated with the prevention of pronation of the foot. The extensors digitorum longus and hallucis longus follow a similar pattern. They reach their peak of contraction almost at the moment of transition between the swinging and the supporting phases, and then relax early in the supporting phase, and commence to contract slightly at the end of this phase.

The gastrocnemius, soleus and tibialis posterior contract slightly in the early part of the supporting phase and moderately in the middle and late parts. In rapid walking this contraction is strong. The peroneus longus follows a similar pattern, but does not seem to contract quite so strongly as the others, except in rapid walking. The peroneus brevis does not start to contract until about the middle of the supporting phase, but contracts more strongly than the longus. In rapid walking it starts earlier and contracts with intensity soon after the halfway mark has been reached.

The flexor digitorum longus contracts slightly during the middle portion of the supporting phase and increases abruptly to moderate contraction in the last portion. In rapid walking the contraction becomes strong. The flexor hallucis longus follows the same pattern, except that it does not start to contract until the middle of the supporting phase.

Lateral balance is maintained by an interplay between the tibialis posterior, flexor hallucis longus and flexor digitorum longus on the one hand, and the peroneus longus and brevis on the other. The supinators are probably contracting almost constantly in order to combat the common tendency of the foot to pronate whenever it is bearing weight.

MUSCLES OF THE TOES. The flexor hallucis longus, flexor digitorum longus, and the short flexors of the toes contract in response to the pressure of the ground against the toes. In the propulsive phase, especially in a vigorous walk, this contraction is intensified. In all parts of the supporting phase the contraction of the toe flexors is greater in barefoot walking than it is when shoes are worn. It is likewise greater when walking on sand than when walking on pavement.

Summary of Mechanical Principles Which Apply to Walking

1. Translatory movement of a lever is achieved by the repeated alternation of two rotatory movements, the lever turning first about one end, then about the other end.[16]

2. A body at rest will remain at rest unless acted upon by a force. Since walking is produced by a pendulum-like motion of the limbs, the inertia of the body must be overcome at every step.

3. A body in motion will continue in motion unless acted upon by a force. Since motion is imparted to the trunk by the backward thrust of the leg, the trunk has a tendency to continue moving forward, even beyond the base of support. A brief restraining action of the forward limb acts as a check on the momentum of the trunk.

4. Force applied diagonally consists of two components, horizontal and vertical. The vertical component in walking serves to counteract the downward pull of gravity. The horizontal component serves (1), in the restraining phase, to check forward motion, and (2), in the propulsive phase, to produce it. The horizontal component of force in the propulsive phase must exceed that in the restraining phase if the end result is to be progressive forward motion.

5. The speed of the gait is directly related to the magnitude of the pushing force and to the direction of its application. This force is provided by the extensor muscles of the hip, knee and ankle joints, and the direction of application is determined by the slant of the lower extremity when the force is being applied.

6. The economy of the gait is related to its timing with reference to the length

and weight of the limbs. The most economical gait is one which is so timed as to permit ballistic motion of the lower extremities.

7. Walking has been described as an alternating loss and recovery of balance.[16] This being so, a new base of support must be established at every step.

8. Since propulsion of the body is effected by the diagonal pressure of the foot against the supporting surface, the efficiency of locomotion depends upon the counterpressure and friction provided by this surface.

9. Stability of the body is directly related to the size of the base of support. In walking, the lateral distance between the feet is a factor in balance.

a. Too narrow a lateral distance between the feet, such as occurs when one foot is placed directly in front of the other, increases the difficulty of maintaining balance, since it decreases the width of the base of support.

b. Too wide a lateral distance between the feet increases stability, but tends to cause a weaving gait and to make the body sway from side to side.

c. The optimum position of the feet seems to be one in which the inner borders fall approximately along a single straight line.

Summary of Anatomic Principles Which Apply to Walking

1. Good alignment of the lower extremities reduces friction in the joints and eliminates the likelihood of strain and injury.

2. Normal flexibility of the joints (i.e., sufficiently long and flexible muscles, ligaments and fasciae) reduces internal resistance, and hence reduces the amount of force required for walking.

3. Speed of walking is increased by increasing both the length of the stride and the tempo of the gait.

4. The longer the stride, the greater the up and down movements of the body, unless the knee is kept slightly flexed during the middle portion of the supporting phase.

5. Unnecessary lateral movements result in an ungainly and uneconomical gait.

a. Failure to keep the gluteus medius contracted when the weight is on the foot results in an exaggerated hip sway caused by the dropping of one side of the pelvis.

b. Excessive trunk rotation may be caused by an exaggerated arm swing, or by restriction of the arm swing. The arm swing should exactly counterbalance the hip swing.

c. Straight, sagittal plane action of the leg is assured by keeping the knee and the foot pointing straight forward in all phases of the gait.

d. The rotation of the pelvis should be only just enough to enable the leg to move straight forward. Too little or too much rotation tends to cause a weaving gait.

e. Minimum lateral motions occur when the feet are placed in such a way that their inner borders fall approximately along a single straight line.

6. The pulley action of the two-joint muscles of the lower extremity contributes to economy of muscular action in walking (see p. 33).

7. Properly functioning reflexes contribute to a well coordinated gait.

8. The stability of the weight-bearing limb and the balance of the trunk over this limb are important factors in the smoothness of the gait.

Individual Variations in the Gait. Although the basic anatomic analysis of the gait is valid for all physically normal persons, individual characteristics are present to such a degree that persons are often recognized by their gaits. These variations may be either structural or functional in origin. The structural differences include unusual body proportions, as well as differences in the limbs themselves such as knock-knees and bowlegs. Extreme variations in the angle between the neck and the shaft of the femur and in the obliquity of the femoral shaft (see pp. 226 to 228) are also responsible for characteristic gaits.

Variations in movement patterns which are not structural in origin are often related to characteristics of the personality. This was brought home forcefully to the author when she attempted to help college students whose gaits were awkward. Almost invariably the students who had the most awkward gaits were those who were extremely shy or lacking in self-confidence. It would seem, therefore, that teachers and therapists who work with such individuals need a good background in psychology as well as in kinesiology.

Running

Easy running, like walking, is a pendulum type of movement. It is doubtful, however, whether running at top speed can be so classified. The most notable factors differentiating the run from the walk are the period of double support, characteristic of the walk, but not present in the run, and the period of no support (a "sailing-through-the-air period"), characteristic of the run, but not present in the walk. In the run the foot hits the ground, not in front of the body as in the walk, but almost directly under the body's center of gravity. This reduces the restraining part of the supporting phase and gives greater emphasis to the propulsive part. As the speed increases, the restraining part of the supporting phase diminishes, disappearing completely as maximum speed is attained. The fact that, in the run, the supporting phase is known as the driving phase indicates its propulsive nature.

In running, as in walking, the force exerted to produce the movement has two components, horizontal and vertical. In running, however, because of the tremendous increase in horizontal force, the vertical component is relatively negligible.

Whether the run is an easy jog or a full-speed sprint, economy of effort is a highly desirable objective. To achieve this it is essential that the runner, either consciously or unconsciously, observe the principles which apply to efficient running. The most noteworthy of these are listed below.

Mechanical Principles of Running*

1. In accordance with the first law of motion, a body at rest remains at rest unless acted upon by a force. In running, the problem of overcoming inertia decreases as the level of speed is reached. It is greatest at the take-off, and least after acceleration has ceased.

* The principles of running as here stated are based largely on the description of sprinting in "Track and Field Athletics" by Bresnahan and Tuttle.

a. The crouching start enables the runner to exert maximum horizontal force at the take-off by:

(1) Providing a surface against which the foot can push horizontally;

(2) Putting the legs in a more horizontal position;

(3) Enabling the runner to use maximum hip, knee and ankle extension in both legs.

b. During acceleration the horizontal component of the leg drive gradually diminishes until a level of speed is maintained, during which period it remains uniform. The period of acceleration is characterized by a gradual decrease in the forward inclination of the trunk, a lengthening of the stride (made possible by the raising of the center of gravity as the trunk becomes more erect), and decrease of the knee thrust, resulting from the gradual straightening of the knee at the moment of contact between the foot and the ground.

2. In accordance with the second law of motion, acceleration is directly proportional to the force producing it. Hence, the greater the power of the leg drive, the greater the acceleration of the runner.

3. In accordance with the third law of motion, every action has an equal and opposite reaction.

4. Since a long lever develops more speed at the end that does a short lever, the length of the leg during the driving phase of running should be as great as possible when speed is a consideration. This is achieved by full extension at the knee joint at the end of the driving phase.

5. The smaller the vertical component of force, the greater the horizontal or driving component.

a. In the most efficient run, vertical movements of the center of gravity are reduced to a minimum.

b. The vertical component of force should be just enough to counteract the downward pull of gravity, but not enough to produce an unnecessary bounce in running.

6. The more completely the horizontal component of force is directed straight backward, the more it will contribute to the forward motion of the body. Lateral movements of the arms, legs and trunk detract unnecessarily from forward propulsion. To assure forward motion of the body:

a. The knees should be lifted directly forward-upward with the entire lower extremity kept in the sagittal plane. (Unathletic girls frequently run with a minimum knee lift and with an inward rotation of the thighs, the feet and lower legs being thrown out to the side.)

b. The arm swing should exactly counterbalance the twist of the pelvis and should not cause additional lateral motion.

7. Efficiency in running, as in any movement, requires the elimination of all unnecessary force.

Figure 214. Sprinting. *A,* Take-off; *B,* acceleration; *C,* full speed.

a. The shorter the lever, the less the force required to move it, and the less the reaction to it. By flexing the leg at the knee and carrying the heel high up under the hip in the recovery phase, the leg is moved more rapidly, as well as more economically.

b. Internal resistance caused by the viscosity of the sarcolemma is reduced by warming-up activities.

c. Internal resistance caused by tight muscles, fasciae and ligaments is reduced by systematic stretching exercises.

d. Unnecessary force in the form of excessively rapid muscular contractions is eliminated by developing as long a stride as can be controlled.

Supplementary Material

Electromyographic Study of the Muscles of the Foot in Walking.   Sheffield, Gersten and Mastellone investigated the action of the ankle and foot muscles used in walking. The subjects who participated in the study were ten normal adult males, and the walking was performed on the level at a rate of 60 steps per minute, one step consisting of the two phases, support and swing. The results are briefly summarized below.

Tibialis Anterior, Extensor Digitorum Longus and Extensor Hallucis Longus. Active throughout both phases with two peaks of intensity, the first during the early part of the swing phase when dorsiflexion was necessary in order to clear the ground, and the second at heel strike, apparently to lower the foot gradually instead of slapping it down.

Flexor Digitorum Longus, Flexor Hallucis Longus, Peroneus Longus and Tibialis Posterior.   The maximum activity of these muscles commenced near the beginning of the support phase, when the metatarsal region struck the ground, and continued until this region was off the ground. There was no activity during the swing phase.

Gastrocnemius and Soleus.   In eight subjects the gastrocnemius became active at the time the metatarsal region touched the ground; in the other two there was slight activity beginning at the time the heel touched the ground. In all ten subjects these muscles showed a high degree of activity throughout the support phase.

On the whole the findings of these investigators substantiate those of the National Research Council of the Advisory Committee on Artificial Limbs in a similar study. The latter group studied the muscular activity of six subjects as they walked at a normal pace, a rapid pace, up and down stairs, and up and down a ramp. The electromyograms made during rapid walking closely resemble the muscular activity as described by Sheffield and his co-workers. There are a few minor discrepancies, however. Sheffield's group appeared to find a greater degree of activity of the dorsiflexor muscles during the early part of the swing phase. They also appeared to find that the second group of muscles began their period of maximum activity earlier than did the Research Council group. The discrepancies may be due to the author's interpretation, however, since her comparison is based on the electromyographic tracings of one study and the written report of another.

Demonstrations and Laboratory Exercises

1. Observe the gait of people on the street; detect individual characteristics; and analyze them in terms of anatomic and mechanical principles.

2. Get a subject to walk in each of the following ways. Observe and note differences in the movements of the head, shoulders, hips, etc.

a. Placing one foot directly in front of the other.

b. Keeping a lateral distance of 10 to 12 inches between the feet.

c. Pointing the toes out.

d. Pointing the toes in.

e. Pointing the toes straight ahead.

f. Taking a short stride.

g. Taking a long stride.

3. Select four or five individuals who are not alike in leg length. Get them to practice walking until each one finds the stride and speed that feels most comfortable to him. Compare their strides and measure the distance between the footprints for each individual.

4. Observe several individuals as they run. Look for the application of the principles listed.

5. Observe other forms of locomotion and discover for yourself what principles apply to them.

Bibliography

1. Advisory Committee on Artificial Limbs, National Research Council: The Pattern of Muscular Activity in the Lower Extremity during Walking. Prosthetic Devices Research Project, Institute of Engineering Research, University of California, Berkeley, September, 1953.

2. Bresnahan, G. T., and Tuttle, W. W.: Track and Field Athletics. St. Louis, C. V. Mosby Company, 1937, Chap. 3

3. Elftman, H.: Measurement of the External Force in Walking. Science, *88:* 152–3, 1938.

4. Elftman, H.: The Function of Muscles in Locomotion. Am. J. Physiol., *125:* 357–66, 1939.

5. Elftman, H.: Forces and Energy Changes in the Leg during Walking. Am. J. Physiol., *125:* 339–56, 1939.

6. Glanville, A. D., and Kreezer, G.: Characteristics of Gait of Normal Male Adults. J. Exper. Psychol., *21:* 109–136, 1937.

7. Grace, M. E.: An Analysis of Certain Factors in the Gait of College Women. Research Quarterly of the Am. Assn. for Health, Phys. Ed. and Recrn., *14:* 294–309, Oct. 1943.

8. Houtz, S. J., Council, W. J., Norris, E. N., Eubank, R. N., and Hellebrandt, F. A.: Fundamental Approach to the Study of Stance Stability and Locomotion in the Cerebral Palsied. Phys. Ther. Rev., *32:* 51–55, 1952.

9. Hubbard, A. W., and Stetson, R. H.: An Experimental Analysis of Human Locomotion. Am. J. Physiol., *124:* 300–13, 1938.

10. Kreezer, G., and Glanville, A. D.: A Method for the Quantitative Analysis of Human Gait. J. Genetic Psych., *50:* 109–36, 1937.

11. Morton, D. J.: The Human Foot. New York, Columbia University Press, 1935, Chaps. 15 and 18.

12. Morton, D. J., and Fuller, D. D.: Human Locomotion and Body Form. Baltimore, Williams & Wilkins Company, 1952.

13. Saunders, J. B. deC.M., Inman, V. T., and Eberhart, H. D.: The Major Determinants in Normal and Pathological Gait. J. Bone & Joint Surg,, *35–A:* 543–558, 1953.

14. Schwartz, R. P., et al.: Kinetics of the Human Gait. J. Bone & Joint Surg., *16:* 343–50, 1934.

15. Sheffield, F. J., Gersten, J. W., and Mastellone: Electromyographic Study of the Muscles of the Foot in Normal Walking. Am. J. Phys. Med., *35:* 223–236, 1956.

16. Steindler, A.: Kinesiology of the Human Body. Springfield, Ill., Charles C Thomas, 1955, Lectures 37 and 38.

17. Steindler, A.: Gait; Physiologic and Pathologic Mechanics. Medical Physics. Chicago, Year Book Pub., Inc., 1944, pp. 468–479.

Recommended Readings

Morton, D. J.: The Human Foot. (See 11 above.)
   Chapter 15. Locomotion.
   Chapter 18. Mechanics of the Foot in Walking.
Steindler, A.: Kinesiology of the Human Body. (See 16 above.)
   Lecture 37. On the Mechanics of the Gait.
   Lecture 38. The Pathomechanics of the Gait.

24 · Applications of Kinesiology to the Teaching of Sports

$\mathbf{T}$HE PURPOSE of this chapter is to illustrate various ways in which kinesiology may be applied to teaching the sports commonly included in physical education programs. A few representative sport techniques and problems have been selected as a means of demonstrating to the student-teacher some of the practical applications of kinesiology in the area of sports. It is a truism that we learn best by doing. Hence no attempt is made to present comprehensive analysis of sport techniques. In fact, to do so would be contrary to the philosophy on which this text is based. The objective of the teacher-in-training should be to develop the ability to analyze movement, rather than to accumulate a collection of ready-made analyses. The effective physical education teacher is one who is able to analyze individual performance and to make helpful suggestions for improvement. The development of this ability is the logical outgrowth of experience in analyzing not only the correct form of specific techniques, but also the common faults in performance. The value of this chapter to the student will be in direct proportion to the extent to which he adopts this objective as his own.

In making a practice analysis the student should first select a specific movement-unit, such as a basketball pass, or a single stroke in swimming. This must be clearly defined and the exact form described. The movement should be divided into logical phases, such as (a) preliminary movement and (b) stroke and follow-through; or in the case of periodic movements, (a) propulsion and (b) recovery. Note that the "follow-through" is not given as a separate phase. Since it is continuous with the stroke, it should be included with it. Taking up one region of the body at a time, the student should then proceed to note the nature and range of motion at each joint. Next, he should analyze the action of the muscles, verifying this by observation and palpation whenever possible. In doing this he needs to keep in mind the relation of the position of the body to the pull of gravity and its effect on the muscular action. The mechanical factors should be identified and the appropriate principles considered. Attention should then be given to common faults and safety precautions. These should be analyzed with reference to the anatomic and mechanical principles concerned. Finally, coaching points based on the complete analysis of the movement should be selected.

Analysis of the Forehand Drive in Tennis

The technique upon which this analysis is based is that advocated by Driver in her book, "Tennis for Teachers." It is suggested that the reader refer to Driver's description in order to understand the kinesiologic analysis.

Purpose.   To return the ball advantageously.

Type of Movement.   Linear for the hand and racket; rotatory for the arm and for the body as a whole. The movement is also ballistic. The speed of the racket is reduced when it makes contact with the ball, and the movement is finally terminated by the contraction of antagonistic muscles.

Skill Classification.   Giving impetus to an object.

Description.   *Starting Position.*   The left side is toward the net, the feet about 18 inches apart, the knees slightly flexed and the weight on the balls of the feet. The racket is held with the eastern grip, as though shaking hands with it.

Backswing (Fig. 215, *A*).   The weight is transferred to the right foot and the trunk rotated to the right as the racket is swung back at about waist height. The elbow is kept away from the body. (It is assumed that the straight backswing is being used, rather than the circular.) There is a pause at the end of the backswing before the forward swing is begun.

Forward Swing and Follow-Through (Fig. 215, *B, C*).   The arm and racket swing forward and slightly upward in a continuous sweep. The racket is held with its head slightly above the level of the wrist at all times. The racket face is either flat or facing slightly upward at the moment of impact, and the grip is firm. The weight is transferred from the right to the left foot, and the body is rotated to the left so that, at the finish of the follow-through, the right shoulder is pointing in the direction of the ball's flight. As the weight is shifted from the right to the left foot, the racket is in contact with the ball and is moving forward in a straight line, rising slightly. The racket is above shoulder height for the follow-through and may finish in a slightly closed position, that is, facing somewhat downward.

Anatomic Analysis*

For the starting position and backswing only the joint analysis is given; for the forward swing and follow-through, both the joint and the muscular analyses.

Starting Position:

Head and neck: Rotation to the left
Trunk: Extension
Hips: Probably slight flexion and possibly slight abduction
Knees: Slight flexion
Ankles: Slight dorsiflexion
Right wrist: Extension; possibly slight hyperextension and radial flexion
Right hand: Flexion of fingers increasing from first to fifth finger; metacarpophalangeal joint of index finger only slightly flexed

Backswing:

Head and neck: Rotation to the left
Trunk: Extension; rotation to the right
Hips (variable)
  Right: Slight flexion, adduction and inward rotation
  Left: Extension or slight flexion; abduction increased; slight outward rotation

Figure 215. Forehand drive. *A,* The backswing; *B,* the forward swing; *C,* the follow-through.

* As in the preceding example, this analysis is systematic rather than chronologic. The correct sequence of movement for giving impetus is stated on page 434.

Knees (vary according to the height of the ball)
  Right: Either extension or slight flexion
  Left: Slight flexion
Ankles
  Right: Dorsiflexion
  Left: Neutral
Feet: Neutral
Shoulders
  Right: Partial abduction; horizontal extension-abduction to the limit of motion; outward rotation
Left: Abduction
Right elbow
  Extension (possibly not complete)
Right wrist: Hyperextension; radial flexion (may be increased or decreased, depending upon the height of the ball)

Forward Swing and Follow-Through:

HEAD AND NECK.   The head and neck are extended in the neutral position by the static contraction of the splenius capitis and cervicis and the capitis and cervicis portions of the sacrospinalis. They are rotated slightly to the right by the left semispinalis capitis and cervicis, left multifidus, left sternocleidomastoid, right splenius capitis and cervicis, right capitis and cervicis portions of the sacrospinalis, right rectus capitis posticus major and right obliquus capitis inferior.

TRUNK.   The trunk is held in a position of extension by static contraction of the sacrospinalis and semispinalis. It is rotated to the left by the left sacrospinalis (dorsal and lumbar portions), left internal oblique abdominal, right semispinalis (dorsal portion), right multifidus (dorsal and lumbar portions); right rotatores and right external oblique abdominal muscle. It flexes slightly to the left, the movement being controlled by the eccentric contraction of the right spinal muscles. (The simultaneous contraction of these muscles as extensors, lateral flexors, rotators of the trunk to the left, and rotators of the head to the right, is not inconsistent. It can be explained in terms of the region involved and of the relative number of fibers that contract for each movement. Actually, each of these muscles is a series of many small muscles, rather than a single, unified muscle in itself.)

RIGHT HIP.   As the weight shifts from the right to the left foot the right thigh becomes slightly abducted. The action is controlled by the eccentric contraction of the adductors. The thigh is extended by the hamstrings and adductor magnus and rotated outward slightly by the six deep outward rotators.

LEFT HIP.   The left thigh goes into a position of adduction, and slight inward rotation, the action being controlled by eccentric contraction of the gluteus medius and minimus. It also becomes slightly flexed in the weight-bearing position. This movement may be initiated by the tensor fasciae latae, the sartorius and the pectineus, but almost immediately it is controlled by eccentric contraction of the hamstrings.

KNEES.   The flexion of the left leg is slightly increased and that of the right slightly decreased. Since the legs are in a weight-bearing position, the movement is controlled by the quadriceps femoris.

ANKLES AND FEET.   The feet assume a position of dorsiflexion in weight-bearing with possibly a slight degree of supination. The weight is well forward. The gastrocnemius, soleus, peroneus longus, tibialis posterior and possibly the tibialis anterior (if the supination is sufficiently pronounced) control the movement. The flexor hallucis longus and flexor digitorum are also contracted in response to the pressure of the ground against the toes. There are individual variations in the position of the feet, there occasionally being plantar flexion of one foot or the other.

RIGHT SHOULDER JOINT.   As the arm swings forward the humerus passes from a position of partial abduction to a position of flexion-adduction. The muscles causing this are the pectoralis major, the anterior deltoid, subscapularis, the coracobrachialis, and short head of the biceps. The middle deltoid and supraspinatus support the weight of the arm. The degree of elevation of the arm depends upon the height of the ball. The flexion-adduction of the humerus is accompanied by inward rotation. This is produced by the subscapularis, anterior deltoid, coracobrachialis and short head of the biceps. At the end of the follow-through the posterior deltoid, infraspinatus and teres minor contract momentarily to check the motion of the arm.

RIGHT SHOULDER GIRDLE.   The scapula is abducted and tilted laterally by the serratus anterior, rotated upward by the serratus anterior and second and fourth parts of the trapezius, and elevated by the levator scapulae and first part of the trapezius.

RIGHT ELBOW AND RADIOULNAR JOINTS.   The forearm is held in a position of incomplete extension throughout the movement. The slight amount of flexion probably serves to protect the joint against the effect of the impact, as well as to keep the racket in the desired position. For about the first three quarters of the swing the biceps, brachialis, brachioradialis and pronator teres are in static contraction. Then, during the last quarter of the movement, they relax and the triceps contracts, first in eccentric, then in static contraction. If the racket ends in a closed position, the forearm has pronated. The pronator teres and pronator quadratus are responsible for this movement.

RIGHT WRIST.   The hyperextension is reduced by means of the action of the flexor carpi ulnaris, flexor carpi radialis and palmaris longus. When the midposition is reached, the extensor carpi ulnaris and extensor radialis longus and brevis contract to check further flexion. The hand remains in a position of slight radial flexion against the downward pull of gravity acting on the racket. The abductor pollicis, extensor carpi radialis longus and brevis, and flexor carpi radialis are in static contraction.

THUMB AND FINGERS OF RIGHT HAND.   These are in strong flexion through the action of the flexor longus pollicis and flexor digitorum sublimis and profundus.

The action of the left arm is not analyzed, since it varies with the individual. It usually moves in opposition to the right arm in order to help maintain balance.

Note: 1. Variations in the muscular action are caused by the height at which the ball is struck and by the foot work required for the approach.

2. The follow-through serves three purposes:

a. It assures an adequate application of force up to the moment of impact.

b. It permits a gradual cessation of the application of force by the "movers."

c. It minimizes the amount of force needed by the antagonistic muscles for terminating the movement.

Mechanical Factors and Principles

Equilibrium

The effectiveness of giving impetus to an object is largely dependent upon the stability of the body at the moment of giving it. A moderately wide base of support, and the use of the left arm to balance the right, both contribute to stability.

Friction

Rubber-soled shoes are worn to increase friction and thus reduce the danger of slipping and to facilitate quick changes of direction.

Inertia

1. In accordance with the Law of Inertia, a straight backswing requires the application of a force to stop the movement, and of another force to overcome

the inertia and start the movement in the reverse direction. This would not be true if a circular backswing were used. The latter method, however, has the disadvantage (for the inexperienced player) of requiring more exact timing.

2. The follow-through provides sufficient distance for "decelerating" (i.e., losing kinetic energy) without necessitating the oversudden contraction of antagonistic muscles.

3. Momentum plays an important part in this movement. It is probably of greater importance than muscular contraction in being responsible for the position of the body at the end of the movement.

Giving Impetus to an Object

1. Maximum velocity is obtained in the racket when maximum distance is used for accelerating. This is accomplished in the forehand drive by (*a*) shifting the body weight; (*b*) rotating the trunk; (*c*) starting the backswing sufficiently early; (*d*) swinging the arm to the comfortable limit of motion in the backswing; and (*e*) keeping the racket at approximately arm's length from the body. The timing of these movements is of utmost importance. For maximum velocity of the racket head, the movement commences with the shifting of weight and continues with rotation of the lower part of the body, progressing to the upper, and then proceeds to the arm, progressing from the proximal to the distal end. Each movement in turn gets under way before the next one commences. If the timing is correct, the cumulative effect of these movements is to produce maximum velocity. If any of the movements is added to the preceding one either too early or too late the potential velocity will not be realized.

2. The use of the arm in an almost fully extended position increases the length of the lever, thereby giving greater velocity to the racket head than would be the case if the upper arm were close to the body.

3. The concentration of mass at the level of the shoulders is moving forward at the moment of impact, thus assuring maximum speed for striking.

4. A skillful player tends to use a relatively heavy racket because, other things being equal, the greater the mass of the striking implement, the greater the striking force, and hence the greater the speed of the struck ball.

5. A new ball and a well strung racket assure a good coefficient of restitution (i.e., elasticity), thereby increasing the speed of the struck ball.

6. The compressibility of the tennis ball causes it to rebound from the racket at an angle slightly less than the angle of incidence.

7. A firm grip on the racket and the use of good wrist force assure the transmission of force from the body to the instrument, and hence to the ball.

8. If the racket is lifted slightly on the forward swing and if the racket face is flat at the moment of impact, top spin will be imparted to the ball. This causes the ball to move in an arc, to have a long bounce, and to rise on its bounce.

9. There is a positive relationship between the speed of the approaching ball and the speed of the struck ball.

10. The application of maximum force to the ball is dependent upon the correct timing of every phase of the stroke. There is a little more leeway, however, with a straight backswing than with a circular backswing.

Common Faults and Means of Correction.   These are covered so thoroughly in Chapter 12 of Driver's book, "Tennis for Teachers," that they are not repeated here.

Safety Precautions.   An adequate warm-up period should be engaged in before playing in a game. Several minutes spent in volleying usually serves this purpose.

Evaluation of the Forehand Drive as Described.   The side-to-the-net position permits a long backswing. If the player were to face the net, as beginners frequently do, a backswing could be obtained only by means of the arm swing and rotation of the trunk, without the help of the shift of weight from one foot to the other. The arm would have a shorter forward swing before the moment of impact, hence would have less distance in which to develop velocity. Another advantage of the side-to-the-net position is that it permits more forceful action of the pectoralis major muscle.

The side-to-the-net position also contributes to greater stability because it means that the base of support is widened both in the direction of the oncoming external force (the ball) and in the direction of the force being imparted by the body to the ball.

A position sufficiently far to the side of the ball to permit a full or nearly full reach with the arm and racket permits a more forceful stroke than could be executed if the player were so close to the ball that a cramped elbow action swing was necessitated. The latter style would be unfavorable both to the leverage and to the muscular action.

The straight backswing necessitates the overcoming of inertia in order to change to the forward swing. This is not true of the circular backswing because, in the latter, the arm moves in one continuous motion. This method is more efficient for players who can control the direction of the racket and the timing of the entire movement.

Of special interest to the kinesiologist is the need for strong wrist and finger flexors for maintaining a firm grip on the racket and a firm wrist at the moment of contact with the ball.

Analysis of the Sprint Crawl

The technique upon which this analysis is based is described by Armbruster and Morehouse in their book, "Swimming and Diving." The position of the head and trunk and the movement of the head in breathing are analyzed briefly. The arm and leg strokes are analyzed in somewhat greater detail. These are divided into phases, and each phase is defined and discussed from the point of view of the mechanics involved and then analyzed anatomically. The arm stroke is divided into the propulsive, recovery and gliding phases, and the leg stroke into the downstroke and the upstroke. The kinesiologic analysis of the sprint crawl is as follows:

Purpose. To swim the crawl stroke with maximum speed, as in a race.

Type of Movement. Linear movement of the body as a whole effected by means of rotatory movements of the upper and lower extremities. The action of the legs in the flutter kick can be classified as an oscillatory movement (see p. 297). It is also somewhat

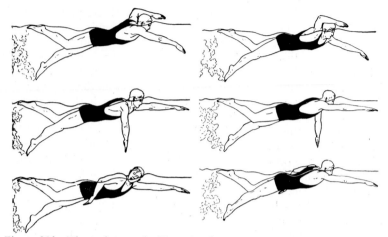

Figure 216. The sprint crawl. (From Armbruster: "Competitive Swimming and Diving," by courtesy of C. V. Mosby Company.)

ballistic, although the resistance of the water makes true ballistic action difficult.

Skill Classification. Moving one's own body in the water.

THE HEAD AND TRUNK

The head and trunk have three important functions in swimming, particularly in speed swimming. These are minimizing resistance, enabling the swimmer to breathe, and providing a stable anchorage for the arm and leg muscles. The position of the body is the key to reducing resistance. The popular term, "streamlining the body," gives the picture. The body is almost horizontal, but not quite, because the feet and buttocks are below the surface of the water, and the head and shoulders are partly above it. The head is held with the chin slightly lifted and the eyes close to the surface of the water, in some cases just below it, and in some cases just above it. The exact position of the body varies with the anatomic build and the buoyancy of the individual, as well as with the speed of the stroke. A common mistake is to overdo the lift of the head. If it is held too high, or tipped back too far, it makes the swimmer overtense and hence reduces his endurance. Armbruster emphasizes the importance of keeping the chin and nose in the midplane of the body in order to keep the body on an even keel. By static contraction of the rectus abdominis the spine is held in a position of slight flexion—or at least of incomplete extension— and the pelvis in a position of slightly decreased inclination.

The turning of the head for inhaling must be accomplished with the least possible interference with the rhythm of the arm and leg action and with the progress of the body through the water. It is essential not to lift the head for breathing, but to rotate it on its longitudinal axis while at the same time tucking the chin in close to the side of the neck. In this position the face appears to be resting on the bow wave, and the mouth is just above the surface of the water. After a quick inhalation the face is again turned forward with the eyes in the horizontal plane and the nose and chin in the midsagittal plane of the body.

In order to provide a firm base of attachment for the muscles of the arms and thighs the trunk must be held steady. By the alternating action of the left and right oblique abdominals and spinal extensors the spine and pelvis are stabilized against the pull of the shoulder and hip muscles, thus permitting the latter to exert all their force on the limbs for the propulsive movements.

THE ARM STROKE

Propulsive Phase

Description

1. THE CATCH.   The arm is in a forward extended position, the hand slightly under the surface of the water. The elbow is slightly bent, and the palm and forearm are pressing slightly against the water. The pressure is mostly downward and slightly backward. As the arm continues to press, the backward component becomes relatively greater. The backward component exceeds the downward when the hand is approximately 6 or 7 inches below the surface. At this point the arm is pulled medialward and downward until the hand is in line with the midline of the body. This helps to prevent undesirable lateral movements. There is little force in the movement until the backward component exceeds the downward component of force. If maximum force were exerted as soon as the hand hit the water, the downward component of force would be so great that it would tend to lift the body, rather than drive it forward.

2. THE PULL.   The pull starts at the moment when the hand reaches the longitudinal midline position and continues until the arm is directed vertically downward. During this phase the arm is pulling downward-backward with the hand in the midsagittal plane of the body. The elbow flexes just enough to permit the long axis of the hand to remain in this plane. As Armbruster points out, the flexed position of the elbow enables the hand and forearm to exert their force in line with the body; it shortens the lever-arm, thereby permitting faster motion; and it facilitates the transition from the pull to the push. It is also responsible for introducing an inward rotatory component in the action of the shoulder joint. The muscular action is of course much stronger in the pull than in the catch.

3. THE PUSH.   As soon as the arm passes beyond the vertical, the movement becomes a push instead of a pull. The movement continues until the upper arm is parallel with the surface of the water and the forearm—owing to the flexion at the elbow—is at approximately a 45-degree angle. At the completion of the movement the hand is "opposite the middle of the thigh, just below the hip."[2] The push is done with maximum power and finishes with an extra push from the hand itself.

It is important not to continue the push beyond this point because the horizontal-backward component of force is constantly diminishing and the upward

Figure 217.   The crawl stroke. Taken through underwater window in Wellesley College swimming pool. The right arm is completing the glide and is about
to begin the pull. (Photo from files of Department of Hygiene and Physical
Education, Wellesley College.)

component increasing. If the latter exceeded the former, it would tend to drive
the body downward instead of forward.

Anatomic Analysis

1. SHOULDER JOINT.   The arm extends at the shoulder joint and rotates
slightly inward throughout the propulsive phase. As the arm pulls toward the
midline slight horizontal flexion-adduction occurs. In the push, this is reduced as
the arm is brought to the side of the body. The muscles responsible for these
movements are the latissimus dorsi, teres major and pectoralis major, particularly the sternal portion. The long head of the triceps and the coracobrachialis
help stabilize the joint. The latter muscle and the short head of the biceps
probably help in the slight inward horizontal movement.

2. SHOULDER GIRDLE.   The scapula is rotated downward through the action
of the rhomboids and the pectoralis minor. Probably some abduction accompanies this movement when the arm is directed vertically downward. If so, the
upper serratus anterior might be working with the pectoralis minor to bring this
about.

3. ELBOW.   The forearm flexes slightly and remains in this position. The
muscles which flex the forearm are the biceps, brachialis, brachioradialis and
pronator teres. Even though the joint action is slight, the muscular action is
strong, since it must resist the pressure of the water against the front of the hand
and forearm.

4. RADIOULNAR JOINTS.   The pronator teres and pronator quadratus hold
the forearm in a position of slight pronation.

5. WRIST AND FINGERS.   The palmaris longus, flexor carpi radialis, flexor
carpi ulnaris, flexor digitorum sublimis, and flexor digitorum profundus contract to hold the wrist and fingers in an extended position against the pressure
of the water. In the final push the hand flexes slightly at the wrist and the fingers
flex at the metacarpophalangeal joints. The fingers and thumb are adducted by
the palmar interossei, the opponens digiti quinti, the adductor pollicis and the
opponens pollicis. In the part of the movement in which the hand is brought

in to the midline, there may be slight ulnar flexion at the wrist if the fingers are pointing directly downward.

Recovery Phase

Description

1. RELEASE.   The propulsive phase ends with the elbow at the surface of the water and the hand close to the front of the thigh, palm up. The forearm is in a backward-downward diagonal position with the hand below and posterior to the elbow. From this position the forearm is lifted with the elbow leading and the ulnar side of the forearm turned toward the surface. This position assures a minimum of resistance as the forearm is lifted from the water.

2. RECOVERY.   The elbow is lifted above the level of the head, and when the hand is clear of the water, the forearm swings outward and forward in a low arc with the hand turned palm down and the thumb side leading forward. After the hand has passed the head the arm reaches forward in preparation for the entry. The upper arm is close to the head, the elbow in a slightly flexed position and carried higher than the hand, the palm is almost parallel with the surface of the water, and the wrist and the fingers are fully extended.

Anatomic Analysis

1. SHOULDER JOINT.   The lifting of the arm out of the water is accomplished by hyperextension at the shoulder joint, with the posterior deltoid, latissimus dorsi and teres major in strong contraction. As the arm reaches forward the movement changes to abduction and horizontal extension-abduction, accompanied by outward rotation. This part of the movement is brought about by the action of the middle deltoid, supraspinatus, infraspinatus and teres minor. The posterior deltoid probably ceases to contract by the time the elbow passes the head.

2. SHOULDER GIRDLE.   During the lifting part of the movement the scapula is adducted by the action of the rhomboids and middle trapezius. During the reach it is rotated upward by the action of the lower serratus and the second and fourth parts of the trapezius.

3. ELBOW.   At first the elbow joint is relaxed, but in the reach the forearm is partially extended by the action of the triceps and anconeus.

4. RADIOULNAR JOINTS.   The forearm becomes less pronated than it was. This is brought about by contraction of the supinator.

5. WRIST AND FINGERS.   As the palm turns downward the extensors of the wrist and fingers come into action to support their weight and to keep them in an extended position.

Gliding Phase

Description

1. THE ENTRY.   From the position with the hand in front of the head, palm down and parallel with the surface of the water, and with the elbow higher than both the shoulder and the hand, the hand reaches forward and the arm is extended at the elbow. With the finger tips just barely in the lead the hand and forearm then enter the water directly in front of the shoulder. A high position of the shoulder and prevention of hyperextension at the elbow joint are both achieved by keeping the top of the elbow pointing out to the side.

2. SUPPORT.   The forearm continues to extend at the elbow joint when the hand is beneath the surface of the water, but stops a little short of complete extension. The hand and forearm, slanting downward only slightly, reach forward and press down against the water until the hand is about 6 or 7 inches beneath the surface.

Anatomic Analysis

1. SHOULDER JOINT. The abduction of the humerus, commenced in the recovery phase, is completed in the entry part of the gliding phase. This is followed in the supporting part of the gliding phase by a slight forward-downward depression of the arm, involving extension and slight inward rotation at the shoulder joint. The muscles producing these movements are the latissimus dorsi, teres major, pectoralis major, posterior deltoid and long head of the triceps.

2. SHOULDER GIRDLE. The shoulder girdle continues to rotate upward until the humerus has completed its abduction. When the hand and forearm start to press down on the water, the scapula starts to rotate downward through the action of the rhomboids and pectoralis minor.

3. ELBOW. The triceps and anconeus continue to extend the forearm, but cease before the elbow is in complete extension.

4. RADIOULNAR JOINTS. The forearm remains slightly pronated.

5. WRIST AND FINGERS. The hands and fingers remain in extension, but as they begin to press against the water the flexor muscles contract in order to protect the joints.

THE LEG STROKE

Downstroke

Description. At the beginning of the downstroke the hip and the knee are in a slightly flexed position and the ankle is in a position of complete plantar flexion. The downward movement is initiated at the hip joint and from there is transmitted to the thigh, knee, leg, ankle and foot. As the lower extremity moves vertically downward, the knee becomes fully extended and the anterior surface of the thigh and leg and the dorsal surface of the foot exert strong downward pressure against the water.

Anatomic Analysis

1. HIP JOINT. The thigh becomes moderately flexed at the hip joint. It is not rotated either inward or outward; neither is it abducted. Either it is neutral, so far as abduction and adduction are concerned, or else it is in a position of slight adduction. The muscles which flex the thigh are the iliopsoas, tensor fasciae latae, pectineus, sartorius and gracilis. The adductors magnus, longus, brevis and gracilis are responsible for any adduction that may be present.

2. KNEE. The leg extends at the beginning of the downstroke and remains extended until the stroke is completed. The extension is performed by the quadriceps femoris. At the end of the stroke the muscles relax momentarily.

3. ANKLE AND FOOT. The ankle and tarsal joints remain in a position of complete plantar flexion. The ankle joint is so constructed that when it is completely extended, the foot is in a slightly adducted position. This is because the axis of the ankle joint is slightly oblique. Instead of being situated in a true frontal plane, it slants slightly posteriorly as it passes from the medial to the lateral aspect. There is probably a slight amount of voluntary adduction and inversion (supination) of the foot also, in addition to the involuntary adduction incidental to the complete plantar flexion. There is no "toeing in" in the same sense that there is in walking. The latter is due to inward rotation at the hip joint, a movement which should not occur in the flutter kick. The plantar flexion is caused by contraction of the soleus, peroneus longus and brevis, tibialis posterior, flexor digitorum longus, and flexor hallucis longus. Of these, the last three also supinate the foot. Whether or not the tibialis anterior contributes to the supination is difficult to say. Experiment shows that it does contract when the foot is supinated against resistance even when the ankle is fully extended

(plantar-flexed). It does not seem likely that the gastrocnemius helps in the plantar flexion in this part of the stroke, because the movement is not performed against resistance. This is difficult to determine experimentally.

Upstroke

Description. The lower extremity is completely extended at the beginning of the upstroke, but there is a momentary relaxation of the muscles as the movement changes from downward to upward. The leg flexes slightly at the knee during the upstroke and the foot is easily extended, but not turned in as it is in the downstroke.

Anatomic Analysis

1. HIP JOINT. The thigh extends throughout the upstroke, but stops before reaching the position of complete extension. The hamstrings, adductor magnus and gluteus maximus are in strong contraction. There is no rotation of the thigh.

2. KNEE JOINT. The leg flexes at the knee joint to an angle of approximately 135 degrees. Hence it moves through an arc of about 45 degrees. The hamstrings, sartorius, gracilis, popliteus and gastrocnemius are all instrumental in flexing the leg, but since the gastrocnemius is in a shortened position, owing to the ankle extension, its contribution to the knee flexion cannot be great.

3. ANKLE AND FOOT. The foot is in a position of plantar flexion, but this is not complete until the very end of the movement, when the sole of the foot exerts maximum pressure against the water. Armbruster refers to this movement of the foot as a lashing action and attributes to it the major propulsive action of the legs. There is no adduction or inversion of the foot until the upstroke is completed. In the terminal position of the upstroke the sole of the foot is just below the surface of the water and is parallel with it. The action of the plantar flexors is even stronger in the upstroke than in the down, because they are working directly against the pressure of the water. The muscles which contract are the gastrocnemius, soleus, peroneus longus, peroneus brevis, tibialis posterior, flexor digitorum longus and flexor hallucis longus.

Additional Aspects

Other aspects of the crawl stroke which are important to the swimmer and the coach include the timing and coordination of the arm and leg strokes and of the breathing, the rhythm of the stroke as a whole, the relaxation of the body and the flexibility of the joints, particularly of the shoulders and ankles. Of these, possibly the last named is of greatest interest to the kinesiologist. The serious swimmer will want to know how to increase the range of motion in his shoulder joints and ankles, specifically, how to stretch the pectorals and anterior ligaments of the shoulders, and to gain greater plantar flexion of the feet. Armbruster has suggested a few exercises for these purposes. The kinesiology student should be able to devise several others.

Analysis of Common Faults in Selected Sport Techniques

One particularly useful application of kinesiology for the sports instructor is the analysis of common faults. A number of such analyses have been made by Vollmer in an original study at Wellesley

College. The material in this section is condensed from portions of her study.* It is included in this text as a means of demonstrating to the reader how he can analyze common faults in sport techniques and use these analyses as the basis for his teaching suggestions. Prior to making the analysis of a fault it is essential to note the respects in which the fault differs from the correct form of the technique. The next step is to analyze the fault kinesiologically. This may include both anatomic and mechanical analyses, or it may be limited to either one or the other, depending upon the nature of the fault. The final step it to devise teaching suggestions. These should be the natural and logical outgrowth of the analysis. Practice of this sort should enable the student-teacher to think analytically about his teaching and should sharpen his awareness of cause and effect relationships. Being forewarned of the nature and cause of the faults, he should be able to teach the techniques in such a way that his pupils will avoid the common faults. If some do develop them, he will presumably be prepared to make appropriate suggestions for overcoming them.

FAULT IN THE CRAWL STROKE: RIGID FLUTTER KICK

Description.   In the rigid flutter kick the movement is one of alternate flexion and extension of the entire lower extremity, with the movement confined to the hip joint instead of being transmitted successively through the thigh to the knee joint and thence through the leg to the ankle and foot. The knee joints are fully extended throughout the kick, and the feet and ankles are held in an unchanging position of plantar flexion, the exact degree of this flexion varying with individuals. The swimmer who commits this fault finds that he has to kick more times to cover the same distance as a swimmer who kicks correctly. This results in a narrower kick. A rigid flutter kick is obviously less efficient than the correct kick. In brief, the rigid flutter kick deviates from the correct form in that there is an absence of knee and ankle flexion, an absence of relaxation at the end of the downkick or beginning of the upkick, and an absence of "fishtail" action of the sole of the foot against the water.

Anatomic Analysis.   In the correct downkick the upward pressure of the water against the lower leg causes flexion to occur at the knee. In the rigid kick, however, this is prevented by the tension of the quadriceps extensors. Normally the slight flexion at the knee is followed by extension during the course of the downstroke, but since the knee is already rigidly extended, this extension cannot take place. Similarly, the reduction of plantar flexion which should take place at the end of the downstroke fails to occur be-

* Used by permission of Lola Vollmer Shepherd.

cause of the continuous contraction of the plantar flexor muscles (soleus, peroneus longus and brevis, tibialis posterior, flexor digitorum longus and flexor hallucis longus).

In the upstroke the tension of the quadriceps extensors again prevents the slight knee flexion which occurs when the kick is correctly performed. (See Figs. 216 and 217.) Throughout the stroke the extensors of the lower back and the abdominal muscles contract to stabilize the pelvis against the pull of the hip flexors and extensors. Normally they relax momentarily just before the legs reverse their direction. The tension in the muscles of the lower extremities spreads to these, however, and the excess tension of these muscles causes interference with the action of the diaphragm. This, in turn, results in less efficient breathing and is an additional factor in causing fatigue.

Mechanical Analysis.   The propulsive component of force which drives the body forward is that which pushes the water directly backward. In the downstroke this is provided most effectively by the instep of the foot, and in the upstroke, by the sole. The amount of propulsive force developed depends upon the angle at which the instep and the sole of the foot are held with respect to the surface of the water. In the upstroke the best angle for the sole of the foot is possible only when the knee is slightly flexed. In the rigid kick the knee is straight, and the sole of the foot is therefore not in the best position for providing propulsive force.

In the correct form each limb acts as a series of levers—thigh, lower leg and foot—but in the rigid kick each limb acts as one long lever with the force arm extending from the distal attachments of the hip flexors and extensors to the axis of the hip joint. The resistance arm consists of the entire length of the lever from the instep or from the sole of the foot to the hip joint. The force acting on this lever comes solely from the muscles of the hip joints. The muscles of the knee and angle do not contribute to the motion of this lever. When the limb is used as a series of levers, these muscles help to provide the force.

Inertia must be overcome with each reversal of direction in the kick. Since, in the rigid flutter kick, the stroke is shorter and faster than it should be, the muscles of the hip joint, which have the double task of overcoming both the inertia of the limb and the resistance of the water, are overburdened. They must work harder and faster to meet the demands made on them by the frequent changes of direction and the increased resistance of the water due to the speed of movement. Ordinarily the upstroke has an advantage over the downstroke because, when the stroke is performed correctly, the sole of the foot is in a better position to push back against the water than is the instep on the downstroke. In the rigid kick this advantage is lost.

Teaching Suggestions. "The rigid crawl flutter kick is associated with undue tension of the quadriceps extensors at the knee joint, and of the plantar flexors at the ankle joint, during the changes of direction in both the downkick and the upkick. There may also be unnecessary tension of the abdominal muscles and the spinal extensors. As the kick is inefficient, it is carried on at a faster rate and through a narrower arc than would be the correct kick for the individual swimmer. Conversely, a rapid, narrow kick tends to be a rigid kick. These factors aid in its recognition. In the teaching of the kick, it would seem the best procedure to insist on a slow, deep kick in the student's first attempts, and to increase the rhythm gradually to the desired rate. Motivation should not be directed toward speed in the performance of the 'kick glide' in the teaching progression. Neither is it desirable to emphasize that the legs be held straight at the knees. The emphasis should be put on the increased action at the hips and at the ankles. Furthermore, land drills to increase ankle flexibility seem to be advisable."[22]

Fault in Archery: Creeping on the Release

Description. The fault known as creeping may be caused by either arm. It may be due to a forward movement of the right hand prior to, or at the moment of, the release; or it may be due to the relaxation of the left arm at both the shoulder and the elbow joints. If the creeping is due to the right arm, the normal follow-through is omitted entirely; if it is due to the left arm, the follow-through is reduced because of the loss of tension between the bow and the string preceding the release.

Anatomic Analysis. The arms are maintained at shoulder level by the deltoid and supraspinatus muscles and are drawn back in horizontal extension-abduction chiefly by the posterior deltoid, infraspinatus and teres minor, assisted by the latissimus dorsi. The scapulae are strongly adducted by the rhomboids and middle trapezius. Both the horizontal extension of the arm and the adduction of the scapula are stronger on the side of the drawing arm than of the bow arm. The muscles of the bow arm are in static, i.e., tonic, contraction, whereas those of the drawing arm are in phasic contraction. The elbow extensors and the ulnar flexors of the wrist on the side of the bow arm are also in static contraction, resisting the pressure of the bow.

When creeping is the fault of the right arm (i.e., the drawing arm), it is caused by premature relaxation or by lengthening contraction of the scapular adductors and the horizontal extensors of the shoulder joint. This results in insufficient resistance to the pull of the string. When creeping is the fault of the left, or bow, arm, it is caused by tiring, and consequent relaxation, of the muscles which must resist the pressure of the bow, particularly the triceps muscle.

Mechanical Analysis.   "Creeping before or during the release reduces the tension between the string and the bow, and thereby reduces the potential energy which the string has acquired. Thus the amount of force imparted to the arrow by the string is decreased. Furthermore, this fault introduces a variable factor, as the amount of creeping will tend to vary with each shot.

"A study has been made on the effect of creeping when the archer holds his anchor and aims correctly.[11] A reduced draw, or a creep, of one half inch resulted in hits 5.9 inches below the target center at forty yards, and 9.4 inches below the center at fifty yards. A creep of three quarters of an inch resulted in hits 8.8 inches below the center of the target at forty yards and 13.8 inches below at fifty yards."[22]

Teaching Suggestions.   The student should be instructed to keep drawing actively with the right arm and to be constantly aware of the pull between his shoulder blades until after the release. Absence of a follow-through is usually an indication of creeping. Since creeping may be caused by using too heavy a bow, the teacher should check to see that the bow is the right weight for the student. He should also make sure that the student has a correct anchor and that he is not holding the draw position too long. If the student has difficulty finding his aim, he should relax his draw and rest a moment before drawing again.

If the student-teacher will select a number of common faults, comparable to those just cited, and will analyze them in a similar manner, he will find this practice to be of value in helping him to become more observant and analytical in his teaching and coaching.

Application of Kinesiologic Principles to the Teaching of Sports

Physical education teachers have found that their students learn sport skills more rapidly and practice them more intelligently when they have at least a rudimentary knowledge of the basic principles which underlie successful performance.[12, 18] The student of kinesiology should keep this in mind and, as he reviews the anatomic and mechanical principles of movement, should think of ways of explaining them in simplified terms. This is a practical application of kinesiology which has received all too little attention in the past.

As an illustration of the way in which simplified kinesiologic explanations and demonstrations may be utilized by the sports instructor in his teaching methods, a portion of an original study by McAuley is presented below in somewhat abridged form.*

* Used by permission of Janet McAuley.

SOFTBALL OVERHAND THROW*

Kinesiologic Explanations	*Demonstrations*

Leverage

The ball is held in the finger tips because the fingers lengthen the throwing lever. The improved leverage serves to increase the speed that can be developed. The longer the lever, the greater the speed that can be developed at its end. Hence the greater the momentum that can be imparted to the ball.

To demonstrate the difference between using a short and a long lever in throwing a softball, have the students throw, first using just the hand and forearm, and then using the entire arm.

Movement of the Body

The weight shifts to the right foot in the preparatory phase so that in the actual throw the momentum caused by the forward shifting weight can be added to the ball as it leaves the hand. The rotation of the trunk to the right in the preparatory phase ensures a larger arc to swing through in the delivery phase.

To demonstrate the value of the weight shift and rotation in throwing a softball, have the students throw, first with a narrow stance and without moving the feet or shifting the weight, and then using the correct form. They should compare the two methods with respect to the distance of the ball's flight.

Angle of Release

If distance is desired, the ball should be released at approximately a 45-degree angle from the horizontal. This assures sufficient vertical force to overcome the force of gravity, yet at the same time provides optimum horizontal force. If the ball is to be thrown a short distance at maximum speed, it should be released in as nearly a horizontal direction as possible.

To demonstrate the effect of the angle of release on the flight of the ball, have the students throw balls, releasing them at various angles and note the results. If they work in pairs, the partner can check on the angle of release.

VOLLEY BALL UNDERHAND SERVE

Relation of Body Position to Flight of Ball

To assure a straight forward swing with the right arm moving in the sagittal plane, the feet are pointed forward toward the net. A moderate stride, with the left foot slightly forward, assures stability for the serve.

The teacher should demonstrate the effect of body position on the flight of the ball, and show how a side-arm swing is required if the side is turned to the net. Note that a ball thus hit will be directed to the side of the court. Have the class try standing incorrectly a few times and serve with some side-arm action, and then have them practice correctly, swinging straight through to the opposite court.

* The authority for all the sport skills referred to in this section is "Technic of Team Sports for Women," by Meyer and Schwartz.

Relation of Stance to Application of Force

A moderate stride with the left foot slightly forward, the left knee slightly flexed, and the weight over the right foot enables the server to shift the weight forward toward the end of the serve. This contributes to greater force in hitting the ball, hence to greater speed of the ball in its flight.

The teacher should demonstrate the way a stiff forward knee acts as a brake to the momentum of the body and necessitates "tipping over" the stiff leg. Point out the way this "tipping" action tends to make the player hit up and to lose momentum. Have the class concentrate for a while on bending the left knee as they practice serving.

Effect of Hitting Ball Off-Center

The direction taken by the ball after it has been struck is determined in part by the angle of contact. For a straight flight, the ball must be hit directly behind its center with the hand moving in the desired direction of flight. In order to hit the ball properly it should be held at the right side of the body.

The teacher should hit the ball first to the left of its center, and then to the right. The students should note the effect on the ball's flight. The effect of hitting off-center can be shown even more clearly by placing the ball on the floor and hitting it gently, first to the left of its center, then to the right, and then in line with its center.

Angle of Application of Force

If the force is applied to the ball at a 45-degree angle from the horizontal, both optimum horizontal distance and height are assured. The ball then has equal forward and upward components of motion. The upward component carries the ball high enough for it to clear the net, and the forward component carries it an adequate distance onto the court. The application of force to the ball at a 45-degree angle depends upon the height at which it is held by the left hand, as well as upon the movement of the right hand. The ball should be hit about midway between center back and bottom. If the ball is contacted from beneath, its flight has too large a vertical component. If it is contacted too high, the horizontal component is too large. These two faults result respectively either in netting the ball, or in causing it to "pop up." If the ball succeeds in crossing the net on a "pop-up," it usually drops so close to the net on the other side that the front line players are able to spike it.

Demonstrate hitting the ball:
1. Midway between center back and bottom;
2. From beneath;
3. Too high.

Have the class note the flight of the ball resulting from each kind of hit. Then have the class work in pairs and take turns practicing serving, attempting to hit the ball at a 45-degree angle. The partner should stand at the side and announce the approximate angle at which each ball is struck. Both partners should note the effect of this angle on the flight of the ball, with reference both to direction and to distance.

Relation of Length of Lever to Speed of Backswing

The right arm is slightly flexed at the elbow to facilitate rapid completion of the backswing. This is based on the principle that "the shorter the lever, the more rapidly it can be moved." If the arm is straight on the backswing, the swing will take longer and the reversal of direction will be more difficult because more momentum is developed. This additional momentum is likely to cause loss of balance.

The instructor should provide himself with two laths or similar sticks. One of these should be sawed in half and the two pieces nailed together at right angles to each other. To demonstrate the relation of the length of the lever to the speed of the swing, both the straight and the bent levers should be suspended by one end, lifted together through approximately a 90-degree arc, and then allowed to swing free. The class should note the difference in the speed of their swings.

Applications of Kinesiologic Principles to the Teaching of New Skills

When the physical education instructor presents a new skill to his class, he will find his teaching more effective if he can point out to his students the similarities between the new skill and a skill with which they are already familiar. For instance, suppose he is introducing his class of young boys to tennis. If they are already thoroughly familiar with softball and have an elementary understanding of the principles which apply to the overhand throw (see p. 399), he should have little trouble in pointing out the way in which most of these principles also apply to a tennis serve. The youngsters will realize then that they are not so much learning a totally new skill, as that they are modifying an old familiar one to fit a new situation. This method of building new skills on old ones is a psychologically sound procedure.

In a similar manner, if the physical education instructor is confronted with the problem of teaching a sport with which he has had little or no experience, he will find it helpful to analyze it kinesiologically and to note the similarity of each technique to a technique with which he is already familiar. As has already been suggested, the value of a classification, such as that found on page 336, is that it enables the instructor to see basic similarities. An awareness of these similarities helps him to recognize the kinesiologic principles which apply to the unfamiliar skill.

Let us assume, for instance, that an instructor is given the assignment of teaching soccer, a sport with which he has had no experience. He has, however, had considerable experience both in playing and in teaching football, baseball and basketball. His first step is to study the rule book and any other books he can find on soccer. If he can observe a game or a film, it will be helpful. His next step should be to identify the various skills involved in soccer, such as running, punting, trapping, and so on. He should then analyze these to see to which category of skill each belongs and to discover the principles which apply to each technique. In the skills involving the giving of impetus he should note whether the emphasis is on distance, speed or direction, and should select the appropriate principles. Whatever the technique under consideration, he should discover how the principles can be applied without violating the limitations of the prescribed form. In field hockey, for instance, the principles of giving impetus to an external object need to be modified when they are applied to a drive in order to conform to the ruling concerning "sticks." This kind of preparation for teaching an unfamiliar sport will give the instructor a basis for confidence which he might not otherwise possess, and will greatly add to the effectiveness of his teaching.

Assignments and Projects

1. Select a team sport, e.g., baseball, field hockey, football, basketball, etc., and list all the types of skills involved. (Refer to the classification of motor skills in Chapter 16.)

2. Make an analysis of the muscular action of a straight backswing in the tennis forehand drive. (The joint action has been given in this chapter.)

3. Analyze the difference, in terms of joint and muscular action, between a forehand drive with a straight backswing and one with a circular backswing.

4. Make a complete anatomic analysis of the following sport techniques:
a. Chest pass in basketball
b. Side-arm pass in basketball
c. Drive in golf
d. Batting a baseball
e. Pitching a baseball
f. Crouching start in sprinting
g. Standing broad jump
h. Breast stroke in swimming

Note: In an analysis of a sport technique it will be extremely helpful if motion pictures can be used, particularly if they have been taken in slow motion.

5. Observe the following paired activities and contrast them both anatomically and mechanically.
a. Serve in tennis and in badminton
b. Shot put and baseball throw for distance
c. Standing broad jump and Sargent vertical jump
d. Running front dive and jackknife dive.
e. Rowing forward and rowing backward

6. Indicate the mechanical similarities and dissimilarities in throwing a baseball, batting a baseball, serving a volley ball, bowling, and a forehand drive in tennis. Note that all involve a ballistic movement of the arms.

7. Select any sport technique, such as those mentioned in questions 4 and 5, and observe several performers executing them. The subjects should represent a wide range in ability. Detect the differences in their form and draw up a list of suggestions for each of the poorer performers.

8. Observe several individuals as they swim and look for the application of the principles listed.

9. Analyze any of the standard strokes, e.g., breast, side, elementary back, back crawl, etc. Either observe or practice the stroke before analyzing it.

10. **Analyze** other forms of aquatic locomotion, e.g., paddling and rowing. Either observe or practice each before analyzing it.

11. Analyze the following common faults kinesiologically and suggest coaching points to avoid or to correct each fault: insufficient body pivot in golf drive, too wide a pull with the arms in the breast stroke, hitting the left arm on the release in archery, a short, choppy stroke in paddling, "catching a crab" in crew rowing.

12. Select a single sport technique and write an elementary explanation of the pertinent kinesiologic principles. This should be worded in such a way that it could be used as teaching material for high school boys or girls.

13. Select a sport with which you have had no experience (e.g., men might select field hockey, and women, football). Identify each skill involved in the sport selected; state its classification (see p. 336); and list several principles which apply to each of the skills identified.

Bibliography

1. Alley. L. E.: An Analysis of Water Resistance and Propulsion in Swimming the Crawl Stroke. Res. Quart. Am. Assn. for Health, Phys. Ed. and Recr., *23:* 253–270, 1952.

2. Armbruster, D. A., Sr., and Morehouse, L. E.: Swimming and Diving. 2d ed. St. Louis, C. V. Mosby Company, 1950.

3. Bowen, W. P., and Stone, H. A.: Applied Anatomy and Kinesiology, 7th ed. Philadelphia, Lea & Febiger, 1953.

4. Chumley, E. M.: Mechanical Analysis of Swan, Back and Front Jack Dives. Unpublished Master's Thesis, University of Wisconsin, 1941.

5. Cureton, T. K.: Mechanics and Kinesiology of Swimming. Res. Quart. Am. Assn. for Health, Phys. Ed. and Recr., *1:* 3–24, 1930.

6. Daughtrey, G.: The Effects of Kinesiological Teaching on the Performance of Junior High School Boys. Res. Quart. Am. Assn. for Health, Phys. Ed. and Recr., *16:* 26–33, 1945.

7. Driver, H. I.: Tennis for Teachers. 2d ed. Philadelphia, W. B. Saunders Company, 1941.

8. Edgerton, H. E., and Killan, J. R.: Flash! 2d ed. Boston, Charles T. Branford, 1954.

9. Groves, W. H.: Mechanical Analysis of Diving. Res. Quart. Am. Assn. for Health, Phys. Ed. and Recr., *21:* 132–144, 1950.

10. Hawley, G.: An Anatomical Analysis of Sports. New York, A. S. Barnes Co., 1940.

11. Hickman, C. N., et al.: Archery, the Technical Side. Milwaukee, North American Press, 1947.

12. Huelster, L. J.: Learning to Analyze Performance. J. Health and Phys. Ed., *10:* 84, 120–121, 1939.

13. Lafler, J.: A Mechanical Analysis of Diving Techniques. Unpublished Master's Thesis, State University of Iowa, 1943.

14. Lanoue, F.: Analysis of the Basic Factors Involved in Fancy Diving. Res. Quart. Am. Assn. for Health, Phys. Ed. and Recr., *11:* 102–109, 1940.

15. McAuley, J. E.: Application of Mechanical Principles to Methods of Teaching Selected Sports Techniques. Unpublished Master's 350 Study, Wellesley College, 1950.

16. Meyer, H. M., and Schwartz, M. M.: Team Sports for Girls and Women. 3rd ed. Philadelphia, W. B. Saunders Company, 1957.

17. Morehouse, L. E., and Cooper, J. M.: Kinesiology. St. Louis, C. V. Mosby Company, 1950.

18. Powell, E.: Kinesiology for Students and Teachers of Physical Education. The Foil (The Semi-annual Publication of Delta Psi Kappa), 39–46, 1942.

19. Scott, M. G.: Analysis of Human Motion. New York, F. S. Crofts, 1945.
20. Sinclair, C.: The Body at Work in the Water: A Study in the Kinesiology and Mechanics of Swimming. Beach and Pool, *23:* Numbers 9, 10 and 11, 1949.
21. Slater-Hammel, A. T.: Action Current Study of Contraction-Movement Relationships in Golf Stroke. Res. Quart. Am. Assn. for Health, Phys. Ed. and Recr., *19:* 164–177, 1948.
22. Vollmer, L. T.: Kinesiological Analysis of Common Faults in Selected Activities. Unpublished Master's 350 Study, Wellesley College, 1951.
23. Wild, M. R.: The Behavior Pattern of Throwing and Some Observations Concerning Its Course of Development in Children. Res. Quart. Am. Assn. for Health and Phys. Ed., *9:* 20–24, 1938.

Recommended Readings

Huelster, L. J.: Learning to Analyze Performance. (See 12 above.)
Morehouse, L. E., and Cooper, J. M.: Kinesiology. (See 17 above.)

25 · The Selection and Evaluation of Exercises for Conditioning and Corrective Purposes

ALTHOUGH THE USE of exercises for corrective and conditioning purposes goes back many centuries, Per Henrik Ling, of the nineteenth century, was the father of modern corrective physical education. Medical gymnastics, as they were called in his day, were given a place of equal importance with educational and military gymnastics at the Royal Central Institute of Gymnastics in Stockholm which Ling directed for a quarter of a century.

Ling put particular emphasis on the remedial aspects of exercise, and he devised many exercises for increasing strength and flexibility and for correcting postural defects. The principles which he professed are unsurpassed even today. He believed that gymnastics were as important for the weak as for the strong, that exercises should be prescribed for individuals, rather than for groups, and that those who taught them should know the purpose and effect of each exercise.

Conditioning exercises constitute an important part of a physical fitness program. They are also valuable for increasing the strength of specific muscle groups and the flexibility of specific joints, as an aid to better posture and to greater skill in sports and the dance. A kinesiology text such as this cannot include an exhaustive discussion of the special uses of exercises. What it can and should do, however, is to serve as an introduction to this specialized field of study. It is the purpose of this chapter to demonstrate some applications of kinesiology to conditioning exercises and posture correction.

In physical education even the nonspecialist is frequently confronted with exercise problems such as the following: A member of the swimming team wants an exercise to increase the range of motion in the ankle joints; a student whose general physical condition is poor wants a systematic plan for building himself up within a few weeks in order to enter competitive sports; a man who has boxed a great deal decides to go out for tennis and finds that he is handicapped by the lack of flexibility in his shoulders; a girl trying out for the swimming club is troubled by her inability to lift herself out of the deep end of the pool onto the deck; another girl wants to improve her posture because she received a grade of D at the time of her physical examination; and another complains of pain in her arches and says her doctor wants her to do foot exercises. Every physical educator should possess the necessary qualifications for handling problems like these. These qualifications include a thorough foundation in anatomy, physiology and kinesiology, an understanding of hereditary and environmental influences on the musculoskeletal structure, and the ability to analyze and evaluate exercises. An understanding of the purpose and effect of every exercise is no less important today than it was in the days of Ling.

Equipped with these qualifications, the physical educator is prepared to analyze the problem in question and to select the appropriate exercises. In the case of the boxer, for instance, he will realize that the pectorals have been overdeveloped and shortened, owing to the nature of the posture and movements required by the activity. And in the case of the girl who cannot lift herself up onto the deck, he knows that exercises to strengthen the triceps, lower pectoralis, latissimus dorsi and teres major are indicated.

In the same way the physical educator who is well trained in kinesiology is able to analyze and evaluate exercises which are brought to his attention, whether these exercises are described in standard texts on corrective exercise, found in popular magazines and newspapers, or seen on television. By studying the pictures, or noting the description, he can analyze the exercise and tell whether or not it is a desirable one for accomplishing the stated purpose. He can also tell whether the exercise is suitable for the inexperienced performer, a performer of moderate experience and ability, or an advanced performer. Because of his familiarity with the normal range of motion in the various joints, he knows whether the exercise is likely to put a strain on any of the ligaments. Furthermore, he is so familiar with the action of the joints and muscles that he almost unconsciously analyzes an exercise every time he sees it performed and knows instantly whether or not it has any undesirable features. He is also so familiar with the patterns of movement common to the human body, particularly the untrained body, that he is able to foresee the ways in which the average individual will react. He knows whether the exercise will tend to produce a forward head, an increased lumbar curve and pelvic tilt, or hyperextended knees. He knows whether it will tend to cause excessive tension or breath-holding. The kinesiologist is so familiar with the mechanical aspects of human motion that he knows immediately whether or not there are any mechanical problems involved in the exercise, such as problems of balance, leverage or momentum.

The physical educator who has thus developed the ability to analyze individual needs, to select exercises for specific purposes, and to evaluate these exercises in terms of their effect on the individual will have become what Huelster aptly calls a "practical kinesiologist."[7] The following questions are suggested to the student as an aid in developing these abilities. For each exercise that he is considering he should attempt to answer these questions:

1. What is its purpose?
2. Does it accomplish the purpose claimed for it?
3. Does it violate any principles of good body mechanics?
4. What is the chief joint and muscular action involved in it?
5. What is its status regarding intensity and difficulty? (Is it suitable for a beginner, a moderately experienced performer, or an advanced performer?)
6. Are there any elements of danger, injury or strain against which precautions should be taken?
7. Is it likely to call forth any undesirable or harmful responses against which the performer should be on his guard?
8. If the exercise is a difficult one, what preliminary exercise would serve to prepare the performer for it?

In order to illustrate the evaluation of exercises for specific purposes a few sample conditions and exercises have been selected for analysis. They represent the areas of general conditioning, specific strengthening and posture correction.

Conditioning

Squat-Thrust and Dip

The squat-thrust, both with and without the dip, is commonly included among conditioning exercises.[16] Without the dip, it is known as the Burpee test for agility.[11] The analysis presented below follows the outline found on page 337.

Description

1. Starting from an erect standing position, the subject drops to a squat with the knees separated, the arms between the knees, and the hands on the floor.

2. With a jump, he thrusts the legs back to a front-leaning-rest position, the weight resting on the hands and toes and the body in a straight line from head to heels.

3. Keeping the body straight, he bends his elbows, lowering his body until his chest nearly touches the floor.

4. He pushes up to the front-leaning-rest position.

5. With a jump, he returns to a squat position.

6. He rises to an erect standing position.

Purpose

1. To strengthen the "pushing muscles" of the arms and shoulder girdle; also the abdominal muscles.

2. To improve agility and coordination.

3. To develop endurance.

Type of Movement

1. Essentially angular. The linear movement of the feet in the thrust and return is accomplished by means of angular movement of the hips and knees.

2. Slow (i.e., moving fixation): Steps 1, 3, 4 and 6.

3. Ballistic: Steps 2 and 5. The thrust is terminated by anatomic

Figure 218. The squat-thrust and dip exercise: *A,* The squat; *B,* the thrust; *C,* the dip.

limitation, and the return movement is terminated by the momentary contraction of antagonistic muscles.

Skill Classification. Moving one's own body when it is supported and receiving the impetus of one's own body.

Anatomic Analysis. This analysis may be as comprehensive or as brief as the kinesiologist wishes. The important requirement is that it should fit the needs of the situation. The present analysis is a very detailed one.

1. *The Squat* (Fig. 218, *A*). Flexion at the hips, knees and ankles, produced by the force of gravity and controlled mainly by the extensor muscles

   Hips
   > Flexion in position of outward rotation: Adductor magnus and gluteus maximus in eccentric contraction

   Knees
   > Flexion: Quadriceps femoris in eccentric contraction

   Ankles
   > Dorsiflexion: Gastrocnemius, soleus, tibialis posterior, peroneus longus and brevis in eccentric contraction

   Shoulder joints
   > Flexion (until hands are placed on floor): Pectoralis major, anterior deltoid and coracobrachialis

   > Inward rotation: Subscapularis, pectoralis major and teres major

   Shoulder girdle
   > Slight abduction of scapulae: Serratus anterior

   Elbows: Extension: triceps and anconeus, especially after weight is put on hands

   Wrists
   > Hyperextension as hands are placed on floor: Extensor carpi radialis longus and brevis and extensor carpi ulnaris until weight is on hands

   Spine
   > Slight flexion of thoracic and lumbar spine: Spinal extensors in eccentric contraction until weight is on hands

2. *The Jump and Thrust* (Fig. 218, *B*). A quick extension of the spine and lower extremities as the hands momentarily support the weight

   Hips
   > Extension (following brief flexion): Gluteus maximus, hamstrings and adductor magnus

   > Adduction: Adductor magnus, longus and brevis

   Knees
   > Extension (following brief flexion): Tibialis posterior, peroneus longus and brevis, gastrocnemius and soleus

   Ankles
   > Plantar flexion (following brief increase in dorsiflexion): Gastrocnemius, soleus, tibialis posterior, peroneus longus and brevis

   Toes
   > Hyperextension: Extensor hallucis longus and extensor digitorum longus until weight is on toes

   Shoulder joints
   > Increased flexion and maintenance of flexion: Pectoralis major, anterior deltoid and coracobrachialis

   Shoulder girdle
   > Maintenance of abduction: Serratus anterior and pectoralis minor

   > Slight upward rotation: Serratus anterior and second and fourth parts of trapezius

Elbows
Extension: Triceps and anconeus
Wrists
Hyperextension: Flexor carpi ulnaris, flexor carpi radialis, palmaris longus, abductor pollicis longus and flexor digitorum sublimis and profundus, first in eccentric, then in static contraction to prevent further hyperextension
3. *The Dip* (Fig. 218, *C*). Flexion at the elbow joints accompanied by a lowering of the body until it almost touches the floor.
Shoulder joints
Horizontal extension abduction: Pectoralis major, anterior deltoid, coracobrachialis and subscapularis in eccentric contraction
Shoulder girdle
Adduction: Pectoralis minor and serratus anterior in eccentric contraction
Elbows
Flexion: Triceps and anconeus in eccentric contraction
Wrists
Reduction of hyperextension: Extensor carpi radialis longus and brevis and extensor carpi ulnaris in eccentric contraction
Maintenance of straight alignment from head to heels against the pull of gravity
Head and Neck: Cervical extensors in static contraction
Lumbar spine: Rectus abdominis and external and internal obliques in static contraction
Hips: Flexors in static contraction
Knees: Quadriceps in static contraction
Ankles: Plantar flexors in static contraction
Toes: Flexors in static contraction
4. *The Push-up.* Extension at the elbow joints until the body is again in the position shown in Figure 218, *B*.
Shoulder joints
Horizontal flexion adduction: Pectoralis major, anterior deltoid, coracobrachialis and subscapularis
Shoulder girdle
Abduction: Serratus anterior and pectoralis minor
Elbows
Extension: Triceps and anconeus
Wrists
Hyperextension: Extensor carpi radialis longus and brevis and extensor carpi ulnaris
Maintenance of straight alignment from head to heels: Same as above
5. *The Jump to Squat Position*
Hips
Flexion: Hip flexors until weight is on feet
Abduction: Gluteus medius and minimus
Knees
Flexion: Hamstrings
Ankles
Quick, forceful plantar flexion, followed by dorsiflexion: Plantar flexors during push-off; dorsiflexors when feet not bearing weight
Shoulder joints
Maintenance of flexion: Pectoralis major, anterior deltoid and coracobrachialis in static contraction
Shoulder girdle
Maintenance of abduction: Serratus anterior and pectoralis minor in static contraction

Maintenance of upward rotation: Serratus anterior and second and fourth
parts of trapezius in static contraction
Elbows
Maintenance of extension: Triceps and anconeus in static contraction
Wrists
Slight increase in hyperextension: Produced by movement of body as a
whole and maintained by wrist flexors in static contraction
6. *Return to Standing*
Hips, knees, and ankles
The same muscles contract as in (1), but this time in concentric contraction
Shoulder joints, shoulder girdle, elbows and wrists
Relaxation of muscles

Mechanical Analysis.   In this type of activity the mechanical
aspect is less obvious and would seem to be of less importance
than the anatomic aspect.

Principles of Motion

1. A body at rest remains at rest unless acted upon by a force, and a body in
motion remains in motion unless acted upon by a force.
   a. In this case, muscular force overcomes the body's inertia in the second,
fourth, fifth and sixth parts of the exercise. Gravity is the motivating force in
parts 1 and 3, although the movement is controlled by muscular force.
   b. The motion of the body is stopped partly by gravity, partly by muscular
contraction, and partly by the natural limitations of movement due to anatomic
structure.
2. To every action there is an equal and opposite reaction. This is illustrated
by the resistance of the ground to the pressure of the hands and feet.

Principles of Balance

1. Since the center of gravity is lowered in this exercise, the stability of the
body is greater at the end of each movement than it is in the starting position.
2. Since the size of the base of support is greater in parts 2, 3 and 4, the stability
of the body is correspondingly greater.
3. Since stability is greater when the center of gravity is kept over the center
of the base of support, the performer can control his stability, to a certain extent,
by keeping his weight centered over his base of support.

Principles of Posture

1. The posture at the beginning and end of the movement is best when the
body segments are arranged in the position of optimum alignment.
2. Because of the body's horizontal position in parts 2, 3 and 4, gravity exerts
a strong rotatory force on the trunk and lower extremities. This force must be
balanced by strong action of the abdominal muscles and hip flexors if hyperextension in the spine and hips is to be prevented and good alignment maintained.

Common Faults and Their Correction.   The most common
fault is allowing the back to sag in the second, third and fourth
parts for this exercise. A second fault is caused by an "overcorrec-
tion" of the first one, namely, maintaining a flexed position at the
hips in order to prevent a sagging back. The correction of both
these faults lies in strengthening the abdominal muscles and train-

ing them to prevent hyperextension of the lumbar spine when the body is in the extended position.

Safety Precautions. There are none in particular, aside from an adequate period of training involving a progression of "lead-up" exercises before attempting such a strenuous exercise as this. A warm-up is advisable before all exercises requiring maximum strength or flexibility.

Evaluation. This is a good exercise for improving agility and coordination. If repeated sufficiently often, it will strengthen the "pushing muscles" of the arms and shoulder girdle; also the abdominal muscles if hyperextension of the lumbar spine is prevented. It will develop endurance if it is repeated the maximum number of times possible every day for an appreciable number of days.

THE HURDLE PUSH-UP—A CONDITIONING EXERCISE FOR THE DANCE*

Exercises such as the one described and analyzed below are often called dance warm-ups or dance techniques. They are essentially conditioning exercises for the dance.

Description

Starting Position. The subject sits on the floor with the right knee bent, the medial surface of the lower leg and foot in contact with the floor, and the heel in line with the buttocks, about five inches from them. The left leg is in front of the body, the knee bent, with the lateral surface of the leg and foot in contact with the floor. The sole of the left foot is close to, but not touching, the right knee, and the two thighs and the leg form a triangle in front of the trunk. With the legs in this position and the left hand resting on the floor behind the body, the subject sits erect. The right forearm is held vertically in front of the body, palm toward the face, the wrist straight, and the hand at eye level with fingers relaxed.

The Movement. From the above-described starting position the subject puts the weight on the left hand, lifts the hips off the floor, arches the back and drops the head backward, and at the same time extends the right arm over the head. This movement of the body causes the left leg to roll onto its anterior surface, and the knee to extend slightly. At the completion of the movement the hips are raised and the spine arched, while the weight of the body is supported by the two legs and the left arm.

The Recovery. The hips are gradually lowered until the buttocks rest on the floor and the upper trunk is rounded. The left elbow bends slightly, and the right arm is lowered to the side of the body with the elbow bent and the fingers relaxed.

* The author is indebted to Miss Gwen M. Stose for permission to use this analysis.

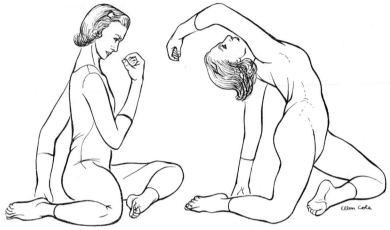

Figure 219.   The hurdle push-up.

Purpose of Exercise
1. To stretch the hip adductors
2. To strengthen the spinal extensors
3. To provide a technique for use in dance compositions

Type of Movement.   This is a slow (non-ballistic), angular type of movement.

Skill Classification.   The exercise belongs in the category of moving one's own body when it is supported on a solid surface. It is non-locomotor in the sense that the areas of support remain relatively constant.

Mechanical Aspect.   As is true of most exercises not involving the use of apparatus, the mechanical aspect of this technique plays a less conspicuous part than the anatomic. Newton's first and third laws of motion and the principles of balance are the main ones that apply. Since the center of gravity remains low throughout this exercise, and the base of support relatively broad, there is no particular balance problem to be considered.

Anatomic Analysis of the Movement.   (The analyses of the starting position and of the recovery are not given.)

    Knees
      Right
        Partial extension: Quadriceps femoris
      Left
        Anterior aspect is rolled onto floor passively as result of hip action
    Hips (both)
        Complete extension; maintenance of abduction and outward rotation:
          Gluteus maximus, adductor magnus, and possibly the hamstrings
    Pelvis
        In position of increased tilt at end of movement due to extension of hips
        and hyperextension of lumbar spine

Spine
  Thoracic and lumbar
    Hyperextension: Sacrospinalis, semispinalis and deep posterior spinal muscles
    Maintenance of rotation and lateral flexion to the left (as in starting position)
  Cervical
    Hyperextension: Sternocleidomastoid, longus capitis and colli, rectus capitis anterior and lateralis, three scaleni and hyoid muscles, in eccentric contraction
    Rotation to left: Right sternocleidomastoid
Shoulder girdle
  Right
    Upward rotation: Lower serratus anterior and upper and lower trapezius
  Left
    Little if any movement, but strong stabilization
Shoulder joints
  Right
    Increased flexion: Anterior deltoid, coracobrachialis and pectoralis major
    Maintenance of outward rotation and slight horizontal flexion-adduction: Subscapularis, infraspinatus and teres minor, in addition to above muscles
  Left
    Increased hyperextension: Posterior deltoid, latissimus and teres major
Elbows
  Right
    Extension: Triceps and anconeus
  Left
    Strong extension: Triceps and anconeus
Radioulnar joints
  Right
    Maintenance of supination: Supinator
  Left
    No action
Wrists
  Right
    Slight hyperextension: Flexor carpi ulnaris and radialis, and palmaris longus to prevent excessive hyperextension by pull of gravity
  Left
    Increased hyperextension: Wrist flexors to support weight of body without increasing hyperextension excessively

Common Faults and Their Correction

Faults.   1. Drawing the forward leg too close to the trunk makes it impossible to roll properly onto the anterior surface of the leg.

2. Placing the hand too far behind the body causes hyperextension of the spine in the starting position and makes it extremely difficult to execute the movement.

3. Incomplete elevation of the hips, i.e., pelvis.

4. Failure to drop the head backward.

Prevention and Correction.   These are accomplished mainly by a good presentation of the exercise, i.e., an accurate demonstration accompanied by a clear description, and vigilance in watching the performers. The technique is a difficult one to teach because the subject cannot see what he is doing. The instructor must be alert to note every detail of the student's execution of the exercise and must endeavor to develop in him a kinesthetic sense of the correct position.

Precautions for Avoiding Strain and Injury.   Since improper execution of the exercise is likely to cause muscular strain, the instructor should make sure that the necessary strength has been developed before the technique is attempted. This requires familiarity with the ability of each member of the class, as well as a good progression of preparatory exercises.

Evaluation.   The anatomic analysis shows that, when done correctly, this exercise accomplishes the first two of the purposes stated at the outset, namely, strengthening the spinal extensors and stretching the hip adductors. Furthermore, it is a good exercise for correcting a forward head and round shoulders. So far as its usefulness in dance composition is concerned, dance instructors and choreographers are in a better position to judge than are kinesiologists.

STRENGTHENING THE ABDOMINAL MUSCLES

Because of the widespread interest in abdominal exercises and because of some common misconceptions about them, two exercises are analyzed in this section, one which observes kinesiologic principles and one which, as usually performed, disregards them. Four principles for abdominal exercises are suggested below.

1. The criterion for an abdominal exercise performed in the supine position is the performer's ability to prevent the tilting of the pelvis and the hyperextension of the lumbar spine. If the pelvic tilt and lumbar curve increase, it would seem to indicate the failure of the abdominal muscles to stabilize the pelvis and spine against the pull of the iliopsoas. Since the task is too great for them, there is danger of straining them.

2. An objective in building a strong abdominal wall is to strengthen all four abdominal muscles: rectus abdominis, external oblique, internal oblique and transversalis. To do this successfully requires a knowledge of the exercises in which these muscles participate and of the relative intensity of their action.

3. It seems reasonable to assume that a protruding abdomen indicates that the abdominal muscles have been stretched. It would seem to be a function of abdominal exercises, therefore, to shorten, as well as to strengthen, these muscles.

4. Exercises which involve the abdominal muscles as prime movers are thought by some kinesiologists to be more effective for

strengthening them than are exercises in which they merely serve as stabilizers. There is no objective evidence of this, however.

Walters and Partridge have recently conducted a series of electromyographic studies of abdominal exercises.[12, 19] Their findings are pertinent. They found that all portions of the rectus abdominis and external oblique were strongly activated in both the trunk curl and the pelvic tuck, performed from the supine, straight-leg position. An exercise in which the internal oblique was strongly activated was double knee rolling from side to side from the supine position with the knees drawn up. The internal oblique, along with the rectus abdominis and the anterior and middle fibers of the external oblique, was also activated in the "reverse curl," an exercise performed from the supine position in which both knees are lifted toward the chest until the buttocks are raised from the floor.

In all forms of the sit-up exercise from the hook-lying position it was found that the hip flexors played a greater part when the feet were held down. The investigators concluded from their experiments that the sit-up type of exercise, including the trunk curl and the "V" sit-up (raising trunk and legs simultaneously from the supine position), was one of the most effective types of exercise for all the abdominal muscles.

ABDOMINAL EXERCISE: THE CURL

Description.   The subject lies on the back with the hands resting on the front of the thighs, the elbows straight. He pulls the chin in, raises the head, shoulders and upper back off the floor in sequence, letting the hands slide down the thighs. The return is done by "uncurling," i.e., a reversal of the original movement. Beginners may use the arms for partial support in the return movement.

Purpose.   To strengthen the abdominal muscles, particularly the rectus abdominis and external oblique.

Type of Movement.   This is essentially an angular movement, although the hands move linearly. It is also a slow movement, hence not ballistic.

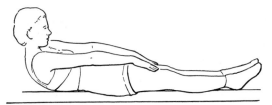

Figure 220.   The curl.

Skill Classification. Moving one's own body when it is supported.

Anatomic Analysis
Flexion of head and neck
  Sternocleidomastoid
  Longus colli and capitis
  Rectus capitis anterior major and minor
  Rectus capitis lateralis
  Infrahyoids and suprahyoids
  Three scaleni
Flexion of thoracic spine (and possibly lumbar)
  Rectus abdominis
  External and internal obliques (external more than internal)
  Stabilization of pelvis and possibly slight hip flexion
  Tensor fasciae latae
  Sartorius
  Pectineus
  Rectus femoris
  Iliopsoas—possibly
  The return movement is performed by the eccentric contraction of the same muscles which flexed the head and spine. The hip flexors continue to stabilize the pelvis. The arm movement is of no consequence in either part of the exercise.

Mechanical Analysis. Since the body is in an extremely stable position, there are no balance problems.

The laws of inertia and reaction apply, just as they do to any movements in which the body, having a firm support, changes its position.

Common Faults and Their Correction. Beginners may try to come up quickly, using momentum rather than gradual muscular contraction. This nullifies the value of the exercise. Unless care is taken to see that the arms are in the right position, the performer may attempt to push off with the elbows. The only way to avoid these faults is by vigilance.

Safety Precautions. An adequate period of training and a preparatory warm-up.

Evaluation. According to the first of the four principles stated earlier, an exercise performed in the supine position should not necessitate hyperextension of the lumbar spine. The average person, performing the curl as described, is not likely to commit this fault. For a weaker person the exercise can be modified. It can be done in the bent knee position; the legs can be held down; or a slight pull may be provided. On the other hand, the exercise can be made more strenuous by gradually raising the position of the arms or by performing the movement against resistance.

The electromyographic studies by Walters and Partridge have shown that the rectus abdominis and external oblique are active in the curl. Doubtless the transversalis would participate if the abdomen were retracted at the beginning of the exercise. Since the internal oblique was found to be only slightly active, this exercise should be supplemented by one which calls for greater activity on its part.

In accordance with the third and fourth principles the abdominal muscles act as prime movers; they are engaged in shortening contraction; and they are not put on a stretch.

ABDOMINAL EXERCISE: SLOW LEG LOWERING (NOT RECOMMENDED)

Description. The subject lies on the back, either with the arms extended on the floor or with the hands clasped under the head. The knees are first brought up to the chest and the legs then extended vertically upward. From this position the legs are slowly lowered to the ground with the knees kept in a position of complete extension (Fig. 221).

Purpose. To strengthen the abdominal muscles.

Type of Movement. Angular.

Skill Classification. Moving one's own body when it is supported.

Anatomic Analysis of the essential part of the exercise, i.e., the leg lowering:

> Extension of the thighs at the hip joints, performed slowly and with resistance to the pull of gravity
> > Iliopsoas (eccentric contraction)
> > Tensor fasciae latae (eccentric contraction)
> > Pectineus (eccentric contraction)
> > Sartorius (eccentric contraction)
> > Gracilis (eccentric contraction)
> > Rectus femoris (eccentric contraction)
>
> Maintenance of extension of the legs at the knee joints
> > Rectus femoris (eccentric contraction because of the action at the hip joints)
> > Vastus lateralis (static contraction)
> > Vastus intermedius (static contraction)
> > Vastus medialis (static contraction)

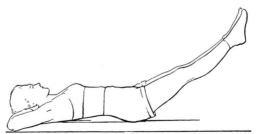

Figure 221. Slow leg lowering. Note the increased curve of the lumbar spine.

Attempted stabilization of pelvis and lumbar spine
Rectus abdominis (static and then eccentric contraction)
External oblique abdominis (static and then eccentric contraction)
    The rectus abdominis and external oblique have the task of stabilizing the pelvis and lumbar spine as the hip flexors control the gradual lowering of the legs. The force needed by the hip flexors to support the weight of the legs increases progressively as the legs approach the floor, and a corresponding increase in force is needed for stabilizing the pelvis. When the feet are about 20 inches from the floor, the back tends to hyperextend, owing (1) to the inability of the abdominal muscles to stabilize the pelvis in this position, and (2) to the reversal of the psoas muscle's usual function at the spine. Because its line of pull, usually anterior to the vertebrae's axes of motion, is now posterior to them, it extends, rather than flexes, the spine (see pp. 76, 77).

Mechanical Analysis:

From the mechanical point of view this exercise is primarily a problem in leverage. The lower extremities act together as twin levers of the third class, that is, levers in which the force point lies between the fulcrum and the weight or resistance point. The fulcrum is situated at the hip joint; the force point at a point representing the average insertion of the hip flexors; and the weight point at the center of gravity of the lower extremities. This is a lever in which both the force and the resistance are applied at angles other than a right angle. Hence, in the case both of the force and of the resistance, only the rotatory component acts on the lever. Since the force of gravity is always directed vertically downward, the more nearly horizontal the lower extremities, the more nearly perpendicular the application of gravitational force to them, therefore the greater the rotatory component of gravitational force. This means that as the lower extremities approach the horizontal position the rotatory effect of the gravitational force becomes relatively greater, and the muscles controlling the movement (i.e., the hip joint flexors) must exert an ever-increasing amount of force.

Applying the familiar equation of balanced levers, $F \times FA = W \times WA$, to this exercise, F is the rotatory component of the resultant of the total muscular force exerted by the hip joint flexors; FA is the perpendicular distance from the hip joint to a line representing the resultant of the total muscular force; W is the rotatory component of the gravitational force acting on the leg; and WA is the perpendicular distance from the hip joint to the limb's line of gravity. Since FA and WA are fixed distances determined by the position of the lower extremity, any increase in W necessitates a corresponding increase in F. Hence the more nearly horizontal the lower extremity, the greater the rotatory component of the gravitational force and, therefore, the greater the muscular force required to balance the lever. Since the hip joint muscles take their origin in part from a movable bony ring (the pelvis), and in part from a movable segmented column (the spine), any increase in their force must be matched by a corresponding increase in the force of the muscles responsible for stabilizing these movable structures. This is the task of the abdominal muscles. The strain put upon these muscles is tremendous as the rotatory component of gravitational force approaches 100 per cent.

Common Faults.   The fault in this exercise is hyperextension of the lumbar spine. The correction, or rather the prevention, is modification of the exercise in order to avoid the tendency to hyperextend. Since the hyperextension is most likely to occur during the last 30 degrees of movement, the modification consists in stopping the movement before this point is reached. This can be done by letting the legs drop, by bending the knees, or by providing an inclined plane or a bench which will support the feet at a height of about 20 inches above the floor.

Safety Precautions. Even when hyperextension of the lumbar spine is prevented, if the subject trembles noticeably while doing this exercise, he should not be allowed to do it. The trembling indicates strain. As in the case of all strenuous or difficult exercises, there should be adequate preparation by means of progressive "lead-up" exercises. Also there should be a warm-up immediately preceding the performance of the exercise.

Evaluation. Since this is a strenuous exercise which involves the danger of strain, only those who already have strong abdominal muscles should be permitted to practice it. Furthermore, it does not even seem to be a particularly effective exercise for strengthening the abdominal muscles. Partridge and Walters experimented with the reverse movement, *double leg raising,* which would seem even more strenuous than slow lowering, and found from their electromyographic recordings that only a small amount of electrical potential was produced. They commented: "Most authorities agree that double leg raising is a strenuous task but contributes little to strengthening of the abdominals. . . . The low voltage recorded from these particular abdominal leads supports the clinical opinion that this procedure can hardly be classified as an abdominal strengthening exercise." Most kinesiologists agree that it is a stronger exercise for the psoas muscle than for the abdominals.

Posture Correction

In this section of the chapter on the selection and evaluation of special exercises it may be well to remind the reader that this unit represents one small sample from the field and that its purpose is merely to demonstrate how kinesiology may be applied to the corrective uses of exercises. No attempt is made to demonstrate its application to all the problems associated with the corrective aspects of posture education. These are far too extensive and complex to be discussed adequately in a general kinesiology text. The appropriate sources for such information are textbooks in corrective physical education, mechanotherapy and kinesiology of corrective exercise. It is well to remember that, in addition to anatomic and mechanical principles, there are physiologic, psychologic and pedagogic principles of posture correction not covered in texts such as this.

To illustrate the application of kinesiology to posture problems, one common fault and two exercises for its correction have been selected for analysis. The postural fault is the condition commonly

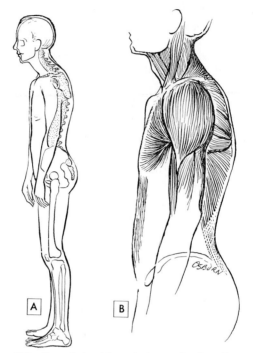

Figure 222. Round shoulders. *A*, Anatomic view; *B*, muscles.

referred to as "round shoulders." It includes a forward head and low chest as well as protracted scapulae.

Anatomic Analysis of "Round Shoulders":

Head and Neck: Hyperextended. The head is tipped back with the chin lifted.

Thoracic Spine: Convexity increased. The increased thoracic curve causes a forward head. Owing to the forward head, the sternocleidomastoid and scaleni muscles, which have their upper attachments on the head and neck, no longer exert their normal tension on the sternum and upper ribs. The thoracic portions of the sacrospinalis and other extensors are elongated because of the increased convexity.

Shoulder Girdle: Abducted and tilted laterally. The rhomboids and middle trapezius are elongated, and the pectoralis minor and serratus anterior shortened. The pectoralis minor fails to exert its usual tension on the third, fourth and fifth ribs. The pectoral fascia is likely to be tight.

Shoulder Joints: Inward rotation. The abduction of the scapulae causes the arms to hang farther forward than usual and to turn slightly inward so that the palms face to the rear. Since the pectoralis major attaches to the upper part of the arm; it no longer exerts its usual tension on the ribs.

Chest: Depressed. The failure of the sternocleidomastoid, scaleni and pectoral muscles to exert their usual lifting effect on the sternum and ribs results in a lowered position of the chest. This in turn lowers the diaphragm, making it impossible for it to travel through as large an excursion as usual during respiration.

This picture does not end here, because compensatory adjustments take place through the entire body. The joints mentioned, however, are the ones most directly concerned in the posture defect of round shoulders. Two typical corrective exercises have been selected for analysis, one which has for its purpose the stretching of the shortened muscles and fascia; and the other, the strengthening and shortening of the muscles which have become unduly stretched.

Passive Chest Lifting

Description. The subject sits on a low stool with the hands behind the neck (not clasped) and the elbows well back. The operator stands behind the subject with the toes of one foot on the edge of the stool and the knee against the subject's spine between the shoulder blades. A small pillow may be used to pad the knee, if desired. The operator grasps the subject's elbows, lifts them slightly and pulls them back with a strong steady pull. He holds the pull for several seconds, then gradually releases the tension. This is repeated from six to fifteen times. It is essential that the pull be applied with gradually increasing intensity, never with a jerk.

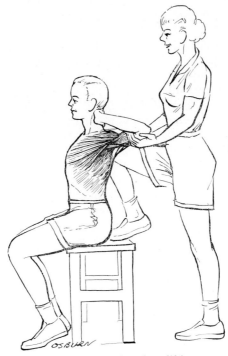

Figure 223. Passive chest lifting.

Care must be taken to see that the subject avoids excessive hollowing of the back by contracting the abdominal muscles.

Purpose.   To stretch the pectoral muscles and fasciae.

Type and Classification.   For the subject: Moving fixation; postural.

Anatomic Analysis.   The upward and backward pull of the arms puts the pectoralis major and minor muscles and the pectoral fascia on a stretch. The tension on the muscles produces a pull on their attachments to the ribs and sternum and results in a lifting of the chest, expansion of the thorax, and hyperextension of the thoracic spine. If the pull is applied with a quick jerk, a strong stretch reflex is likely to occur. This is an involuntary protective contraction of the pectoral muscles. It defeats the purpose of the exercise, since the muscles cannot be stretched when they are contracted. When the pull is applied slowly and gradually, the reflex action is either avoided or overcome. It is also less likely to occur if the subject is told to pinch the shoulder blades together just as the operator is pulling the elbows back. According to the law of reciprocal innervation, the scapular abductors relax when their antagonists, the adductors, are contracting. Experience has shown that an appreciably wider range of motion is possible when the movement is performed slowly and when the subject contracts the scapular adductors (see p. 44).

Mechanical Analysis.   The subject is in a stable position because of the relatively wide base of support and low position of the center of gravity.

The operator uses the subject's arms as levers. They serve as second class levers, the fulcrum being at the shoulder joint, the power point at the elbow, and the resistance point at the upper arm where the pectoralis major inserts. If the operator holds the arms at a point nearer the body, he loses leverage by shortening the length of the force arm, and either has to use more force to compensate, or else be content to give a less forceful stretch.

The stretching of the pectoralis minor is caused by the transmission of the force applied to the arm through the shoulder joint (due to the ligamentous attachments) to the coracoid process of the scapula, to which the pectoralis minor is attached.

It is important to note that if the trunk were free to move, the operator's pull on the elbows would simply result in a backward inclination of the trunk. But because of the resistance afforded by the pressure of his knee against the subject's back, movement at the hip joints is prevented. Likewise, if the spine were completely free to move, the backward pull on the arms would produce hyperextension of the entire spine. The subject himself must prevent this by contracting his abdominal muscles.

Common Faults:

Of Operator:
1. Pulling so suddenly that a strong reflex action of the pectoral muscles results
2. Pulling so hard that the subject hyperextends the lumbar spine rather than endure the discomfort
3. Pulling so gently that no stretch results
4. Placing the knee too low. This encourages hyperextension of the lumbar spine and detracts from the pull on the pectorals.

Of Subject:
1. Failure to contract the abdominal muscles
2. Failure to hold the head in good position
3. Failure to contract the rhomboids and middle trapezius
4. Failure to relax the pectoral muscles.

Evaluation.   This is an excellent pectoral stretching exercise when done correctly. The intensity can be controlled to the required degree.

FRONT LYING, HEAD RAISING WITH PALMS TURNING OUTWARD

Description.   The subject lies face downward with the arms at the sides, palms down. He raises the head from 3 to 6 inches, looking at the floor directly beneath the nose. He should attempt to stretch the top of the head forward, making the body feel as long as possible. As he raises his head, he lifts the hands from the floor, turning the thumbs up and the palms outward. At the same time that he is raising and turning his arms he should pull his shoulder blades together vigorously. After holding the position for at least five seconds he returns to the starting position and relaxes. The exercise should be repeated ten to twenty times.

A more effective but more difficult form of this exercise is to precede the head and arm movement with contraction of the abdominal and gluteal muscles, holding this contraction throughout the movement of the head and arms.

Purpose.   To correct a forward head and round shoulders by strengthening the extensors of the head and spine, the adductors of the scapulae, and the outward rotators of the arms.

Type of Movement.   Angular, both for the spine and for the arms.

Skill Classification.   Moving's one's own body when it is supported.

Anatomic Analysis:

Head and Neck: Holding in extension (but not hyperextension) against the pull of gravity

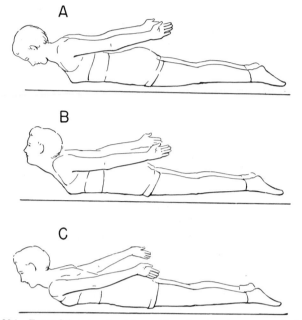

Figure 224. Front lying, head raising with palms turning outward. *A,* Correct form; *B,* incorrect; the head and neck are hyperextended; *C,* incorrect; the arms are rotating inward instead of outward.

> Splenius cervicis and capitis (static contraction)
> Upper portions of sacrospinalis, semispinalis, etc. (static contraction)
> *Thoracic and Lumbar Spine:* Extension and slight hyperextension; maintaining position against the pull of gravity
>> Sacrospinalis (concentric, followed by static contraction)
>> Semispinalis (concentric, followed by static contraction)
>> Multifidus (concentric, followed by static contraction)
>> Rotatores (concentric, followed by static contraction)
> *Shoulder Joints:* Outward rotation and hyperextension
>> Infraspinatus
>> Teres minor
>> Posterior deltoid
>> Latissimus dorsi
>> Teres major
> *Shoulder Girdle:* Adduction and reduction of lateral tilt
>> Rhomboids
>> Middle trapezius
> *Elbows and Forearms:* Extension and supination
>> Triceps
>> Anconeus
>> Supinator
> *Stabilization of Pelvis*
>> Gluteus maximus
>> Hamstrings

Mechanical Analysis. The subject is in a completely stable position because of the large base of support and low position of the center of gravity. There are no mechanical problems evident in this exercise.

Common Faults and Their Correction:

1. Hyperextending the head and neck. This can be prevented by insisting that the subject look at a spot beneath his nose.

2. Lifting the body too high, thereby hyperextending the lumbar spine. This can be prevented by telling the subject to lift his head not more than 3 inches off the floor. (Although he will probably lift his head more than this, it is not likely that he will exceed the 6-inch limit.)

3. Rotating the arms inward instead of outward. This is more likely to occur if the subject is not told to start with the palms down. If he continues to have trouble after the movement of the hands has been carefully explained, he should try turning the arms both ways several times and learn to recognize the kinesthetic "feel" of the adduction and abduction of the shoulder blades. Once he can distinguish these movements, he will know when he has turned his arms the wrong way. He should aim at "pinching the shoulder blades together."

Evaluation. This is one of the best exercises for correcting a forward head and round shoulders when it is done correctly. Unless the subject can be carefully supervised, however, it might be wise not to give it to anyone who has a tendency toward lordosis (hollow back). In such cases the exercise should be done with abdominal and gluteal contraction and the amount of lifting should be carefully regulated.

The exercise is more strenuous than those involving the same movements in a sitting or standing position, because in the horizontal position the movements are performed against the resistance of gravitational force.

POSTURE AND SPORTS

Besides prescribing special corrective exercises such as the two just described, the physical education instructor should guide the student who has posture limitations, in his choice of sports. For instance, a student with round shoulders might well be encouraged to participate in archery, the back crawl and breast stroke in swimming, and exercises on the rings and horizontal bar. But he should be discouraged from boxing or using the crawl stroke excessively because of the abduction of the scapulae and shortening of the pectoral muscles which these activities involve.

Assignments and Projects

1. Find a subject who has an increased lumbar curve and increased pelvic tilt. Analyze his posture, select two or three appropriate exercises, and suggest a sport which might be beneficial, also one which might be harmful to his posture.
2. Do the same for a subject who has weak, relaxed abdominal muscles.
3. Do the same for a subject who has weak lower back muscles.
4. Do the same for a subject who has severely pronated feet.
5. Select from three to ten exercises seen in popular magazines or newspapers, or heard over the radio. Using the outline on page 337, analyze and evaluate these exercises and answer the eight questions on page 454.
6. Observe someone doing a conditioning exercise. Analyze the exercise, using the outline on page 337 as a guide.
7. Originate an exercise for stretching the hamstring muscles which will not tend to accentuate a round upper back.

Bibliography

1. Bowen, W. P., and Stone, H. A.: Applied Anatomy and Kinesiology. 7th ed. Philadelphia, Lea & Febiger, 1953.
2. Drew, L. C., and Kinzly, H. L.: Individual Gymnastics. 5th ed. Philadelphia, Lea & Febiger, 1945.
3. Ewerhardt, F. H., and Riddle, G. F.: Therapeutic Exercise. Philadelphia, Lea & Febiger, 1947.
4. Gardiner, M. D.: The Principles of Exercise Therapy. 2nd ed. New York, Macmillan Company, 1957.
5. Goldthwait, J. E., Brown, L. T., Swaim, L. T., and Kuhns, J. G.: Essentials of Body Mechanics in Health and Disease. 5th ed. Philadelphia, J. B. Lippincott Company, 1952.
6. Hawley, G.: The Kinesiology of Corrective Exercise. 2nd ed. Philadelphia, Lea & Febiger, 1949.
7. Huelster, L. J.: Learning to Analyze Performance. J. Health and Phys. Ed., 10: 84, 120–121, 1939.
8. Kraus, H.: Principles and Practice of Therapeutic Exercises. 2nd ed. Springfield, Ill., Charles C Thomas, 1955.
9. Kiphuth, R. J. H.: How to Be Fit. 2nd ed. New Haven, Yale University Press, 1956.
10. Lee, M., and Wagner, M. M.: Fundamentals of Body Mechanics and Conditioning. Philadelphia, W. B. Saunders Company, 1949.
11. McCloy, C. H.: Tests and Measurements in Health and Physical Education. 2nd ed. New York, F. S. Crofts and Company, 1946. (Burpee test, p. 84.)
12. Partridge, M. J., and Walters, C. E.: Participation of the Abdominal Muscles in Various Movements of the Trunk in Man. Phys. Ther. Rev., 39:791–800, 1959.
13. Phelps, W. M., et al.: The Diagnosis and Treatment of Postural Defects. 2nd ed. Springfield, Ill., Charles C Thomas, 1956.
14. Rathbone, J. L.: Corrective Physical Education. 6th ed. Philadelphia, W. B. Saunders Company, 1959.
15. Stafford, G. T., and Kelly, E. D.: Preventive and Corrective Physical Education. 3rd ed. New York, Ronald Press Company, 1958.
16. Steinhaus, A. H., Hawkins, A. M., Giauque, C. D., and Thomas, E. C.: How to Keep Fit and Like It. Chicago, Consolidated Book Publ., Inc., 1943.
17. Truslow, W.: Body Poise. Baltimore, Williams & Wilkins Company, 1943.
18. U.S. Office of Education Committee on Wartime Physical Fitness for Colleges and Universities. Handbook on Physical Fitness for Students in

Colleges and Universities. Washington, D.C., U.S. Govt. Printing Office, 1945.

19. Walters, C. E., and Partridge, M. J.: Electromyographic Study of the Differential Action of the Abdominal Muscles During Exercise. Am. J. Phys. Med., *36:* 259–268, 1957.

20. War Department Field Manual FM 21–20. Physical Training. Washington, D.C., U.S. Govt. Printing Office, 1946.

21. War Department Technical Manual 8–292. Physical Reconditioning. Washington, D.C., U.S. Govt. Printing Office, 1944. (The exercises in this manual were prepared by C. H. McCloy.)

22. Williams, M., and Worthingham, C.: Therapeutic Exercise in Body Alignment and Function. Philadelphia, W. B. Saunders Company, 1957.

26 · Applications of Kinesiology to Physical Therapy and Occupational Therapy

$\mathbf{P}$ERHAPS IN no profession is a thorough knowledge of kinesiology more vitally needed than in the twin professions of physical therapy and occupational therapy. In both fields an accurate knowledge of the structure and function of the joints and muscles, and an appreciation of the mechanics of human motion, are prerequisite to the intelligent selection and use of therapeutic techniques. It is the purpose of this chapter to introduce the prospective physical and occupational therapist to some of the practical uses of kinesiology, and to suggest a few of the specific ways in which his knowledge of this subject may be applied to the techniques of his future profession. This does not pretend to be an authoritative presentation of the techniques of the therapist, or a comprehensive discussion of the kinesiologic principles underlying them. It is intended, rather, to serve as an introduction to this field. It is designed, not so much for the professional student as for the student enrolled in a preprofessional college curriculum. It seeks to give him a preview of the wide variety of kinesiologic applications with which he will later be dealing, and thus to motivate him to build a solid foundation for this aspect of his work.

Kinesiology provides both an anatomic and a mechanical basis for the therapist's choice of techniques and for his method of using them. In fact, the accuracy and effectiveness of the technique used depend to a large degree upon the therapist's grasp of anatomy and biomechanics—the sciences which comprise kinesiology.

The majority of techniques and activities used by physical and occupational therapists fall into one of two major categories, namely, techniques of evaluation and techniques of treatment. The techniques of evaluation include measuring the range of motion in a joint, muscle testing, postural analysis and testing performance in the activities of daily living. The techniques of treatment include massage, stretching tight tissues in order to increase the range of motion in a joint, muscle re-education, therapeutic exercise (including progressive resistance exercise), bandaging and strapping, training in the activities of daily living, occupational activities (crafts, household tasks, and so on) and prevocational activities, such as typing, printing and simple assembly work.

Techniques of Testing

Measuring the Range of Joint Motion.   The measurement of the range of motion in a joint presupposes an understanding of its structure, of the movements of which it is capable, the muscles which produce these movements, the normal range of each movement, the structures which normally limit each movement and the pathologic conditions which commonly restrict normal motion. In addition, the therapist needs to be familiar with the individual variations frequently found in the structure and range of motion of a given joint.

The therapist who has a working knowledge of anatomy and kinesiology learns to view every joint with an "x-ray eye." He understands the interrelationships between various joints, such as the shoulder and shoulder girdle, the elbow and radioulnar joints, and the hip joints and the lumbar spine. In measuring joint motions he is aware of the necessity of preventing motion in one joint in order to get a true picture of the movement in another. For instance, if he desired to measure outward rotation of the humerus, he would not do so in terms of the facing of the palm because he would know that, when the elbow is extended, rotation of the humerus is accompanied by rotation (pronation and supination) of the forearm. Similarly, if he desired to measure abduction of the humerus at the shoulder joint, he would hold the scapula to prevent it from rotating upward. If he simply measured the movement of the arm away from the side of the body, he would have no way of judging the degree to which movement of the scapula might be compensating for restricted motion in the shoulder joint. In like manner, a patient may unwittingly compensate for restricted forward elevation of the arm, i.e., flexion of the humerus, by leaning backward and hyperextending his lumbar spine. If the measurement was made in terms of the angle between the arm and a vertical line, the measurement could scarcely be said to represent the range of motion in the shoulder joint.

A knowledge of reciprocal innervation and inhibition helps the therapist to understand why a patient can achieve a greater range of motion by moving a part actively than by letting the therapist move it for him. The resistance of the antagonist muscles, due to their normal tonus, and the factor of reciprocal inhibition are dramatically illustrated by dorsiflexion of the foot, first performed passively by another person, and then actively by the subject himself.

The various problems which need to be considered in measuring the range of motion have been amply discussed in the literature. References to the methods of measuring joint motion may be found at the end of Chapter 2, as well as at the end of the present chapter.

Manual Muscle Testing.   In order to test muscular strength accurately it is essential that the therapist know the location of each muscle, its attachments and its direction of pull. He should be familiar with its various functions, not only as principal or assistant mover in a movement, but also as neutralizer, stabilizer and even as antagonist. He should know the peculiar characteristics of the two-joint muscles, and should understand the relation of the degree of the muscle's shortening to the amount of force it can exert. He needs to know the optimum position in which the part should be placed for testing, when to, and when not to, use gravity, and when to give assistance and when resistance. He needs to know how to rule out the action of one muscle in order more accurately to test another which has a similar function, and he must be able to recognize when a patient is substituting some other muscle for the one desired. Many of these and other problems are ably discussed by H. O. and F. P. Kendall in their book, "Muscles: Testing and Function."[10]

In an investigation of the way in which muscular forces vary during different phases of the range of motion, Williams and Stutzman measured the amount of force exerted by the elbow flexors in several different positions of the joint. They found, for instance, that when the angle of the elbow joint was 150 degrees (i.e., when the forearm had moved through an arc of 30 degrees from the position of extension), the flexors exerted 53 pounds of force; at a 90-degree angle they exerted 86 pounds of force; and at a 60-degree angle they exerted a force of 61 pounds.[17]

Postural Evaluation.   Skill in judging posture can be acquired only by practice and the constant sharpening of one's powers of observation. There are no fool-proof, rule-of-thumb measurements which will give an accurate and adequate analysis of posture. The measurements used by some examiners are useful for supplementing the subjective examination, but they cannot replace it. Even so-called objective measurements are based on subjective factors such as locating anatomic landmarks. They must be interpreted in the light of the patient's physique, sex, age and nutritional status. Since there is no universal posture norm, the trained examiner must have a mental concept of the posture that he thinks would be normal for the patient in view of age, sex, skeletal structure and occupation. By comparing the image he visualizes with the body he actually sees, and by using some sort of predetermined rating scale, he decides on the amount of deviation shown by the patient in each aspect of posture observed, e.g., total alignment, position of head, depth of spinal curves, comparative height of shoulders, and the like. Many examiners use a plumb line as a guide in judging both anteroposterior and lateral posture. In judging the former, common practice to the contrary, there appears to be little justification for using the plumb line as a precise point of reference for specific anatomic landmarks, such as the lateral malleolus, patella, greater trochanter, acromion process and lobe of the ear. Such an inflexible concept of "good posture" makes no allowance for variations in body build. A more flexible method of using the plumb line is to use it as a general guide for judging the alignment of the weight-bearing segments of the body. If a vertical line is erected at the patient's side from a point in line with the apex of the longitudinal arch (roughly opposite the prominence of the fifth metatarsal head), and if the patient is standing with his weight distributed evenly between his heels and toes, it seems reasonable to expect the major weight-bearing segments of the body, with the exception of the leg below the knee, to be approximately centered behind this line. The leg from the knee down must be excepted, for, since the leg articulates with the posterior part of the foot, it cannot be expected to be vertical when the weight is centered anteroposteriorly over the feet. When the plumb line is used as a guide in judging bilateral symmetry, it is reasonable to accept as the norm exact correspondence between the line and such anterior landmarks as the nose, chin, suprasternal notch and umbilicus; and such posterior landmarks as the spinous processes of the vertebrae and the gluteal cleft. Deviation of these points from a vertical line would suggest an abnormality.

Palpation is frequently used as an aid in evaluating certain aspects of posture, such as relative height of the iliac crests, lateral curvature of the spine, tonus of the abdominal muscles, relative tension of the muscles on the left and right sides of the back, and so forth.

Some attempts have been made, especially by physical educators, to measure and grade posture objectively. This has been done both by means of measurements made directly on the body, and, more frequently, through the medium of posture photographs or silhouettes. These attempts have met with varying degrees of success, but most of them have proved either too time consuming or too expensive to be practical for routine use for large numbers of subjects.

Posture measurements have also been used by orthopedic specialists and by physical therapists. Kraus and Weber used a series of structural and functional measurements in their work with children. The Kendalls, likewise, have used plumb line measurements and manual muscle tests in their posture examinations. It is their belief that muscle testing is as useful for indicating the kind and amount of exercise therapy needed for faulty posture as for paralysis and other pathologic conditions. They emphasize the role of muscular imbalance in postural defects, and hence the need for using muscle testing as a guide to the selection of appropriate exercises.

Activities of Daily Living (A.D.L.) Testing. Testing a patient's ability to perform the basic activities of daily living is now routine procedure in rehabilitation centers. The activities tested are usually classified according to whether or not they are related to locomotion. The following list, based on the tests used at the Institute of Physical Medicine and Rehabilitation of Bellevue Medical Center, is probably typical of those used generally in physical therapy and occupational therapy clinics. It illustrates the wide scope of activities included in A.D.L. testing.

Non-walking activities
    Bed activities
    Hygiene (toilet activities)
    Eating activities
    Dressing and undressing activities
    Hand activities
    Wheelchair activities
    Elevation activities
Walking activities
    Progressing activities
    Gait
    Climbing activities
    Traveling activities

There are many subdivisions under each of these categories. For instance, under hand activities there are twenty-seven items, including such diverse uses of the hand as writing, turning the pages of a book, dialing a telephone number, opening and closing locks, doors, drawers, windows, hooks and safety pins, striking a match and ringing a doorbell.

Although it does not take a person trained in kinesiology to determine the patient's success or failure in the test items, such training is essential for analyzing the reasons for failure, for understanding the treatment prescribed by the doctor, and for suggesting modifications in the method of performing a task in order to make it more consistent with the patient's limited abilities.

Techniques of Treatment

Massage.   In giving a massage for therapeutic purposes it is essential that the masseur have an exact knowledge of the structure and function of the part he is massaging. In the case of a muscle massage he needs to know the location and the direction of the fibers of each muscle to be massaged. In a joint massage he must be able to visualize the structure of the joint and should know the location of the capsule and its reinforcing ligaments. Furthermore he must know the normal range of motion of the joint, also the action of each muscle which acts upon it, in order to give the correct passive, active or resistive movements at the conclusion of the massage.

By applying his knowledge of kinesiology and body mechanics to the use of his own body in giving the massage, the masseur can work more efficiently and with less fatigue than when he disregards this matter. He should see to it that the patient is high enough so that he can stand erect as he works, yet not so high as to make it difficult to use the weight of the arms and body for applying the necessary pressure. When the patient is too high, the operator has to use more muscular effort to exert adequate pressure. When on a bed or table, the patient should be close enough to the edge so that the masseur does not have to reach across unnecessarily. By facing in the direction that his arms are moving the masseur will find that he can save himself considerable muscular effort. For instance, when using stroking (effleurage) on the muscles of the back, if he stands opposite the patient's hips and faces the head, he will be able to shift his weight forward and backward, and thus supplement the push from his arms. This position will also make it easier for him to exert equal pressure with both hands.

Increasing the Range of Motion.   Whether the patient does this himself by means of active stretching exercises, whether he engages in handicrafts that require him to use a joint to the limit of its range, or whether the therapist stretches the tight tissues manually—whatever method of stretching is used—the therapist needs to be thoroughly familiar with the structure and function of the joint in question. He must know not only the degree of limitation of motion, but also what tissues are responsible for the limitation.

He should also know under what conditions the stretch reflex is

likely to defeat his purposes. In the preceding chapter an exercise
for stretching the pectoral muscles was analyzed. It was shown how,
by having the patient cooperate actively in the movement and by
the therapist's taking care to pull the elbows back gradually, the
resistance of the pectorals to stretching could be minimized.

The therapist also needs to be aware of the possibility that the
return movement from a stretching exercise may encourage further
shortening of the tight muscles. For instance, another exercise that
is sometimes used for stretching tight pectorals is for the patient to
lie on his back on a narrow plinth with an iron weight in each hand,
with his arms bent and his hands close to his shoulders. He extends
his arms obliquely sideward, somewhat above shoulder level. In this
position he relaxes his arms and lets the weights pull them toward
the floor. After several seconds he returns his arms to the starting
position. If he should return them by first raising them vertically
before bending them, he would be defeating the purpose of the
exercise, because raising the arms in this position requires concentric contraction of the pectorals. It takes an alert therapist who is
familiar with muscle actions, to see when an exercise is being performed in such a way that the return movement is counteracting
the desired effect.

Muscle Re-education.   The application of theoretic knowledge to practical problems is illustrated by a comparison of the different types of resistance that can be used in progressive resistance
exercises for the quadriceps muscles. Weights can be attached to
the foot, in which case the direction of the resistance force is always
downward, and the angle of application progressively increases from
zero to 90 degrees as the knee is extended and the leg raised from
a vertical to a horizontal position. If a pulley-weight rope is attached
to the ankle in such a way that it pulls backward at 90 degrees when
the leg is hanging vertically downward, the angle will decrease progressively as the leg is raised to the horizontal. A third method of
providing resistance is by the use of a mechanism which moves with
the leg in such a way that the resistance, applied to the ankle, remains at right angles to the leg throughout the movement.

An interesting problem for the student to solve for any of the
foregoing methods of applying resistance is to determine mathematically each of the following values for any stated resistance and
for any degree of joint movement: (a) the rotatory component of
the resistance; (b) the rotatory component of the muscular force;
(c) the total muscular force needed to balance the resistance. An
example of such a problem is presented in the Supplementary
Material at the end of this chapter.

Bandaging and Strapping.*   The physical therapist should be

* The techniques described here are those advocated by Dr. A. R. MacAusland
of Boston, Mass.

able to put on a good bandage or strapping. This requires an understanding of anatomy, as well as a knowledge of bandaging techniques. For instance, in applying a cotton elastic bandage or a strapping to the foot and ankle it is necessary to differentiate between a sprained ankle and a "fallen" arch. Whereas the site of a sprain is usually at the lateral side of the ankle or foot, the site of the difficulty associated with a strained arch is usually on the medial and inferior aspects of the foot. The sprained ankle should be supported in a position that will favor the injured tissues, giving them a chance to repair themselves, and that will permit locomotion without risk of further injury. The bandage should therefore hold the ankle in a right-angle position with a slight tendency toward eversion. This is accomplished by applying the bandage in such a way that it comes from under the instep toward the lateral border of the foot, with tension exerted on it as it runs from here diagonally across the top of the foot toward the medial side of the ankle.

In a fallen arch, on the contrary, the foot should be held in a position of slight inversion or supination. With the ankle held at right angles, the bandage should be applied to the foot in such a way that it comes from under the instep toward the *medial border* of the foot, with tension exerted on it as it runs from here diagonally across the top of the foot toward the lateral side of the ankle.

In applying a strapping for either a sprained ankle or a strained arch it is important that the foot be maintained in a position of 90 degrees dorsiflexion. A person with a knowledge of kinesiology would know that the patient could more easily hold his foot in this position during the strapping if he kept his knee slightly bent. Furthermore, he would understand the reason for this: namely, that the gastrocnemius is on a stretch when the knee is straight and the ankle dorsiflexed, and that this stretch is relieved when the reverse position of either of the joints is assumed.

When strapping the metatarsal arch, care should be taken to start the strapping back far enough so as not to bind the toes together. It is also important not to pull the tape tight as it passes over a bony prominence. Great discomfort can be caused if the tape is pulled too tightly over the base of the fifth metatarsal bone.

A.D.L. Training. The types of activities included in this training program have already been listed in the discussion of A.D.L. testing. This is a challenging area for the therapist because he frequently must invent special gadgets, or adapt regulation implements, in order to make it possible for a patient to perform ordinary tasks, such as brushing his teeth, fastening and unfastening clothing, opening and closing doors, feeding himself, and in general to achieve as much independence as possible. It takes a good understanding of kinesiology, as well as a spark of inventiveness, for a therapist to see how the patient's environment may be modified and how he can learn to substitute movements for the ones that are no longer possible.

As preparation for gait training and for the use of wheel chairs or crutches, it may be necessary for the therapist to teach the patient exercises for strengthening certain muscle groups. Most women patients need to spend considerable time strengthening their triceps muscles before they can be taught to get in and out of wheel chairs or to use crutches.

Occupational and Prevocational Activities. Occupational therapy techniques, as used in the treatment of orthopedic conditions, are functional rather than diversional. They are a specific form of treatment—"treatment by means of participation in occupations or activities devised to attack specific problems resulting from disease or injury" (Willard and Spackman, p. 10). Among the physical problems for which occupational therapy is frequently prescribed are specific muscle weaknesses, such as that resulting from anterior poliomyelitis; uncoordinated neuromuscular behavior, such as that resulting from cerebral palsy; limitation of joint motion, such as that resulting from injury and arthritis; and general debility, such as that resulting from a prolonged stay in bed. In these cases, activities are chosen with care to increase the motion of joints, to improve muscular strength, or to develop specific coordinations, according to the needs of each case. The activities must meet certain requirements in order to be useful as therapeutic agents. They must be adaptable to the patient's needs and limitations and to the position he must maintain; they must also be adaptable to gradation in order that the patient may follow a program of gradually increasing difficulty and intensity; they must be safe; and finally, they must be appealing and creatively stimulating to the patient. Activities differ with respect to these criteria. Some meet one requirement better than another. Among the activities which have been found to meet the greatest number of qualifications, particularly for the treatment of physical disabilities, are clay modeling, drawing, leather work, metal work, woodworking, weaving, basketry, cord knotting, and needlework.

Occupational therapy should not be thought of as a substitute for physical therapy; it is rather a supplement to it. Physical therapy is frequently given earlier in the treatment of certain conditions; in others the two forms of treatment may be given concurrently. Occasionally occupational therapy may be given first.

Since activities are prescribed for the purpose of fulfilling specific purposes, and since they frequently must be adapted to the patient's limitations of joint and muscle function, it is imperative that the occupational therapist have thorough training in anatomy, physiology and kinesiology. In spite of the fact that it is the physician's responsibility to prescribe the treatment, he frequently leaves it to the occupational therapist to select the specific activity. Furthermore, he rarely supervises the treatment. Hence it is the occupational therapist's responsibility to see that the patient's needs are met and that all necessary precautions are taken to protect him from harm. The occupational therapist must be familiar with the kinesiologic demands of each activity. He should analyze every activity he uses, both from the point of view of the joint and muscular action involved and with reference to its qualifications as a therapeutic agent.

In their book, "Principles of Occupational Therapy," Willard and Spackman give detailed analyses of two crafts frequently used for therapeutic purposes, namely, woodworking and braid weaving.[16] They analyze the former from the point of view of using it as a treatment for limitation of joint motion, and the latter as treatment for flaccid paralysis. Each analysis consists of two parts, General Considerations, and Specific Exercise Involved. The General Considerations serve as a means of evaluating the activity with reference to its use as a treatment for physical disabilities. These considerations consist of a few pertinent questions and their answers. The second section, Specific Exercise Involved, presents a detailed joint and muscle analysis for each phase of the activity. As an illustration of this type of analysis of activities used in "Occupational Therapy," a portion of Willard and Spackman's analysis of braid weaving is reproduced. Even this partial quotation will doubtless serve to convince the student of the need for acquiring an accurate and thorough knowledge of kinesiology.

AN ANALYSIS OF BRAID WEAVING FOR THE TREATMENT OF PATIENTS WITH FLACCID
PARALYSIS*

GENERAL CONSIDERATIONS

Does the activity have a majority of the required characteristics?
1. Action rather than position? ....Yes
2. Repetition? ....Yes
3. Adaptability to grading
   Time? ....Yes
   Range of motion? ....Yes
   Resistance? .... Only in part. Many of the actions in the classification of motions used "against gravity and resistance" from tools or equipment cannot be graded
   Coordination? ....Yes
   Specific Exercise Involved
Elbow
   Flexion: Pulling weft through. May be with gravity eliminated or against gravity.

* From Willard and Spackman: Principles of Occupational Therapy. J. B. Lippincott Company, 1947, pages 247, 250 and 251.

Position (1): Gravity eliminated: shoulder abducted to 90° and supported in that position either by table or sling. Shuttle is pulled through, flexing elbow in position desired, either pronation, supination, or neutral position.

Position (2): Against gravity: Frame vertical or horizontal, arm held against side, elbow is flexed in pulling through weft thread and is allowed to return to side slowly.

Localization: Return motion, with gravity eliminated. Eccentric contraction against gravity.

Muscles: Biceps brachii, brachialis, brachioradialis and pronator radii teres. With the forearm supinated the elbow is flexed mainly by the biceps brachii and the brachialis. With the forearm in neutral position all four muscles act. With the forearm pronated the elbow is flexed by the pronator radii teres and the brachioradialis assisted on resistance by the biceps.

Extension: Pulling weft through. Gravity eliminated.

Position: Weft is pulled through, extending elbow out to the side with shoulder abducted to nearly 90°. Sling support may be used if necessary. If the thread is pulled through normally down to the side it will result in eccentric contraction of the biceps brachii without using the triceps.

Localization: Return motion.

Muscles: Triceps and anconeus.

In addition to the use of weaving, woodwork and other crafts for therapeutic purposes, modified household tasks and simple vocational activities, such as typing, using a printing press and elementary assembly work, are taught as a means of facilitating the patient's return to home and to the world of work. In many cases experimenting with prevocational activities in the clinic or rehabilitation center serves to guide the patient in the choice of a new vocation when he can no longer engage in the old one. This aspect of rehabilitation helps to bridge the gap between therapy and the resumption of duties as a homemaker or a wage earner. It may be the occupational therapist's task to show a woman who is confined to crutches or a wheel chair how she can prepare a meal, clean house, iron clothes and perform the many duties of housekeeping, or to teach a man with a new prosthesis how to master simple skills of business and industry. This will frequently necessitate modifications of both equipment and method, and will challenge the resourcefulness of the therapist.

This chapter has attempted to show a number of the ways in which physical and occupational therapists apply their knowledge of kinesiology to the techniques of their respective professions. Besides learning the applications already in use, they should be alert to new suggestions that appear in the literature or are demonstrated at workshops. Advances and modifications are being made constantly in therapeutic methods as new information is gained through research. New principles are discovered and new applications made of old, familiar principles. Unfortunately, there is too often a lag between the discovery of theoretic knowledge and its application to practical situations. For instance, the overload principle of increasing muscular strength was known to physiologists for a long time before it was applied to therapeutic procedure in the form of progressive resistance exercise. There may well be other familiar principles of anatomy, physiology or mechanics waiting for someone with insight to discover their potentialities in therapeutic practice. This book can perform no greater service than that of demonstrating to the student-therapist the importance of acquiring a sound foundation in the basic sciences, and of stimulating him to be alert to opportunities for making new applications of his theoretic knowledge to the clinical problems with which he is confronted.

Supplementary Material

Progressive resistance exercises present some interesting problems which demonstrate nicely the effect that the direction and point of application of the resistance have on the muscular force needed to balance an anatomic lever. The problems* presented here and in No. 11 of the Laboratory Exercises provide a basis for comparing objectively two methods of giving resistance to leg extension, both of which are performed with the subject sitting on a table with his thighs fully supported and his legs hanging down over the edge of the table. In one method a weight is attached to the under side of the foot near its center. In the other a pulley-weight is adjusted in such a way that the rope, attached to the ankle by means of a cuff, pulls backward at right angles to the leg when the latter is hanging vertically downward. This angle, of course, changes as the leg moves through extension. For purposes of simplification in solving the following pulley-weight problem it may be assumed that the pulley is located directly behind the ankle when the leg is in the starting position.

Problem: For each of the three positions of the leg, representing respectively, 20 degrees, 60 degrees and 90 degrees of extension from the starting position (leg hanging vertically from edge of table), compute the three values listed below. (Note: If the pulley is located beneath the center of the knee joint, the resistance angles in the three positions will be 80 degrees, 60 degrees and 45 degrees, respectively.)

    a. The total muscular force necessary to balance the resistance.
    b. The rotatory component of the muscular force.
    c. The rotatory component of the resistance.

Data

    1. The angle between the long axis of the leg and a vertical line dropped from the center of the knee joint is 20 degrees.
    2. The weight is 30 pounds.
    3. It may be assumed that the pull of the quadriceps is applied to the front of the leg 4 inches below the center of the knee joint at an angle of 20 degrees, and that this angle remains constant in all positions of the joint.

* The author is indebted to Dr. Marian Williams of Stanford University for the idea on which these problems are based.

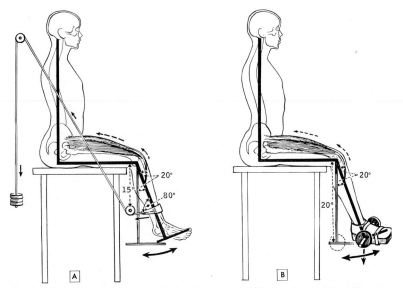

Figure 225. Knee extension against resistance. *A*, Using pulley-weights; *B*, using weighted boot.

4. For the position of the leg defined in 1, the angle between the pulley-rope and the axis of the leg, known as the resistance angle, is 80 degrees.

5. Assume that the length of the lever (distance from knee joint to point where rope is attached) is 15 inches.

Procedure

a. Finding the Total Muscular Force Necessary to Balance the Resistance. As with any lever, the force may be determined if the other three values in the leverage equation are known. In this case, since the weight is known and since we have the information necessary for finding the true force arm and the true resistance arm, the total muscular force can be derived from the equation,

$$F \times FA = W \times WA.$$

The first step is to determine the true force and weight arms of the lever. Diagrams are helpful for this, but are not essential. To find the former, a perpendicular may be drawn from the fulcrum (center of knee joint) to the line representing the direction of force. This represents the true force arm and, together with the long axis of the leg and the force line, forms a right triangle. Using the equation, $\text{sine} = \dfrac{O}{H}$ (see page 316), solve for O, the side opposite, or true force arm of the lever. Refer to a table of sines for the sine of a 20-degree angle. The hypotenuse is the apparent force arm, i.e., the distance from the fulcrum to the point at which the force is applied. This was given as 4 inches. Substituting the values for "sine" and "H," we now have $0.342 = \dfrac{O}{4}$. Hence the side opposite, or true force arm, is 1.368 inches. Since it was assumed that the angle of application would not change as the leg moved, the true force arm would also remain constant for the different positions of the leg.

The true resistance arm is found in similar manner. In this case the angle of application is 80 degrees and the hypotenuse of the right triangle is 15 inches, i.e., the distance from the fulcrum to the point at which the resistance is applied. (The foot may be disregarded in the pulley-weight problems.) Since the sine of an 80 degree angle is 0.985, the equation will read, $0.985 = \dfrac{O}{15}$, and the side opposite, or true resistance arm, will prove to be 14.78 inches when the resistance is applied at an angle of 80 degrees.

Now we are ready to solve for F in the equation: $F \times F'A' = W \times W'A'$.

$$F \times 1.368 = 30 \times 14.78$$
$$F = 324.12 \text{ lbs.}$$

b. Finding the Rotatory Component of the Force

It is not necessary actually to draw this, but let us assume that we have constructed a right triangle in which one angle is 20 degrees (the angle at which the force is applied) and the hypotenuse represents 324.12, the force value found in the first part of this problem. Solve for the side opposite, i.e., the rotatory component, by using the familiar formula, $\text{sine} = \dfrac{O}{H}$. (Note that this formula can be used for either linear or weight measurements.)

$$0.342 = \frac{O}{324.12}$$
$$O = 110.85 \text{ lbs.}$$

c. Finding the Rotatory Component of the Resistance

Assume that we have constructed a right triangle in which one angle is 80 degrees (the angle at which the resistance is applied) and the hypotenuse represents a resistance of 30 pounds.

$$0.985 = \frac{O}{30}.$$
$$O = 29.55 \text{ lbs.}$$

If these procedures are repeated for 60 degrees and for 90 degrees of motion, the resistance angles will be 60 degrees and 45 degrees respectively, and the values will be as follows:

	Resistance Angle of 60°	Resistance Angle of 45°
True resistance arm of lever	12.99 in.	10.61 in.
Total muscular force	284.87 lbs.	232.68 lbs.
Rotatory component of force	97.43 lbs.	79.58 lbs.
Rotatory component of resistance	25.98 lbs.	21.21 lbs.

Demonstrations, Laboratory Exercises and Projects

1. Measure the range of motion in hip flexion with the subject lying on his back:

 a. With the subject's knee straight.

 b. With the subject's knee bent as fully as possible.

What accounts for the difference?

2. Measure the range of motion in dorsiflexion of the foot:

 a. With the subject's knee straight.

 b. With the subject's knee bent.

What accounts for the difference?

3. Measure the range of motion in dorsiflexion of the foot:

 a. When the movement is performed by an operator, the subject remaining as relaxed as possible.

 b. When the movement is performed actively by the subject.

What accounts for the difference?

4. Press on a bathroom scale until it records 50 pounds of pressure:

a. With the scale on a level with the mid-point of the thighs.

b. With the scale on a level with the hips.

Which method takes less muscular effort, *a* or *b?* What implications does this experiment have for giving a back massage?

5. Apply an elastic bandage (*a*) for a sprained ankle; (*b*) for a weak or strained arch.

6. Practice the Kraus-Weber posture measurements on at least three different subjects.

7. Practice the Kendalls' method of examining posture on at least three different subjects.

8. Analyze the joint movements involved in making a reed waste basket.

9. Analyze the muscular action involved in making a knotted belt.

10. Analyze both the joint and muscular action involved in making a tooled leather book cover.

11. In the Supplementary Material a problem based on the pulley-weight method of providing resistance in a progressive resistance exercise for the quadriceps muscles was presented and solved. Using the same data, solve for the corresponding values when the resistance is provided by a weight attached to the under side of the foot, as by means of a DeLorme boot, instead of by pulley-weights. Assume that the length of the lever in this case (distance from center of knee joint to bottom of weight on foot) is 20 inches. (Hint: The resistance angle may be determined by constructing three diagrams to scale, one for each position of the leg, drawing the line representing the direction of the resistance, and measuring the angle with a protractor.) A table of sines and cosines may be found in Appendix B.

In order to compare the two methods of providing resistance in knee extension exercises, record the results in the following spaces.

		20°	60°	90°
Total muscular force	⎰Weight-on-foot:	____	____	____
	⎱Pulley-weight:	____	____	____
Rotatory component of force	⎰Weight-on-foot:	____	____	____
	⎱Pulley-weight:	____	____	____
Rotatory component of resistance	⎰Weight-on-foot:	____	____	____
	⎱Pulley-weight:	____	____	____

Bibliography

1. Bennett, R. L.: Muscle Testing: A Discussion of the Importance of Accurate Muscle Testing. Physiotherapy Rev., *27:* 242–243, 1947.

2. Bennett, R. L.: Muscle: Reeducation: A Brief Discussion of Some of the Basic Principles. Physiotherapy Rev., *27:* 243–246, 1947.

3. Bennett, R. L., and Stephens, H. R.: Functional Testing and Training: Physical Therapy Aspects. Phys. Therapy Rev., *29:* 99–107, 1949.

4. Bierman, W., and Yamshon, L. J.: Electromyography in Kinesiologic Evaluation. Arch. Phys. Med., *29:* 206–211, 1948.

5. Brown, M. E.: Daily Activity Testing and Teaching. Physiotherapy Rev., *27:* 249–253, 1947.

6. Daniels, L., Williams, M., and Worthingham, C.: Muscle Testing: Technics of Manual Examination. 2nd ed. Philadelphia, W. B. Saunders Company, 1956.

7. DeLorme, T. L., and Watkins, A. L.: Progressive Resistance Exercise. New York, Appleton-Century-Crofts, Inc., 1951.

8. Dorinson, S. M., and Wagner, M. L.: An Exact Technic for Clinically Measuring and Recording Joint Motion. Arch. Phys. Med., *29:* 468–475, 1948.

9. Dunton, W. R., and Licht, S.: Occupational Therapy. 2nd ed. Springfield, Ill., Charles C Thomas, 1957.

10. Kendall, H. O. and F. P.: Muscles: Testing and Function. Baltimore, Williams & Wilkins Co., 1949.

11. Kraus, H., and Eisenmenger-Weber, S.: Evaluation of Posture Based on Structural and Functional Measurements. Physiotherapy Rev., *25:* 267–271, 1945.

12. Meyer, S. W.: Kinetic Bandaging. Philadelphia, F. A. Davis Company, 1943.

13. Moore, M. L.: The Measurement of Joint Motion. Phys. Ther. Rev., *29:* 195–205; 256–264, 1949.

14. Noland, R. P., and Kuckhoff, F. A.: An Adapted Progressive Resistance Exercise Device. Phys. Ther. Rev., *34:* 1–6, 1954.

15. Thorndike, A.: A Manual of Bandaging, Strapping and Splinting. Philadelphia, Lea & Febiger, 1941.

16. Willard, H. S., and Spackman, C. S.: Principles of Occupational Therapy. 2nd ed. Philadelphia, J. B. Lippincott Co., 1954.

17. Williams, M., and Stutzman, L.: Strength Variation through the Range of Joint Motion. Phys. Ther. Rev., *39:* 145–152, 1959.

Recommended Readings

Kendall, H. O., and F. P.: Muscles: Testing and Function. (See 10 above.)

Willard, N. S., and Spackman, C. S.: Principles of Occupational Therapy. (See 16 above.) Chapters 2, 4 and 9.

Williams, M., and Stutzman, L.: Strength Variation through the Range of Joint Motion. (See 17 above.)

27 · Applications of Kinesiology to Daily Life Skills

KINESIOLOGY IS not limited to the sports field, corrective gymnasium and treatment room. It has its place in the home, in the garden, on the farm, in the office and in the shop. Wherever man moves, kinesiology and body mechanics are applicable. Man uses his body constantly. Either he observes the principles of good body mechanics or he violates them. To the extent that he observes these principles, his motions contribute to a strong, efficient upright body; to the extent that he violates them, his motions pave the way for postural strains, abnormal tensions and other pathologic conditions of the bones, joints and muscles. The kinesiologist—be he physical education instructor, physical therapist, occupational therapist or athletic coach—has a real responsibility in pointing out and demonstrating the applications of the basic principles of body mechanics to all the daily life skills. Along with learning how to swim an efficient crawl stroke, serve a tennis ball with speed and accuracy, and drive a golf ball with force and precision, the individual needs to master the more modest skills of lifting a heavy package, moving a large piece of furniture, and using a spade, hoe, rake, broom or vacuum cleaner with efficiency and safety. He should learn to perform these skills both from the point of view of the results accomplished and from the point of view of using his body effectively and without strain. Poor body mechanics means not only a task poorly done, but also a poor machine for doing the task. Good body mechanics, on the other hand, means not only a task efficiently done, but also a strong, capable machine for doing it.

If it is desirable to use the body efficiently in sports and exercises, it is infinitely more desirable to use it efficiently in the movements which characterize one's daily occupation.

The majority of the daily life skills may be classified under the following categories:

1. Locomotion, including ascending and descending.
2. Stooping to reach a lower level; taking a seat; rising.
3. Lifting and carrying.
4. Moving heavy objects by pushing and pulling.
5. Working with long-handled implements (such as those used for housecleaning, gardening, wood chopping and snow clearing).
6. Working with small implements and materials at a work surface.

On studying this list it is seen that practically every phase of kinesiology is represented. A complete analysis of representative activities from each category would necessitate a repetition of a large portion of the first three parts of this book. Hence, the procedure adopted is a discussion of the major kinesiologic problems involved and the application of the most noteworthy anatomic and mechanical principles to a few sample activities.

Locomotion: Ascending and Descending (Fig. 226). For the principles which apply to locomotion one should refer to Chapter 19. The problems in the more common uses of locomotion have to do with the anatomic aspects, rather than the mechanical. The alignment of the weight-bearing joints is the major problem in locomotion. Poor alignment causes strain and fatigue. If locomotion forms a relatively large portion of a person's daily occupation,

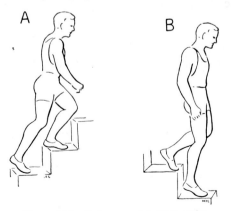

Figure 226. Going up and down stairs.

the good alignment of his feet, knees, and hips is of utmost importance.

One specific problem relating to locomotion in the home is the problem of safety when there is insufficient friction between the feet and the supporting surface. Wet linoleum and scatter rugs on polished floors constitute hazards in the home. An appreciation of the effects of the horizontal component of force in walking and running would make one more aware of the danger and more cautious in one's locomotion about the house.

Housekeeping frequently involves going up and down stairs. The major problem in going up is economy of effort; in coming down the chief problem is safety. Economy of effort in going up can be achieved by keeping the center of gravity forward, thus minimizing the resistance arm of the thigh lever; and by avoiding superfluous joint and muscle action, such as that involved in plantar flexion of the foot. The most economical way of climbing stairs, therefore, is by inclining the body slightly forward (preferably from the feet, not the hips) and by depending upon extension at the knee for lifting the body, rather than extension (plantar flexion) in the ankle joint.

Descending the stairs with safety can be accomplished by keeping the center of gravity approximately over the center of the base of support. Both hurrying and leaning too far forward endanger the equilibrium by causing the line of gravity to come precariously close to the anterior margin of support. Hurrying also increases the danger due to other factors, such as high heels and slippery surfaces.

Stooping, Being Seated and Rising (Figs. 227, 228 and 229). The chief problems here are economy of effort, maintaining equilibrium, and avoiding strain. So far as stooping is concerned, these three objectives are interrelated. In taking a seat there may be a more economical way than the one in which equilibrium is preserved, but it is scarcely acceptable from the point of view of aesthetics or social custom.

In stooping to pick up something from the floor or from a low shelf, stability is enhanced if the feet are slightly separated, both laterally and anteroposteriorly. This serves to enlarge the base of support. To perform the movement with maximum efficiency and minimum danger of strain requires that the stooping should be effected by bending at the knees and inclining the trunk slightly forward. The thigh thus becomes the major lever involved. The fulcrum of this lever is the center of motion at the knee joint; the force is furnished by the knee extensors and is applied at their average point of proximal attachment (not the distal, because the thigh is being extended on the lower leg rather than the leg on the thigh); and the resistance is the weight of the body, represented by the line of gravity. Its point of application to the lever depends upon the position of the body. When the trunk is inclined slightly forward, the line of gravity falls through the approximate center of the base of support. This assures a shorter weight arm (i.e., the horizontal distance from the fulcrum to the line of gravity) than is the case when the trunk is held vertically erect. Given a lever in which the force arm and the weight are constant, an increase in the weight arm will necessitate an increase in the force required to balance the lever. Thus stooping with the trunk held in a vertical or near-vertical position actually requires more muscular effort than does stooping with the trunk inclined slightly forward. Figure 227 illustrates the two styles of stooping. The position of the line of gravity with reference to the base of support was actually found for the subject in each of these positions and the weight arm of the lever measured. In the original photographs ($3\frac{7}{8}$ by $2\frac{3}{4}$ inches) the weight arm in Figure 227, A, was 17 mm. and in B, 14 mm. Since the 100-cm. board measured 66 mm. in the photograph, the actual difference in the two weight arms was approximately 4.5 cm. (See pp. 347–349.)

When one bends from the waist to reach the floor, the center of gravity is considerably higher than when one stoops; hence the body is in a less stable position (Fig. 228). The close position of the feet also decreases stability. The leverage is not clear-cut. The trunk seems to be the major lever in the motion, but it fails to meet the requirements of a lever in that it is not a rigid bar. It is a flexible bar, turning about the common axis of the two hip joints, and at the same time, flexing within itself. The most obvious mechanical disadvantage of this method of reaching the floor lies in the fact that the horizontal position of the trunk permits the force of gravity to act on it with a 100 per cent rotatory component. This requires

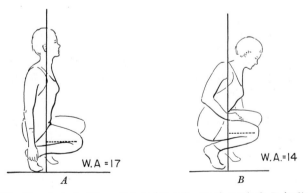

Figure 227. Stooping. A, Attempting to keep the trunk vertical; B, inclining the body slightly forward. (W.A. = the weight arm of the thigh lever.)

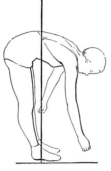

Figure 228. Bending from the waist to reach the floor.

strong action of the spinal extensors to stabilize the flexible spine, and of the hip joint extensors to control the movement of the trunk as a whole at the hip joints. The strong extensors of the knee, located on the front of the thigh, give no help at all in this movement. All the work is performed by the extensors of the hip and spine. Furthermore, the spinal muscles work in a stretched position. The "approved" method of stooping, by bending the knees and inclining the body slightly forward, has the advantage of giving the major portion of the work to the strong knee and hip extensors, with only a small share taken by the extensors of the spine. This method calls upon the spinal extensors to make a reasonable contribution to the movement, but it does not subject them to strain, nor does it require that they work in a stretched position.

In seating oneself gracefully, the major problem is to provide a base of support which will remain under the backward-shifting center of gravity. When the style of the chair permits, this can be accomplished by placing one foot well back under the chair, bending at the knees, and inclining the body forward just enough to keep the center of gravity over the base of support (Fig. 229). The body will be eased into the chair, rather than dropped into it, if the knee extensors are made to control the movement against the pull of gravity. In rising from the chair the problem is to provide a base of support with the feet immediately, so that the transfer of weight can be made gradually instead of by having to throw the body forward or by depending upon the hands for a push-off from the seat of the chair. This is accomplished by placing one foot well back under the chair, inclining the body slightly forward, pushing the feet down against the floor and extending the knees. As the knees are extended the weight is gradually shifted from the rear to the forward foot.

It is more difficult to keep the base of support under the center of gravity when seating oneself on a chair with a low rung or a solid front. In the case of a straight chair with a low rung it is possible to put one foot back close to the side of the chair instead of under it and then to lower oneself onto the side of the seat, later shifting to the center. When taking a seat in a deep upholstered chair or davenport which has a solid front, a different technique must be used. With these the only way to keep the base of support under the center of gravity is to stand with the side to the seat, place the near foot forward, bend the knees and lower oneself sideways onto the front edge of the seat, turning slightly forward at the last moment. One or two additional movements are then needed to complete the forward facing and to get the body well back on the seat. In rising, the reverse procedure is followed. The body is shifted forward and turned sideways; the near foot is placed forward and the other foot backward; the weight is shifted over the feet, the feet pushed down against the floor and the legs and thighs extended.

Lifting and Carrying (Figs. 230, 231 and 232).   In addition to the problems involved in stooping to reach the object, lifting a heavy object from the floor involves the dual problems of keeping the weight arm of the lever used for lifting as short as possible, and the angle at which the gravitational force applies to the lever as small as possible. This is in the interest both of economy of effort and of reducing the likelihood of strain. When the arm used for lifting is in a horizontal position, whether flexed or extended at the elbow, the gravitational force pulls at right angles to the lever. This means that it is 100 per cent rotatory force, and the *true* weight arm of the lever (the perpendicular distance) is coincidental with the *apparent* weight arm. Since $F \times FA = W \times WA$, the longer the weight arm, the more force it takes to balance the lever, other things being equal. If the object were held in the hand with the arm fully extended horizontally, the weight arm of the lever would be extremely long—approximately 30 inches. Great muscular force would be required to balance the lever under these condi-

Figure 229. In seating oneself gracefully the body is balanced and the movement is controlled.

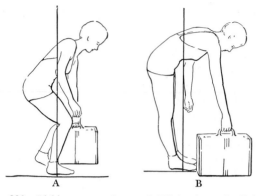

Figure 230. Picking up a suitcase. *A,* Efficiently; *B,* inefficiently.

tions. One instinctively avoids lifting a heavy object in this un-economical manner, but not everyone recognizes the fact that the most economical manner of lifting is the exact reverse of the above: namely, by keeping the lifting arm as nearly vertical as possible and by holding the object as close to the body's line of gravity as possible (Fig. 230, *A*).

In the discussion of stooping, attention was called to the fact that bending over from the waist to reach the floor is not only mechanically disadvantageous, but also requires strong action of the extensors of the spine and hips, and that the spinal muscles are made to work on a stretch. If the body is used in this manner for lifting a heavy object, an additional burden is put upon the muscles of the back, one that they can ill afford to take (Fig. 230, *B*). Strait, Inman and Ralston have made the interesting observation that bending from the waist to touch the floor, without flexing the knees, creates a tensile force of 450 pounds in the sacrospinalis muscle and a compressional force of nearly 500 pounds on the fifth lumbar vertebra. If a 50-pound weight is held in the hands, the tensile force is increased to 750 pounds and the compressional force to 850 pounds.[10] The spinal extensors are not powerful muscles and are easily strained. It is unintelligent to expose them to the danger of strain when this can be avoided by observing the principles of good mechanics.

The same principles of leverage that apply to lifting a heavy object apply also to carrying it. In carrying a weight there is the further problem of assuming a balanced position with the center of gravity centered over the base of support. During the process of lifting, the equilibrium is temporarily disturbed. Once the body is erect, however, it should adjust itself in such a way that it compensates for the load and the new center of gravity (of body and load combined) lies over the center of the supporting base. For instance, when one carries a heavy suitcase, it is no longer good body mechanics to keep the body erect with the head and spine carried in the midsagittal plane of the body. In the presence of a heavy unilateral load, good mechanics requires a compensatory movement, e.g., lifting the arm or inclining the trunk to the opposite side. Failure to make this compensation necessitates additional work by the muscles on the opposite side of the trunk (see Figs. 193 and 194).

In lifting a heavy box down from a high shelf the chief problems are those of avoiding strain and of keeping the movement of the box under control. As the individual tugs on the box to pull it off the shelf he is imparting horizontal momentum to the box. If he pulls quickly or if the box comes free suddenly, as soon as the box is free of the shelf its momentum will be transferred to him. If he is not prepared for this, it may swing his trunk backward and strain his lower back (Fig. 232, *A*). To avoid this likelihood he should observe the principles of widening the base of support in the direction of the oncoming force. In other words, he should stand with one foot forward (Fig. 232, *B*). This will permit him not only to shift his weight from the forward to the rear foot, but also to take a step backward if necessary. This provides additional space in which the box can lose its horizontal momentum. Whether the box is pulled off the shelf slowly or quickly, there is the problem of maintaining equilibrium when reaching forward for the box and when the weight of the box is first transferred to the hands. For a brief moment, at least, the center of gravity is precariously near the front margin of the base of support. By placing one foot well forward, the lifter provides an adequate base of support for the anteriorly displaced center of gravity.

Pushing or Pulling Heavy Objects (Fig. 233).   The main problem in attempting to move a heavy object either by pushing or by pulling is the efficient application of force. This serves two

Figure 231.   A safe and efficient method of lifting a heavy object.

Figure 232. Lifting a box down from a high shelf. *A,* Inefficiently; *B,* efficiently.

purposes: first, the successful moving of the object, and, second, the conservation of the mover's energy. There are two factors to be considered in the problem of applying force efficiently. These are the direction of the force, and the point at which it is applied. Whenever feasible, the force should be applied squarely in the direction in which the object is expected to move. When this is not feasible, the undesirable component of force should be as small as possible. For instance, if one desires to push a low trunk across the floor, it would be difficult to stoop low enough to push with the arms in a horizontal position. One should stoop as low as conveniently possible, however, in order to reduce the downward component of force which would tend to increase friction. If it were necessary to move the trunk down the street, and no cart or wheelbarrow were available, it would be more efficient to tie a rope to it and to pull it. By using a long rope, the horizontal component of force would be relatively great and the vertical or lifting component relatively small. Some lifting component would actually be desirable because it would serve to reduce friction.

The point at which the pushing or pulling force is applied to the object depends upon which kind of motion is desired, linear or rotatory. If one wishes to push a large box or a heavy chair across the floor, he should place his hands in line with the object's center of gravity, provided the amount of friction is inconsequential. This would probably be true of the chair if it had castors. In the case of the box, however, there would probably be considerable friction. In such a situation the force should be applied below the object's center of gravity. The exact spot would have to be determined by experimentation. The criterion would be the object's tendency to tip. There is no tipping in efficient linear motion.

If one wishes to move the box by turning it end over end, he should then place his hands as far above its supporting surface as possible. In this way the box is being used as a lever, with the fulcrum located at its point of contact with the floor. Since the amount of force necessary to turn the box is in inverse proportion to the distance of the hands from the floor (i.e., the force arm of the lever), the higher the hands are placed, the less force is needed. If one wishes to rotate a box horizontally or to move it across the floor by a series of alternating partial rotations, he should place his hands on the top of the box at diagonally opposite corners.

An anatomic principle that applies to pushing and pulling when great force is required is that of using the strong muscles of the body to supplement the weaker ones. This means supplementing the action of the arms with that of the legs. By inclining the body toward the object being pushed, it is possible to add to the force of the push by using the leg extensors. Likewise the force of pulling can be increased by inclining the body away from the object and extending the legs in as nearly a horizontal plane as possible.

Working with Long-Handled Implements.   Working with implements such as a hoe, rake, mop or vacuum cleaner involves a combination of pushing, pulling and, in some instances, lifting. The last is usually only for short distances, but it may occur with

Figure 233. Pushing a tall piece of furniture. *A,* Inefficiently; *B,* efficiently.

considerable frequency. One characteristic of working with implements such as those named is that the body must maintain a more or less fixed posture for relatively long periods of time. This causes tension and fatigue. Hence the chief problem is that of using the body in such a way that tension will be minimized and fatigue postponed as long as possible. If the implement is used back and forth in front of the body, the tendency of the worker is to lean forward. This necessitates static contraction of the extensors of the spine in order to support the trunk against the downward pull of gravity. As implements such as the rake and hoe are lifted at the end of each stroke and carried to position for the next stroke, the force of gravity acts on the implement as well as on the worker's body. Although the implement may not weigh much in itself, its forward position means that the lever has a long weight arm, the effect of which must be balanced by the muscles. This gives an added burden to the back muscles and not infrequently causes a backache. This can be avoided by standing with the side turned toward the working site with the feet in a fairly wide stride and by using the implement from side to side. The reach can then be obtained by bending the knee of the leg on the same side as the implement, and by inclining the body slightly to the same side. Those who are familiar with gymnastics will recognize this as a side lunge position. On the recovery, the knee and the trunk are both straightened. Thus there is an alternating contraction and relaxation of muscles and there is no necessity for any of the trunk muscles to remain in static contraction.

The use of a spade or snow shovel involves primarily the act of lifting. Because the load is taken on the end of a mechanical lever held in a more or less horizontal position, it is inevitable that the weight arm of the lever be relatively long. It can be shortened somewhat, however, by sliding one hand as far down the shaft as possible, using this hand as a fulcrum, and providing the force with the other hand by pushing down on the outer end of the handle. As a variation of this, when getting a particularly heavy load on a shovel, it is possible to bend one knee and brace the shaft against the thigh, thus using the thigh as a fulcrum. This is only for the initial lift, however; the hands must then be shifted to the position previously described in order to carry or throw the load.

Aside from taking and lifting the load on the spade, there is the factor of lowering the body to reach the load and of assuming the erect position for moving it. As in the case of stooping to lift a heavy object from the floor, the chief problems are economy of effort, maintenance of stability and avoidance of strain. These problems are intensified by the additional factor of taking the load on a long-handled implement instead of directly in the hand. As before, separating the feet to widen the base of support, bending at the knees instead of bending from the waist to lower the body and inclining the trunk forward only slightly will respectively increase stability, shorten the anatomic levers involved in the stooping and divide the muscular work among the knee, hip and back extensors instead of making the back muscles assume too large a share of the work. Since the lower back is easily strained by heavy shoveling, it is of great importance to protect it by observing the principles of good body mechanics.

Working with Small Materials and Implements at a Work Surface. The two chief factors to be considered in working with small materials and implements at a work surface are the height of the surface and the position of the materials with reference to the body. So much attention has been given to these in recent years that a detailed discussion would be superfluous. A work surface that is too low makes it necessary for the worker to bend over his work, thus keeping the muscles of his neck and back in static contraction. Hence he becomes fatigued much sooner than he would if he could remain erect. If, on the other hand, the surface is too high, the worker tends to keep his shoulder girdle elevated in order to use his hands effectively. This necessitates contraction of the upper trapezius, levator and rhomboids. He may have to keep his arms elevated from the shoulders, thus keeping his deltoid and supraspinatus muscles in static contraction.

An inefficient arrangement of the materials on the work surface means that the worker has to reach unnecessarily far for some of them and has to make more movements than he would if some thought were given to the advantageous placing of his materials. The time and motion studies by efficiency experts have done much in recent years to show that production can be stepped up considerably by giving attention to small details such as these. Kinesiologically, the problem is a dual one of reducing the length of the reach, thereby reducing the weight arm of the lever (the arms) and of reducing the number of movements, thereby economizing on muscular contractions. These details would not be of great significance for short work periods, but if the motions are repeated hour after hour, attention to these factors makes a great difference in the fatigability of the worker.

Projects

1. Experiment to find the best way to shovel snow or dig earth. Describe and analyze the method selected.

2. Experiment to find the best way to pick up and carry a tray of heavy dishes. Describe and analyze the method selected.

3. Experiment to find the best way to pick up and carry a large bag of flour or cement. Describe and analyze the method selected.

Bibliography

Body Mechanics in Daily Life Skills

1. Fash, B.: Body Mechanics in Nursing Arts. New York, McGraw-Hill Book Company, Inc., 1946.
2. Frost, L.: Posture and Body Mechanics. State University of Iowa Extension Bulletin No. 479, March 1940.
3. Hazelton, H. W., and Russell, M.: Keeping Fit for Farm Work. Purdue University Department of Agriculture Extension Bulletin No. 299, Aug. 1943.
4. Lee, M., and Wagner, M. M.: Fundamentals of Body Mechanics & Conditioning. Philadelphia, W. B. Saunders Company, 1949.
5. Mensendieck, B. M.: It's Up to You. New York, Little & Ives, 1931.
6. Metheny, E. R.: Are Sports Enough? J. Health and Phys. Ed., *14:* 249–251, 286–288, May, 1943.
7. Metheny, E.: Body Dynamics. New York, McGraw-Hill Book Company, Inc., 1952.
8. Mettert, M. T.: Women's Effective War Work Requires Good Posture. Special Bulletin No. 10, Women's Bureau, U.S. Dept. of Labor, Washington, D.C., U.S. Govt. Printing Office, 1943.
9. Newton, K.: Preventing Backstrain in Nursing. Am. J. Nursing, *43:* 921, Oct. 1943.
10. Strait, L. A., Inman, V. T., and Ralston, H. J.: Sample Illustrations of Physical Principles Selected from Physiology and Medicine. Am. J. Physics, *15:* 375–382, 1947.
11. U.S. Dept. of Labor, Div. of Labor Standards: A Guide to the Prevention of Weight-Lifting Injuries. Special Bulletin No. 11, Washington, D.C., U.S. Govt. Printing Office, 1943.
12. Winters, M. C.: Protective Body Mechanics in Daily Life and in Nursing. Philadelphia, W. B. Saunders Company, 1952.
13. Women's Bureau, U.S. Dept. of Labor: Lifting Heavy Weights in Defense Industries. Special Bulletin No. 2, Washington, D.C., U.S. Govt. Printing Office, 1941

Motion Studies

14. Barnes, R. M.: Motion and Time Study. New York, John Wiley & Sons, Inc., 1940.
15. Barnes, R. M.: Motion and Time Study; Applications. New York, John Wiley & Sons, Inc., 1942.
16. Barnes, R. M.: Work Methods Manual. New York, John Wiley & Sons, Inc., 1944.
17. Dunwoody, K. M.: Time and Motion in Physical Education. J. Health and Phys. Ed., *10:* 218, 219, 265, April 1939.
18. Gilbreth, R. B., and L. M.: Applied Motion Study. New York, Sturgis & Walton Company, 1917.
19. Gilbreth, L. M.: Motion Study. Handbook of Business Administration, W. J. Donald, Ed., New York, McGraw-Hill Book Company, Inc., 1931.
20. Hartee, W., and Hill, A. V.: Factors Determining Maximum Work and Mechanical Efficiency. Proc. Roy. Soc. S. B., London, *103:* 234–251, Aug. 1, 1928.

Recommended Readings

Lee, M., and Wagner, M. M.: Fundamentals of Body Mechanics & Conditioning. Chapter 7. (See 4 above.)

Metheny, E.: Body Dynamics. Chaps. 9 and 10. (See 7 above.)

Winters, M. C.: Protective Body Mechanics in Daily Life and in Nursing. Pages 19–56. (See 12 above.)

Appendix A

Outline for a Forty-Five Hour Course in Kinesiology

This OUTLINE is suggested in response to the many requests received by the author for help in adapting the material in this text to a one-semester undergraduate course in kinesiology. Although it is highly desirable to devote sixty or even ninety hours to a kinesiology course, the author recognizes the fact that the kinesiology course in the average undergraduate major program is only one semester in length. If the students have had an adequate course in anatomy immediately preceding the kinesiology course, only a brief review of anatomy, with the emphasis on the function of the joints and muscles, need be included. It is suggested that the time thus gained be devoted to the section on applications of kinesiology. The factual material in the text should be covered by assignments. Class time should be devoted to demonstrations and laboratory exercises, and to explanations of materials which the class does not understand.

Lesson 1. Introduction; Chapter 1, Fundamental Concepts
Lesson 2. Chapter 2, The Joints: Their Structure and Function; Chapter 3, The Muscular System
Lesson 3. Chapter 4, Neuromuscular Function
Lesson 4. Review or quiz
Lessons 5 and 6. Chapter 5, The Spinal Column
Lesson 7. Chapter 6, Movements of the Thorax in Respiration
Lesson 8. Review or quiz
Lessons 9, 10, 11, 12. Chapter 7, The Shoulder Region
Lesson 13. Chapter 8, Elbow Joint and Radioulnar Articulations
Lesson 14. Chapter 9, The Wrist and Hand. (Omit text on smaller muscles of fingers. Study illustrations of these.)

Lesson 15. Review or quiz
Lesson 16. Chapter 10, Hip Joint and Pelvic Girdle
Lesson 17. Chapter 11, Knee Joint
Lesson 18. Chapter 12, Ankle and Foot
Lesson 19. Review
Lesson 20. Mid-term examination
Lessons 21 and 22. Chapter 13, Machinery of the Musculoskeletal System
Lesson 23. Chapter 14, Fundamental Principles of Motion
Lesson 24. Chapter 15, Fundamental Principles of Force and Work
Lesson 25. Review or quiz
Lesson 26. Chapter 16, Bases for the Development of Motor Skills. Emphasis on classification.
Lesson 27. Chapter 17, Principles of Stability
Lesson 28. Chapter 18, Postural Principles
Lessons 29 and 30. Chapter 19, Principles of Moving One's Body
Lesson 31. Review or quiz
Lesson 32. Chapter 20, Principles of Receiving Impetus
Lessons 33 and 34. Chapter 21, Principles of Giving Impetus to External Objects
Lesson 35. Review or quiz
Lesson 36. Chapter 23, Locomotion: Walking and Running
Lessons 37, 38, 39 and 40. Chapter 24, Applications of Kinesiology to the Teaching of Sports
Lessons 41 and 42. Chapter 25, Selection and Evaluation of Exercises for Conditioning and Corrective Purposes
Lesson 43. Chapter 22, Selection and Classification of Principles Pertaining to the Prevention of Injury; Chapter 26, Applications of Kinesiology to Physical Therapy and Occupational Therapy
Lesson 44. Chapter 27, Applications of Kinesiology to Daily Life Skills
Lesson 45. Review or Final Examination
As a final project each student should analyze one activity technique of his own choice.

Appendix B

Table of Sines and Cosines

DEGREES	SINES	COSINES	DEGREES	SINES	COSINES
0	.0000	1.0000	46	.7193	.6947
1	.0175	.9998	47	.7314	.6820
2	.0349	.9994	48	.7431	.6691
3	.0523	.9986	49	.7547	.6561
4	.0698	.9976	50	.7660	.6428
5	.0872	.9962	51	.7771	.6293
6	.1045	.9945	52	.7880	.6157
7	.1219	.9925	53	.7986	.6018
8	.1392	.9903	54	.8090	.5878
9	.1564	.9877	55	.8192	.5736
10	.1736	.9848	56	.8290	.5592
11	.1908	.9816	57	.8387	.5446
12	.2079	.9781	58	.8480	.5299
13	.2250	.9744	59	.8572	.5150
14	.2419	.9703	60	.8660	.5000
15	.2588	.9659	61	.8746	.4848
16	.2756	.9613	62	.8829	.4695
17	.2924	.9563	63	.8910	.4540
18	.3090	.9511	64	.8988	.4384
19	.3256	.9455	65	.9063	.4226
20	.3420	.9397	66	.9135	.4067
21	.3584	.9336	67	.9205	.3907
22	.3746	.9272	68	.9272	.3746
23	.3907	.9205	69	.9336	.3584
24	.4067	.9135	70	.9397	.3420
25	.4226	.9063	71	.9455	.3256
26	.4384	.8988	72	.9511	.3090
27	.4540	.8910	73	.9563	.2924
28	.4695	.8829	74	.9613	.2756
29	.4848	.8746	75	.9659	.2588
30	.5000	.8660	76	.9703	.2419
31	.5150	.8572	77	.9744	.2250
32	.5299	.8480	78	.9781	.2079
33	.5446	.8387	79	.9816	.1908
34	.5592	.8290	80	.9848	.1736
35	.5736	.8192	81	.9877	.1564
36	.5878	.8090	82	.9903	.1392
37	.6018	.7986	83	.9925	.1219
38	.6157	.7880	84	.9945	.1045
39	.6293	.7771	85	.9962	.0872
40	.6428	.7660	86	.9976	.0698
41	.6561	.7547	87	.9986	.0523
42	.6691	.7431	88	.9994	.0349
43	.6820	.7314	89	.9998	.0175
44	.6947	.7193	90	1.0000	.0000
45	.7071	.7071			

Index